Precalculus
with Trigonometry

CONCEPTS AND APPLICATIONS

Assessment Resources

PAUL A. FOERSTER

DEBORAH PRESTON

SECOND EDITION

Key Curriculum Press
Innovators in Mathematics Education

Project Editor: Andres Marti
Editorial Assistants: Elizabeth Ball, Brady Golden
Production Editors: Donna Crossman, Kristin Ferraioli
Accuracy Checker: Dudley Brooks
Copyeditor: Tom Briggs
Editorial Production Supervisor: Christine Osborne
Production Coordinator: Jennifer Young
Production Director: McKinley Williams
Art Editor: Jason Luz
Technical Art: Lineworks, Inc., Interactive Composition Corporation
Compositor: Interactive Composition Corporation
Cover Designer: Jensen Barnes
Cover Photo Credit: ©Grafton Marshall Smith/Corbis
Prepress and Printer: Versa Press, Inc.

Textbook Product Manager: James Ryan
Executive Editor: Casey FitzSimons
Publisher: Steven Rasmussen

Key Curriculum Press
1150 65th Street
Emeryville, CA 94608
510-595-7000
editorial@keypress.com
www.keypress.com

Printed in the United States of America
10 9 8 7 6 5 4 3 2   12 11 10 09
ISBN 978-1-55953-791-9

Contents

Overview of *Assessment Resources*

The *Precalculus with Trigonometry: Concepts and Applications Assessment Resources* contains a complete set of testing materials with solutions. These blackline masters can be reproduced to use with your students.

You can also modify the electronic files of these tests to customize them. The tests are available in Microsoft Word format on the *Instructor's Resource CD* that accompanies the *Instructor's Guide* and also at *www.keypress.com/keyonline,* where you can become a registered user of *Precalculus with Trigonometry: Concepts and Applications.* Equations are set in MathType.

- The Assessment Suggestions are based on the National Council of Teachers of Mathematics' *Assessment Standards for School Mathematics.* This section provides supplementary material to meet these standards, as well as specific suggestions and examples from the author's classroom on how to use the text.

- The Tests include up to three tests for each chapter. There are two forms of each test. Each Section Test covers material from one or more sections, and the Chapter Test covers material from the whole chapter.

- Three Cumulative Tests are also provided, covering Chapters 1-6, Chapters 7-9, and Chapters 10-15.

- Complete solutions to each test are provided.

Assessment Suggestions

Assessment is an opportunity for you to learn more about your students. Through assessment you can discover what students know and understand, how they think, what they still need to learn, and how they feel about their learning. Assessment is also an opportunity for students to learn more about themselves.

Assessment does not always mean recording a grade. You assess students when you read their journals or when you observe them interacting with other members of a group.

You might be one of the many instructors who structure mathematics classrooms and lessons differently from traditional methods of the past. For this reason you need assessment practices that match your changing classroom. For example, instructors argue that if students work cooperatively, we should assess the work they do in groups. If we ask students open-ended questions, we should use open-ended questions as assessment items. If students connect mathematics with the world outside their classroom, we should evaluate projects that make these connections.

Instructors want assessment methods that are genuinely helpful to themselves and their students. They are finding that this kind of constructive assessment requires more than grading the results of a paper-and-pencil test.

According to *Assessment Standards for School Mathematics* (NCTM 1995), there are four major purposes of assessment:

- Monitoring students' progress
- Making instructional decisions
- Evaluating students' achievement
- Evaluating programs

In this section I will share with you some of the assessment techniques I use in my classroom and will point out some of the ways you can address these purposes using the text and supplementary materials for *Precalculus with Trigonometry: Concepts and Applications.*

For more general information on assessment, I recommend *Constructive Assessment in Mathematics: Practical Steps for Classroom Teachers* (Key Curriculum Press 1997) by David Clarke. It offers a good overview of assessment as well as some guidance in specific assessment strategies.

Precalculus with Trigonometry: Concepts and Applications Student Text and Ancillaries

The student text and support materials for *Precalculus with Trigonometry: Concepts and Applications* provide you with ample opportunities to assess student learning. These include a precalculus journal; Concept Problems; projects; technology activities; Section, Chapter, and Cumulative Tests; Explorations; and Quick Review problems. In addition, supplemental resources for projects, graphing calculator activities, precalculus laboratories, problems, and research papers are listed in the Bibliography of Precalculus Resources of the *Instructor's Guide.*

Monitoring Students' Progress

Progress is distinct from achievement. Achievement is a measure of how well a student can do on predetermined tasks. Progress is a measure of how far a student has come along the path toward achievement of broader goals from his or her starting point.

One of the better sources of monitoring student progress for this precalculus course is the journal each student is expected to keep. In this journal students write what they have learned over the past few days and anything about which they are still unsure. By reading sequential journal entries, you and the student can see what progress is being made. Typically, students learning mathematics feel as though they will never master what they have been exposed to today. Tomorrow, when the "Aha!" has hit, they realize that what was difficult before is easy now. But the *next* task seems insurmountable. Students who go back and read their journals will find out a lot about their own learning styles and about how they are making progress in the course.

Another way to monitor progress is to have students keep portfolios into which they put samples of their work. The project problems and experiments throughout the text and the Concept Problems at the ends of chapters make excellent candidates for portfolio entries. With ready access to computer graphing utilities (not just graphing calculators) and word processors, students can write their work on the computer, plot graphs and paste them electronically into their papers, and print near-professional-quality work. The word processor allows students to edit their papers based on your review and comments, turning first drafts into polished products in a time-efficient way. Thus students gain experience with how they will submit papers when they get out into the workforce. The portfolio provides the instructor with a way of monitoring progress and provides potential employers with samples of what the student can do.

> **The main reason you *write* something is for someone else to *read*.**

This maxim appears on the bulletin board in my classroom. It focuses on the importance of the verbal component of mathematics education and gives credence to the reasons students write in their journals and keep portfolios.

> **The safest place to be is at the board!**

Having students work at the board will give you insight into how they are progressing, both individually and as a class. I use a procedure in which a student volunteers or is picked to be at the board. This student then calls on other students, by name, to read the problem, tell what to do first, take the next step, and so forth. The student called upon must supply an answer, whether or not he or she knows the answer when the question is asked. If Tom, for example, is asked a question he cannot answer, I say to the class, "You have a classmate in distress. Tom must answer the question, and you are obligated to help him." Then someone gives Tom hints about how to answer the question, and Tom supplies the answer to the student at the board. (The safest place to be, in this mode of presentation, is at the board!) You can tell how well your students are progressing in the course by how well they respond to the questions.

Note that monitoring progress does not necessarily mean assigning grades. Sometimes the most important result of the monitoring is the one-on-one discussions that you may initiate as a result of having read journal entries or portfolio papers or having seen boardwork presentations.

Precalculus with Trigonometry: Assessment Resources
© 2007 Key Curriculum Press

Making Instructional Decisions

This phase of assessment focuses on you rather than on the student. In its simplest form, this process can involve such things as deciding what to do next based on how well students have done on the previous test. The boardwork previously mentioned might call your attention to the need to try a different approach for a particular topic. On their papers or at the board, you will find students coming up with insightful ways to do things that you can add to your repertoire. For instance, Mary Alice Watkins, Virginia Morales, Jacob Talbot, and Sergio Peña (my former students) found this constructive way to express a product of sine and cosine as a sum:

$$2 \sin 13° \cos 48° = \sin 13° \cos 48° + \sin 13° \cos 48°$$
$$= (\sin 13° \cos 48° + \cos 13° \sin 48°) + (\sin 13° \cos 48° - \cos 13° \sin 48°)$$
$$= \sin(13° + 48°) + \sin(13° - 48°) = \sin 61° + \sin(-35°) = \sin 61° - \sin 35°$$

Their insight came from having learned techniques *verbally,* such as "If you have one term and want two terms, *make* two terms, and then operate on the result." From there the *verbal* knowledge of the composite argument properties, ". . . sine of first, cosine of second, plus cosine of first, sine of second," allowed them to think of adding and subtracting cos 13° sin 48°. When you see such creativity among your students, you will think of ways to orient your instruction to encourage this creativity.

The Quick Review problems in each section can provide a way of checking your instruction. We all omit a topic from time to time, occasionally unintentionally. Sooner or later that topic will arise as a quickie problem. When it does, just say, "Oh, here's how you do that." In five minutes you have filled a gap in their knowledge that might have taken a whole day of instruction if you had presented it as an independent topic.

One thing to remember as you assess your instruction is that variables really *vary*—they don't just stand for unknown constants. The independent variable x and the dependent variable $f(x)$ stand for different numbers at different times in the same problem. Like all concepts, this one must form in students' minds; it cannot be taught. If what you propose to teach encourages the growth of this concept, it is worth teaching in this course. If not, it is a candidate for skipping. If your students finish the course with this concept in their repertoire, they will be well prepared for calculus, in which they will deal with the rate at which variables vary.

Evaluating Students' Achievement

As instructors we are all familiar with the classic written test to evaluate achievement. This text and its supplementary materials have many such testing instruments and suggestions.

> **You don't get paid till the job's done *right*!**

I use this maxim as a guide to grading students' work. If a student's raw score on a regular test is below passing, he or she is assigned a zero until the corrections are completed *(correctly!)*. When the corrections are satisfactory, the student is assigned a score halfway between the raw score and the passing grade. This scheme lets the students know that I will not accept unsatisfactory work, but it gives them a chance to turn a disastrously low score into something that will not ruin their average. Yet the student cannot get a passing score simply by doing corrections. I do not use this grading procedure for cumulative tests, such as semester exams. The regular tests are regarded as "rehearsals" for these exams, and the student is expected to do satisfactorily the *first* time on the actual performance. This correction/new score grading procedure can be time-consuming, but it is rewarding from the standpoint of getting your students to do superior work.

> **You worry about the mathematics.**
> ***I* worry about your grade!**

This maxim gets at the idea that a grade is a *dependent* variable. The way to control a dependent variable is through the independent variable, mathematical knowledge in this case. I mention the correction/new score grading scheme to students only when it comes up in context, not at the beginning of the course. I count tests as 100 points each and homework (when it is graded) or group work as 10 or 20 points each. A cumulative test counts twice if it is above the individual student's average and just once if it is below. I determine the average simply by adding up the student's points and dividing by the total possible points.

> **Keep your pencil moving!**
> **You can't afford the luxury of feeling sorry for yourself.**

This maxim relates to maintaining concentration during a test. As long as a student is aggressively trying to work a problem, adrenaline will help with the concentration. If a student stops and starts thinking, "I don't know how to do this," the momentum is lost and the student's performance suffers. The analogy can be made to such diverse activities as winning at sports and the elephant Dumbo's ability to fly!

Sometimes during a test a student will ask a question like "How much is Problem 5 worth?" Worrying about grades while taking a test can cause students to score lower than they would if they had just concentrated on the mathematics. I deliberately leave off the point values of the problems. Students must decide from the context whether a particular problem is hard or easy.

> **You can't afford to use up your creative energy**
> **on tasks that should be routine.**

Students should be able to do certain tasks by reflex, without a lot of thought. The Quick Review problems give you a chance, almost daily, to assess students' ability to do so. Multiple-choice questions appear occasionally in these problem sets but are avoided elsewhere. As I found from writing problems for the College Board's Mathematics Achievement Tests (now called SAT-2), it is harder to write good, unambiguous multiple-choice questions than it is to grade free-response questions on a classroom set of papers.

> **If in doubt, try it out!**

Making and testing conjectures is a skill you can assess more effectively now that there are graphing calculators. This maxim gets at this fact. The Explorations in the *Instructor's Resource Book* are a particularly rich source of opportunities for conjecture. Students use conjecture for such purposes as finding the product of complex numbers in polar form, determining whether a combination of sinusoids is another sinusoid, or determining whether the point-to-focus distance on a conic section is really equal to the eccentricity times the point-to-directrix distance.

The availability of graphing technology has a drawback for grading students' tests. Students can plot the graph quickly. But if they have to transcribe the graph onto their papers, they lose time and may draw it inaccurately. One remedy is to include an accurately drawn graph on the test, as is done in problems in the student text, in Explorations, and in Section, Chapter, and Cumulative Tests. Students draw on these graphs, measuring angles and distances, before using algebraic techniques to confirm the conjecture. If your objective is to see if students can produce the graph on their graphers, such as in the fractals graphs of Chapter 11, ask them to show you their graphers with the completed graph. Put a checkmark on their papers when the graph is correct. Be sure to put such problems on a later part of the test so that everyone is not crowding around your desk at the same time!

Evaluating Programs

One way to evaluate your course is to solicit student input. I use a four-item questionnaire at the end of the first semester and at the end of the course. For midyear the questions are:

- What is the *one* most important thing you have learned in precalculus so far?
- What has been the most interesting part of the course?
- What has been the hardest part to understand?
- What changes would you suggest for the last half of the course?

I modify the questions slightly for the end of the course. Students fill out the questionnaires anonymously. You will receive interesting insights into how effective you have been! Sometimes students find that the hardest part of the course has also been the most important or most interesting part.

> **What you know, you might never use.**
> **What you don't know, you'll *definitely* never use!**

This maxim is useful for students who ask, "When will I ever *use* this stuff?" It is good to be able to show students applications for what they are learning. However, your assessment of the worth of a particular topic in your course must be based on your knowledge of where it fits into the big picture of mathematics, not on whether the students can see an immediate application.

A primary concern in evaluating your course involves the existence of externally written comprehensive exams, such as departmental finals or state-mandated tests. You must assess what you are doing and make decisions about whether your instruction will lead students to success on these exams.

Conclusions

> **Precalculus should draw students in, not filter them out.**

This maxim is at the heart of the reform mathematics movement. When higher mathematics was entirely dependent on algebraic methods, students had to "demonstrate their worthiness" for higher mathematics by mastering the algebra. Those found "unworthy" were filtered out. With ready access to graphing, numerical, and word processing technology, students can be "pumped into" the pipeline of people who must have mathematical skills. As you do the pumping, keep in mind these important attributes of assessment laid out in "The Assessment Principle" of NCTM's *Principles and Standards for School Mathematics*:

- *Assessment should enhance students' learning.* Assessment of activities such as observations, conversations, interviews, and interactive journals can help students learn through articulating their ideas and answering their instructor's questions. Also, when students understand what a correct response should entail, they will assume more responsibility for their own learning. This can be done through the use of a scoring guide, feedback on assessment tasks, and group discussions in which students present and evaluate different approaches to solving complex problems.

- *Assessment is a valuable tool for making instructional decisions.* Multiple approaches to assessment allow students to show in different ways what they know and can do. This gives students the opportunity to show their strengths. Also, instructors should make an effort to find out what students think about the tasks they are given, which will give insight into how to proceed with the course.

Precalculus with Trigonometry: Assessment Resources
© 2007 Key Curriculum Press

Section, Chapter, and Cumulative Tests

The Section, Chapter, and Cumulative Tests are adaptations of those used in the author's classroom in recent years. Most tests are designed for a 50-minute class period. Some of the cumulative tests are longer, and are so noted on the tests themselves. There are two forms of each test for your convenience.

You can use the tests in this section as they are, or as a basis for writing your own tests. The most effective tests for your students are often the ones you write with knowledge of your own students' abilities and levels of learning, using applications of current and local interest. For instance, use of names such as Darth Vader (and his daughter Ella) was current a number of years ago when the Star Wars movies were made, and became current again when the movies were revived in 1997. At other times such problems might seem outdated.

This table lists each test and the sections or chapters to which it corresponds.

Test Number	Sections/Chapters Covered	Test Number	Sections/Chapters Covered
1	1-1 to 1-3	22	Chapter 8
2	1-4 to 1-5	23	9-1 to 9-5
3	Chapter 1	24	Chapter 9
4	2-1 to 2-4	25	Chapters 7–9
5	2-5	26	10-1 to 10-4
6	Chapter 2	27	10-4 to 10-6
7	3-1 to 3-3	28	Chapter 10
8	3-4 to 3-8	29	11-1 to 11-4
9	Chapter 3	30	Chapter 11
10	4-1 to 4-3	31	12-1 to 12-4
11	4-4	32	Chapter 12
12	Chapter 4	33	13-1 to 13-4
13	5-1 to 5-3	34	13-5
14	5-4	35	Chapter 13
15	Chapter 5	36	Chapter 14
16	6-1 to 6-4	37	15-1 to 15-3
17	Chapter 6	38	Chapter 15
18	Chapters 1–6	39	Chapters 10–15
19	7-1 to 7-3		
20	7-4 to 7-6		
21	Chapter 7		

Tests on the *Instructor's Resource CD*

On the CD accompanying the *Instructor's Guide* you'll find PDF and Microsoft Word files of both forms of the Section, Chapter, and Cumulative Tests. You can use the tests in these ways:

• To make minor changes to text and numbers in the problems, or to reorder problems to create additional versions of tests for different classes

• To add problems of your own

- To delete problems from tests that are too long, or that cover content in the book that you have chosen to skip

- To compile and edit problems from various tests or explorations to make cumulative tests or extra practice masters

Consult the Read Me file on the CD for explicit instructions, warnings, and tips for working with the test files.

Test 1, Sections 1-1 to 1-3

Form A

Objective: Identify and transform functions and their graphs.

Part 1: No calculators allowed (1–8)

1. The grade you could get on a precalculus test depends on the number of hours you study the night before. If you study too long, however, you might score lower because you are too sleepy on the day of the test. Sketch a reasonable graph.

2. What type of function has a graph like the one you sketched in Problem 1?

3. If $f(x) = 2 \times x^3$, what type of function is f?

4. If $f(x) = 5 \times 3^x$, what type of function is f?

5. The graph shows a polynomial function. The domain of the function is $-4.2 \leq x \leq 4.7$. What is the range of the function?

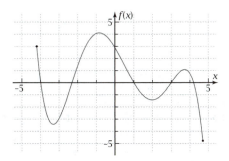

6. What type of function has a graph like this?

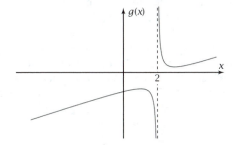

7. The graph of $f(x)$ is shown. Sketch the graph of function g, a horizontal dilation by a factor of $\frac{1}{4}$. Write $g(x)$ in terms of $f(x)$.

Equation: _____

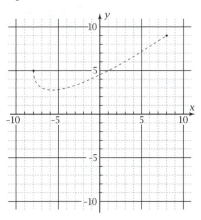

8. If $g(x) = f(x) - 7$, describe the transformation, and sketch the graph of function g.

Verbally: _____

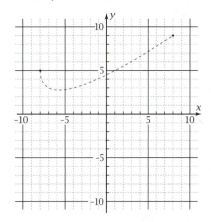

(Hand in this page to get the rest of the test.)

Part 2: Graphing calculators allowed (9–21)

9. The graph shows $f(x) = x^2 - 2x - 3$ plotted in the domain $-1 \le x \le 4$. Plot this graph using a friendly window. Divide by the Boolean variable $(x \ge -1$ and $x \le 4)$ to get the domain shown. Check your graph with your instructor.

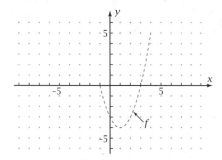

For Problems 10-14, identify the transformation of the graph of f (dashed) to get the graph of g (solid). Plot the graph of g on your grapher and state whether it checks.

10.

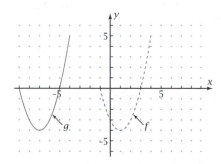

11.

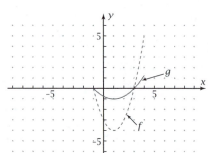

12.

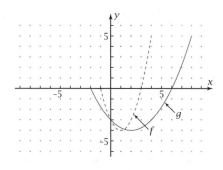

13.

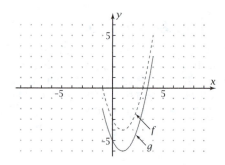

14.

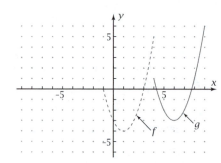

Shopping Cart Problem: For Problems 15–20: The shopping carts at a grocery store are each 52 in. long. A line of 6 carts pushed together has a total length of 109 in.

15. Make a sketch showing what the line of 6 carts would look like.

16. How many inches are added to the line for each cart? Show how you get your answer.

17. Let $f(n)$ be the length in inches for a line of n carts. Write an equation for $f(n)$ in terms of n.

18. What kind of function did you write in Problem 17?

19. Based on your equation in Problem 17, how long would a line of 15 carts be?

20. The store has a space exactly 20 ft long (240 in.) in which to put lines of carts. What is the greatest number of carts they can put in a line without exceeding the 240 in.? Show how you get your answer.

21. What did you learn as a result of taking this test that you did not know before?

Precalculus with Trigonometry: Assessment Resources
© 2007 Key Curriculum Press

Test 1, Sections 1-1 to 1-3

Form B

Objective: Identify and transform functions and their graphs.

Part 1: No calculators allowed (1–8)

1. You pour a cup of freshly brewed coffee but forget to drink it. As the coffee sits there, its temperature depends on the number of minutes that have passed since you poured it.

2. What type of function has a graph like the one you sketched in Problem 1?

3. If $f(x) = \dfrac{2}{x^2}$, what type of function is f?

4. If $f(x) = \dfrac{x^2}{2}$, what type of function is f?

5. The graph shows a polynomial function. The domain of the function is $-3 \le x \le 2.3$. What is the range of the function?

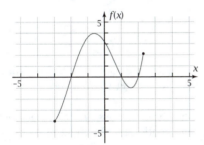

6. What type of function has a graph like this?

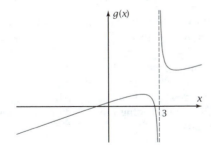

7. The graph of $f(x)$ is shown. Sketch the graph of function g, a horizontal dilation by a factor of $\frac{1}{2}$. Write $g(x)$ in terms of $f(x)$.

Equation: _____

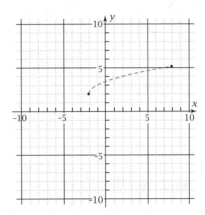

8. If $g(x) = f(x) - 7$, describe the transformation, and sketch the graph of function g.

Verbally: _____

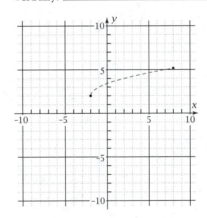

(Hand in this page to get the rest of the test.)

Test 1, Sections 1-1 to 1-3 continued   Form B

Part 2: Graphing calculators allowed (9–21)

9. The graph shows $-x^2 + 2x + 3$ plotted in the domain $-1 \le x \le 4$. Plot this graph using a friendly window. Divide by the Boolean variable ($x \ge -1$ and $x \le 4$) to get the domain shown. Check your graph with your instructor.

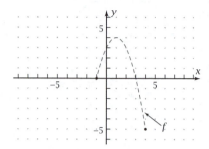

For Problems 10-14, identify the transformation of the graph of f (dashed) to get the graph of g (solid). Plot the graph of g on your grapher and state whether it checks.

10.

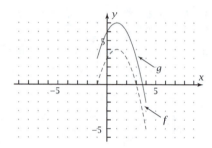

11.

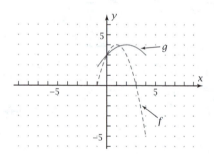

12.

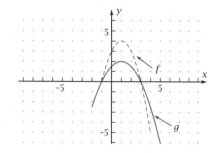

13.

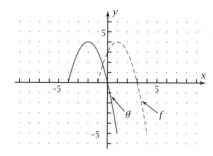

14.

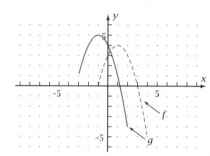

Drinking Cup Problem (15–20): Disposable drinking cups can be stacked so that one cup fits inside the next. A stack of 5 cups is 9.5 cm tall. Each cup is 7.5 cm tall.

15. Make a sketch showing what a stack of 5 cups would look like.

16. How many centimeters are added to the stack for each cup? Show how you get your answer.

17. Let $f(n)$ be the height in centimeters for a stack of n cups. Write an equation for $f(n)$ in terms of n.

18. What type of function did you write in Problem 17?

19. Based on your equation in Problem 17, how tall would a stack of 15 cups be?

20. The manufacturer packages the cups in boxes 32.2 cm tall. Each box holds a single stack of cups. What is the greatest number of cups that can be put in a stack without exceeding the 32.2 cm? Show how you get your answer.

21. What did you learn as a result of taking this test that you did not know before?

Test 2, Sections 1-4 and 1-5   Form A

Objective: Find the composition of two functions and the inverse of a function.

Part 1: No calculators allowed (1–10)

For Problems 1–7, the figure shows the graphs of two linear functions, $y = f(x)$ and $y = g(x)$.

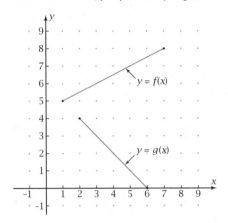

1. Write the domain and range of each function.

   f: Domain: _____ Range: _____

   g: Domain: _____ Range: _____

2. Read values of $g(x)$ from the graph. If the value of x is out of the domain of g, write "none."

x	$g(x)$
0	
1	
2	
3	
4	
5	
6	
7	
8	
9	

3. The value of $f(g(4))$ is 5.5. Show the two-step process by which you find this answer.

4. Put another column in the table for the values of $f(g(x))$. Write "none" where appropriate.

5. Circle a value of x in the table for which $g(x)$ is defined but $f(g(x))$ is undefined.

6. Plot the values of $f(g(x))$ on the given figure. If the points do not lie in a straight line, go back and check your work.

7. From your graph in Problem 6, write the domain and range of the composite function $f \circ g$.

   Domain: _____

   Range: _____

8. Suppose that a function has $f(5) = 7$. If the inverse of f is a function, what would $f^{-1}(7)$ equal?

9. The figure shows the graph of function f. On the figure, sketch the graph of the inverse of f.

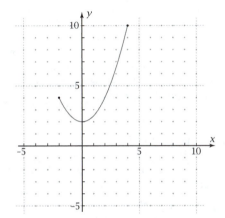

10. Prove that the inverse of f is not a function by showing that the inverse of f at $x = 4$ has two values.

(Hand in this page to get the rest of the test.)

Test 2, Sections 1-4 and 1-5 continued   Form A

Part 2: Graphing calculators allowed (11–24)

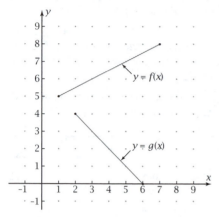

For Problems 11–15, the figure shows functions f and g from the first part of this test. The equations are

$f(x) = 0.5x + 4.5$ for $1 \le x \le 7$

$g(x) = 6 - x$ for $2 \le x \le 6$

11. To find the domain of the composite function $f \circ g$ algebraically, you must first make sure that $g(x)$ is in the domain of f. Show the steps in finding this requirement for the domain of $f \circ g$.

12. To finish finding the domain of $f \circ g$, you must make sure that x is in the domain of g. Combine this requirement with the requirement in Problem 11 to find the domain of $f \circ g$.

13. Plot $f(g(x))$ on your grapher by entering f as y_1, g as y_2, and $f \circ g$ as $y_3 = y_1(y_2(x))$. Use the window shown. Use thick style for y_3. Draw the resulting graph on the given figure.

14. Find an equation for $f(g(x))$ by substituting the expression for $g(x)$ into the equation for $f(x)$. Simplify as much as possible.

15. Plot the answer to Problem 14 as y_4. Does the result agree with the graph of y_3?

For Problems 16–18, let $f(x) = 0.5x + 4$.

16. Plot function f on this graph paper.

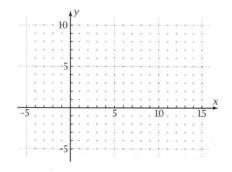

17. By appropriate substitution, find the equation for the inverse function, f^{-1}. Plot the answer on the graph paper in Problem 16.

18. Plot the line $y = x$ on the figure in Problem 16. How are the graphs of f and f^{-1} related to this line?

Problems 19-23 refer to the graph shown in the figure,

$f(x) = 0.5x^2 + 2$ for $-2 \le x \le 4$

This is the same function for which you found the inverse in Problem 9. In these problems you will learn an easy way to plot the inverse relation on your grapher.

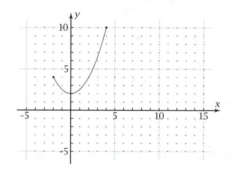

19. Plot these parametric equations.

$x_{1T} = t$

$y_{1T} = 0.5t^2 + 2$

Use a t-range of $[-2, 4]$ and the window shown in the figure. Does your graph agree with the figure?

20. Recall that the inverse of a function is found by interchanging the x and the y. Plot

$x_{2T} = 0.5t^2 + 2$

$y_{2T} = t$

Sketch the result on the given figure.

21. How are the domain and range of the inverse of f related to the domain and range of f?

22. Find a way to plot the line $y = x$ on the same screen as that in Problem 20. What did you enter in your grapher to do this?

23. How are the graphs of f and its inverse relation related to the line $y = x$?

24. What did you learn as a result of taking this test that you did not know before?

Precalculus with Trigonometry: Assessment Resources
© 2007 Key Curriculum Press

Test 2, Sections 1-4 and 1-5 Form B

Objective: Find the composition of two functions and the inverse of a function.

Part 1: No calculators allowed (1–10)

For Problems 1–7, the figure shows the graphs of two linear functions, $y = f(x)$ and $y = g(x)$.

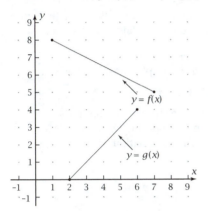

1. Write the domain and range of each function.

   f: Domain: _____ Range: _____

   g: Domain: _____ Range: _____

2. Read values of $g(x)$ from the graph. If the value of x is out of the domain of g, write "none."

x	g(x)
0	
1	
2	
3	
4	
5	
6	
7	
8	
9	

3. The value of $f(g(4))$ is 7.5. Show the two-step process by which you find this answer.

4. Put another column in the table for the values of $f(g(x))$. Write "none" where appropriate.

5. Circle a value of x in the table for which $g(x)$ is defined but $f(g(x))$ is undefined.

6. Plot the values of $f(g(x))$ on the given figure. If the points do not lie in a straight line, go back and check your work.

7. From your graph in Problem 6, write the domain and range of the composite function $f \circ g$.

   Domain: _____

   Range: _____

8. Suppose that a function has $f(3) = 1/5$. If the inverse of f is a function, what would $f^{-1}(1/5)$ equal?

9. The figure shows the graph of function f. On the figure, sketch the graph of the inverse of f.

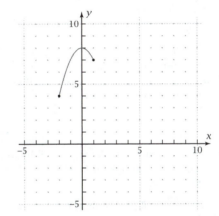

10. Prove that the inverse of f is not a function by showing that the inverse of f at $x = 7$ has two values.

(Hand in this page to get the rest of the test.)

Test 2, Sections 1-4 and 1-5 continued   Form B

Part 2: Graphing calculators allowed (11–24)

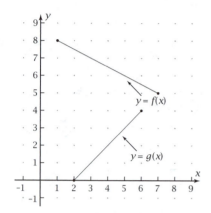

For Problems 11-15, the figure shows functions f and g from the first part of this test. The equations are

$$f(x) = -0.5x + 8.5 \qquad \text{for } 1 \le x \le 7$$

$$g(x) = x - 2 \qquad \text{for } 2 \le x \le 6$$

11. To find the domain of the composite function $f \circ g$ algebraically, you must first make sure that $g(x)$ is in the domain of f. Show the steps in finding this requirement for the domain of $f \circ g$.

12. To finish finding the domain of $f \circ g$, you must make sure that x is in the domain of g. Combine this requirement with the requirement in Problem 11 to find the domain of $f \circ g$.

13. Plot $f(g(x))$ on your grapher by entering f as y_1, g as y_2, and $f \circ g$ as $y_3 = y_1(y_2(x))$. Use the window shown. Use thick style for y_3. Draw the resulting graph on the given figure.

14. Find an equation for $f(g(x))$ by substituting the expression for $g(x)$ into the equation for $f(x)$. Simplify as much as possible.

15. Plot the answer to Problem 14 as y_4. Does the result agree with the graph of y_3?

For Problems 16-18, let $f(x) = -2x + 3$.

16. Plot function f on this graph paper.

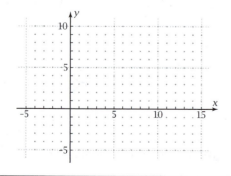

17. By appropriate substitution, find the equation for the inverse function, f^{-1}. Plot the answer on the graph paper in Problem 16.

18. Plot the line $y = x$ on the figure in Problem 16. How are the graphs of f and f^{-1} related to this line?

Problems 19-23 refer to the graph shown in the figure,

$$f(x) = -x^2 + 8, \, -2 \le x \le 1$$

This is the same function for which you found the inverse in Problem 9. In these problems you will learn an easy way to plot the inverse relation on your grapher.

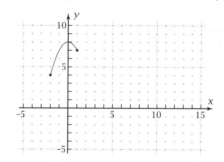

19. Plot these parametric equations.

$$x_{1T} = t$$

$$y_{1T} = -t^2 + 8$$

Use a t-range of $[-2, 1]$ and the window shown in the figure. Does your graph agree with the figure?

20. Recall that the inverse of a function is found by interchanging the x and the y. Plot

$$x_{2T} = -t^2 + 8$$

$$y_{2T} = t$$

Sketch the result on the given figure.

21. How are the domain and range of the inverse of f related to the domain and range of f?

22. Find a way to plot the line $y = x$ on the same screen as that in Problem 20. What did you enter in your grapher to do this?

23. How are the graphs of f and its inverse relation related to the line $y = x$?

24. What did you learn as a result of taking this test that you did not know before?

Precalculus with Trigonometry: Assessment Resources
© 2007 Key Curriculum Press

Test 3, Chapter 1   Form A

Objective: Find the composition of two functions and the inverse of a function.

Part 1: No calculators allowed (1–11)

For Problems 1–4, name the type of function graphed, and write its general equation.

1. Type: _____ Equation: _____

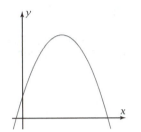

2. Type: _____ Equation: _____

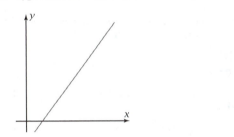

3. Type: _____ Equation: _____

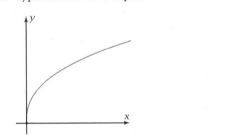

4. Type: _____ Equation: _____

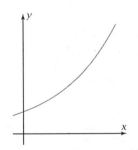

5. If $f(-x) = -f(x)$ for all x, f is an _____ function.

6. If $f(-x) = f(x)$ for all x, f is an _____ function.

For Problems 7 and 8, describe how the graph of f (dashed) was transformed to get the graph of g (solid). Write an equation for $g(x)$ in terms of f.

7. Verbally: _____

   Equation: _____

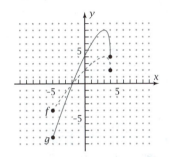

8. Verbally: _____

   Equation: _____

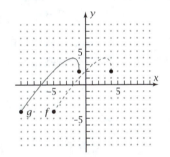

9. The figure shows the graph of a function f. On this figure, sketch the graph of the inverse relation.

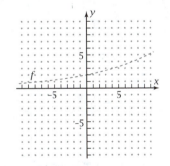

10. On the figure in Problem 9, sketch the graph of the line $y = x$. Explain how the graph of f and its inverse is related to this line.

11. Is the inverse relation in Problem 9 a function? How can you tell?

(Hand in this page to get the rest of the test.)

Part 2: Graphing calculators allowed (12–26)

Problems 12–15 refer to this graph of $y = f(x)$.

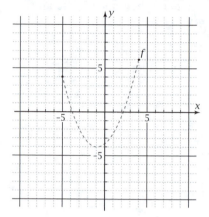

12. Give the domain and range of f.

13. If $y = 1.5\, f(x)$, describe the transformation, and sketch the graph of the transformed function.

14. If $y = f\left(\frac{1}{2}x\right)$, describe the transformation, and sketch the graph of the transformed function here.

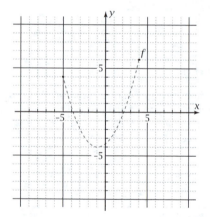

15. Explain why the inverse relation for f is not a function.

For Problems 16–19, the figure shows the graphs of

$y_1 = f(x) = -0.5x + 5$ for $4 \le x \le 7$

$y_2 = g(x) = -x + 9$ for $1 \le x \le 6$

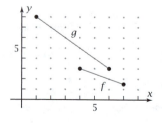

16. On your grapher, plot the graphs of f and g, and the composition $f \circ g$. From your graph, what appears to be the domain and range of the composite function?

17. Show the two-step process in finding $f(g(3))$.

18. Explain why $f(g(6))$ is undefined even though $f(6)$ and $g(6)$ are both defined.

19. Show the algebraic steps in calculating the domain of $f \circ g$. Does the answer agree with your graphical answer in Problem 16?

20. In Problem 9, the given function has the equation $y = 2 \cdot 1.1^x$. Plot the graph of this function and the graph of the inverse function on the same screen, using parametric mode. Use the same scale on both axes. Show how you entered the equations. Sketch the graph.

Flower Pot Problem (21–25): Flora Lee owns a plant nursery. She wants to stack together flower pots of a given size and pack them into cartons. Her employee Jack Potts figures out that the height of a stack of these kinds of pots is given by the function

$$f(n) = 2.7n + 6.3$$

where n is the number of pots and $f(n)$ is the height of the stack in centimeters.

21. What kind of function is this?

22. How high is one pot?

23. Find the height of a two-pot stack. Explain to Flora why this isn't twice as high as one pot.

24. Let $y = 2.7n + 6.3$. Solve this equation for n in terms of y.

25. The cartons in which Flora plans to pack the pots are 35 cm tall. What is the tallest stack of pots she can fit into a carton? Show how you got your answer.

26. What did you learn as a result of taking this test that you did not know before?

Precalculus with Trigonometry: Assessment Resources
© 2007 Key Curriculum Press

Test 3, Chapter 1

Form B

Objective: Find the composition of two functions and the inverse of a function.

Part 1: No calculators allowed (1–11)

For Problems 1–4, name the type of function graphed, and write its general equation.

1. Type: _____ Equation: _____

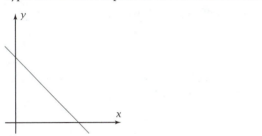

2. Type: _____ Equation: _____

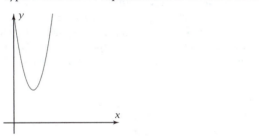

3. Type: _____ Equation: _____

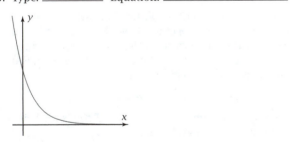

4. Type: _____ Equation: _____

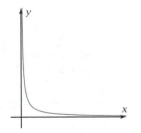

5. The function f is an even function if and only if
   _____ .

6. The function f is an odd function if and only if
   _____ .

For Problems 7 and 8, describe how the graph of f (dashed) was transformed to get the graph of g (solid). Write an equation for $g(x)$ in terms of f.

7. Verbally: _____

   Equation: _____

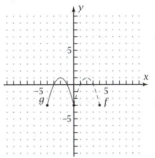

8. Verbally: _____

   Equation: _____

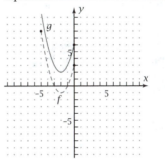

9. The figure shows the graph of a function f. On this figure, sketch the graph of the inverse relation.

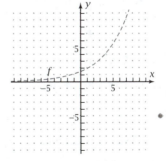

10. On the figure in Problem 9, sketch the graph of the line $y = x$. Explain how the graph of f and its inverse is related to this line.

11. Is the inverse relation in Problem 9 a function? How can you tell?

(Hand in this page to get the rest of the test.)

Test 3, Chapter 1 continued   Form B

Part 2: Graphing calculators allowed (12–26)

Problems 12–15 refer to this graph of $y = f(x)$.

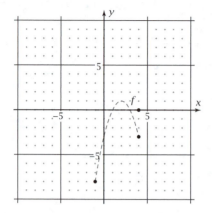

12. Give the domain and range of f.

13. If $y = 0.5 f(x)$, describe the transformation, and sketch the graph of the transformed function.

14. If $y = f\left(\frac{1}{2}x\right)$, describe the transformation, and sketch the graph of the transformed function here.

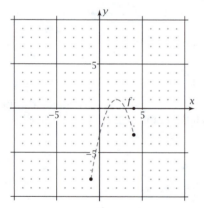

15. Explain why the inverse relation for f is not a function.

For Problems 16–19, the figure shows the graphs of

$$y_1 = f(x) = -2x + 5 \quad \text{for } 1 \le x \le 4$$
$$y_2 = g(x) = x + 1 \quad \text{for } 2 \le x \le 7$$

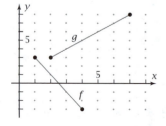

16. On your grapher, plot the graphs of f and g, and the composition $f \circ g$. From your graph, what appears to be the domain and range of the composite function?

17. Show the two-step process in finding $f(g(2))$.

18. Explain why $f(g(4))$ is undefined even though $f(4)$ and $g(4)$ are both defined.

19. Show the algebraic steps in calculating the domain of $f \circ g$. Does the answer agree with your graphical answer in Problem 16?

20. In Problem 9, the given function has the equation $y = 1.5 \cdot 1.3^x$. Plot the graph of this function and the graph of the inverse function on the same screen, using parametric mode. Use the same scale on both axes. Show how you entered the equations. Sketch the graph.

Flower Pot Problem (21–25): Flora Lee owns a flower shop. She wants to stack together flower baskets of a given size and pack them into cartons. Her employee Jack Potts figures out that the height of a stack of these kinds of baskets is given by the function

$$f(n) = 1.5n + 3.5$$

where n is the number of baskets and $f(n)$ is the height of the stack in inches.

21. What kind of function is this?

22. How high is one basket?

23. Find the height of a two-basket stack. Explain to Flora why this isn't twice as high as one basket.

24. Let $y = 1.5n + 3.5$. Solve this equation for n in terms of y.

25. The cartons in which Flora plans to pack the baskets are 36 inches tall. What is the tallest stack of baskets she can fit into a carton? Show how you got your answer.

26. What did you learn as a result of taking this test that you did not know before?

Precalculus with Trigonometry: Assessment Resources
© 2007 Key Curriculum Press

Test 4, Sections 2-1 to 2-4   Form A

Objective: Use the definitions of the six trigonometric functions to find function values and plot graphs.

Part 1: No calculators allowed (1–4)

1. • Sketch angle θ with terminal side containing the point $(-5, -2)$.
   • Mark the reference angle.
   • Write the six trigonometric functions of θ.

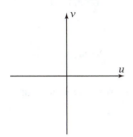

2. • Sketch an angle of 300° in standard position.
   • Mark the reference angle and its measure.
   • Write the six trigonometric functions of 300°.

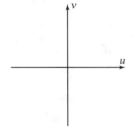

3. • Sketch an angle of 135° in standard position.
   • Mark the reference angle and its measure.
   • Write the six trigonometric functions of 135°.

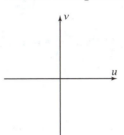

4. The figure shows the periodic function $y = \cos\theta$ (dashed) and a transformed function $g(\theta)$ that involves two transformations. Name the transformations and write an equation for $g(\theta)$.

   Verbally: _____

       and _____

   Equation: $g(\theta) =$ _____

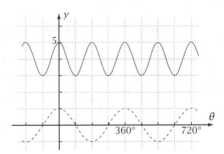

(Hand in this page to get the rest of the test.)

Part 2: Graphing calculators allowed (5–19)

For Problems 5–7, use your calculator to find the indicated value.

5. cot 179°

6. sec (−58°)

7. csc 290°

8. Sketch an angle of −100° in standard position. Mark the reference angle and write its measure.

9. Sketch an angle of 2272° in standard position. Mark the reference angle and write its measure.

10. Sketch an angle of 85° in standard position. Mark its reference angle and write its measure.

11. Find sin 153° and sin 207°. Draw a sketch showing both angles and their reference angles. Based on the sketch, explain why sin 153° and sin 207° have the same magnitude but opposite signs.

12. Find cos 180° on your calculator. Then draw a sketch showing 180° in a *uv*-coordinate system. Pick a point on the terminal side and write the values of *u*, *v*, and *r*. Explain why your calculator's answer for cos 180° is consistent with the definition of cosine.

13. The figure shows a right triangle with acute angles of 20° and 70°. Find sin 20° and cos 70°. Based on the "opposite, adjacent, hypotenuse" definitions of sine and cosine, explain why the two answers are equal.

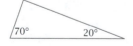

14. You have learned that $f^{-1}(x)$ is the inverse function for $f(x)$, the same function with *x* and *y* reversed. The $\sin^{-1}$ key on your calculator does the same thing for the sine function.

    • Find sin 30°.

    • Find $\sin^{-1} 0.5$.

    • What do you notice about the two answers?

    • Show that $\frac{1}{\sin 0.5°}$ does *not* equal $\sin^{-1} 0.5$.

15. Using what you observed in Problem 14,

    • Find θ if sin θ = 0.9.

    • Without clearing the answer, press sin (Ans).

    • What do you notice?

16. The figure shows an angle whose terminal side contains the point (5, 7). Based on what you observed about inverse trigonometric functions in Problems 14 and 15, find the measure of θ.

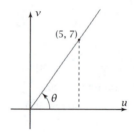

17. On your grapher, make a table of values of cos θ for each 30°, starting at −90°. Plot the values on the graph paper, starting at −90° and ending at 360°. Connect the points with a smooth curve.

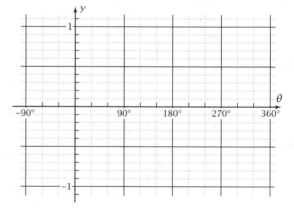

18. On your grapher, plot the graph of y = cos θ. Use the same window as the one shown in Problem 17. Does the graph agree with Problem 17?

19. What did you learn as a result of taking this test that you did not know before?

Precalculus with Trigonometry: Assessment Resources
© 2007 Key Curriculum Press

Test 4, Sections 2-1 to 2-4   Form B

Objective: Use the definitions of the six trigonometric functions to find function values and plot graphs.

Part 1: No calculators allowed (1–4)

1. • Sketch positive angle θ with terminal side containing the point (4, −2).

   • Mark the reference angle.

   • Write the six trigonometric functions of θ.

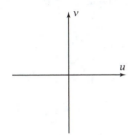

2. • Sketch an angle of 150° in standard position.

   • Mark the reference angle and its measure.

   • Write the six trigonometric functions of 150°.

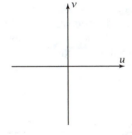

3. • Sketch an angle of 225° in standard position.

   • Mark the reference angle and its measure.

   • Write the six trigonometric functions of 225°.

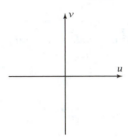

4. The figure shows the periodic function $y = \sin \theta$ (dashed) and a transformed function $g(\theta)$ that involves two transformations. Name the transformations and write an equation for $g(\theta)$.

   Verbally: _____

   and _____

   Equation: $g(\theta) =$ _____

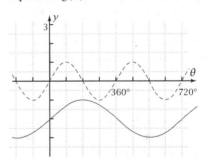

(Hand in this page to get the rest of the test.)

Part 2: Graphing calculators allowed (5–19)

For Problems 5–7, use your calculator to find the indicated value.

5. cot 129°

6. sec (−98°)

7. csc 171°

8. Sketch an angle of −220° in standard position. Mark the reference angle and write its measure.

9. Sketch an angle of 5661° in standard position. Mark the reference angle and write its measure.

10. Sketch an angle of 54° in standard position. Mark its reference angle and write its measure.

11. Find sin 147° and sin 213°. Draw a sketch showing both angles and their reference angles. Based on the sketch, explain why sin 147° and sin 213° have the same magnitude but opposite signs.

12. Find sin 270° on your calculator. Then draw a sketch showing 270° in a *uv*-coordinate system. Pick a point on the terminal side and write the values of *u*, *v*, and *r*. Explain why your calculator's answer for cos 270° is consistent with the definition of cosine.

13. The figure shows a right triangle with acute angles of 35° and 55°. Find sin 35° and cos 55°. Based on the "opposite, adjacent, hypotenuse" definitions of sine and cosine, explain why the two answers are equal.

14. You have learned that $f^{-1}(x)$ is the inverse function for $f(x)$, the same function with *x* and *y* reversed. The $\cos^{-1}$ key on your calculator does the same thing for the cosine function.

   • Find cos 60°.

   • Find $\cos^{-1}$ 0.5.

   • What do you notice about the two answers?

   • Show that $\frac{1}{\cos 0.5°}$ does *not* equal $\cos^{-1}$ 0.5.

15. Using what you observed in Problem 14,

   • Find θ if cos θ = 0.9.

   • Without clearing the answer, press cos (Ans).

   • What do you notice?

16. The figure shows an angle whose terminal side contains the point (2, 3). Based on what you observed about inverse trigonometric functions in Problems 14 and 15, find the measure of θ.

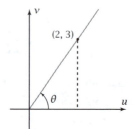

17. On your grapher, make a table of values of sin θ for each 30°, starting at −90°. Plot the values on the graph paper, starting at −90° and ending at 360°. Connect the points with a smooth curve.

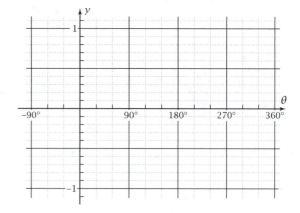

18. On your grapher, plot the graph of $y = \sin \theta$. Use the same window as the one shown in Problem 17. Does the graph agree with Problem 17?

19. What did you learn as a result of taking this test that you did not know before?

Test 5, Section 2-5   Form A

Objective: Use trigonometric functions to find inverse functions and sides and angles in right triangles.

Part 1: No calculators allowed (1–9)

1. For this right triangle, write

   sin M =

   cos M =

   tan M =

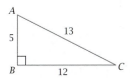

Problems 2–5 refer to right triangle *ABC*.

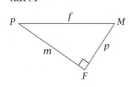

2. If the two legs are 5 and 12, as shown, show by calculation that the hypotenuse is 13.

3. How would you find the measure of angle *C* using the inverse sine?

4. How would you find the measure of angle *C* using the inverse cosine?

5. How would you find the measure of angle *C* using the inverse tangent?

Problems 6–8 refer to the graph of $y = \sin \theta$.

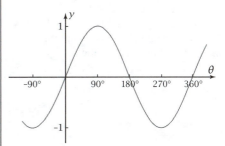

6. Darken the principal branch of the graph.

7. The principal branch is said to be a *one-to-one* function. Explain what this means.

8. Explain why the principal branch is an invertible function but the entire sine function is not.

9. Draw a sketch showing the difference in meaning between an angle of elevation and an angle of depression.

(Hand in this page to get the rest of the test.)

Test 5, Section 2-5 continued

Form A

Part 2: Graphing calculators allowed (10–20)

Calvin's Hill Problem (10–14): Calvin is walking on hills in Berkeley, California. The figure shows that when he is standing "flat-footed" on level ground, his center of gravity is 90 cm above the ground. The tip of his toe is 20 cm from the point where this vertical line meets the ground.

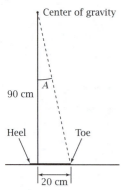

10. Calculate the measure of angle *A* between the vertical and a line from the center of gravity to the tip of his toe.

11. Calvin walks down Marin Ave., one of the steepest streets in the United States. In one block the street makes an angle of 13° with the horizontal. Sketch a figure representing Calvin standing flat-footed and facing downhill on Marin Ave. (Use the space above.)

12. If Calvin stands flat-footed as in Problem 11, he will not fall over if a vertical line from his center of gravity is not beyond his toe. Would he fall over if he stands flat-footed on Marin Ave.? Explain how you decided.

13. Calvin takes one pace downhill on Marin Ave., going a slant distance of 65 cm.
    • How far does he go down?
    • How far does he go horizontally?

14. On Calvin's street map, this block of Marin Ave. measures 330 m. This, of course, is a horizontal distance.
    • How far downhill will Calvin go if he walks the entire block?
    • What slant distance will he have gone?

Ship Sailing Problem (15–19): A ship is sailing due east. The captain sights a buoy ahead of the ship at an angle of 25° to the right of the path of motion. By radar, she determines that the buoy is 9 miles from the ship.

15. Draw a horizontal line representing the path of the ship. Draw accurately the position of the buoy, using a scale of 1 cm for 1 mile.

16. Using only the given information, calculate
    • The closest the ship will come to the buoy
    • How far the ship must go to reach this closest point of approach

17. Measure on the drawing in Problem 15 the two distances you calculated in Problem 16. How close do they come to the calculated distances?

18. If the ship sails 5 miles from its initial point in Problem 15, calculate the angle to the path at which the captain must look to see the buoy.

19. The ship sails 3 miles beyond the closest point of approach to the buoy. To see the buoy now, the captain must look *back* along a line that is at an *obtuse* angle to the ship's path. Calculate the measure of this obtuse angle.

20. What did you learn as a result of taking this test that you did not know before?

Precalculus with Trigonometry: Assessment Resources
© 2007 Key Curriculum Press

Objective: Use trigonometric functions to find inverse functions and sides and angles in right triangles.

Part 1: No calculators allowed (1–9)

1. For this right triangle, write

   $\sin P =$

   $\cos P =$

   $\tan P =$

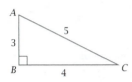

Problems 2–5 refer to right triangle *ABC*.

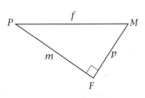

2. If the two legs are 3 and 4, as shown, show by calculation that the hypotenuse is 5.

3. How would you find the measure of angle *C* using the inverse sine?

4. How would you find the measure of angle *C* using the inverse cosine?

5. How would you find the measure of angle *C* using the inverse tangent?

Problems 6–8 refer to the graph of $y = \cos \theta$.

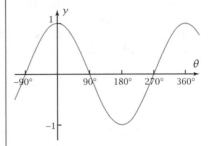

6. Darken the principal branch of the graph.

7. The principal branch is said to be a *one-to-one* function. Explain what this means.

8. Explain why the principal branch is an invertible function but the entire cosine function is not.

9. Draw a sketch showing the difference in meaning between an angle of elevation and an angle of depression.

(Hand in this page to get the rest of the test.)

Test 5, Section 2-5 continued   Form B

Part 2: Graphing calculators allowed (10–20)

Calvin's Hill Problem (10–14): Calvin is walking on hills in San Francisco, California. The figure shows that when he is standing "flat-footed" on level ground, his center of gravity is 80 cm above the ground. The tip of his toe is 25 cm from the point where this vertical line meets the ground.

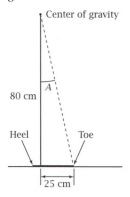

10. Calculate the measure of angle *A* between the vertical and a line from the center of gravity to the tip of his toe.

11. Calvin walks down Jones St., one of the steepest streets in the United States. In one block the street makes an angle of 20° with the horizontal. Sketch a figure representing Calvin standing flat-footed and facing downhill on Jones St. (Use the space above.)

12. If Calvin stands flat-footed as in Problem 11, he will not fall over if a vertical line from his center of gravity is not beyond his toe. Would he fall over if he stands flat-footed on Jones St.? Explain how you decided.

13. Calvin takes one pace downhill on Jones St., going a slant distance of 55 cm.
    • How far does he go down?
    • How far does he go horizontally?

14. On Calvin's street map, this block of Jones St. measures 350 m. This, of course, is a horizontal distance.
    • How far downhill will Calvin go if he walks the entire block?
    • What slant distance will he have gone?

Ship Sailing Problem (15–19): A ship is sailing due east. The captain sights a buoy ahead of the ship at an angle of 20° to the right of the path of motion. By radar, she determines that the buoy is 8 miles from the ship.

15. Draw a horizontal line representing the path of the ship. Draw accurately the position of the buoy, using a scale of 1 cm for 1 mile.

16. Using only the given information, calculate
    • The closest the ship will come to the buoy
    • How far the ship must go to reach this closest point of approach

17. Measure on the drawing in Problem 15 the two distances you calculated in Problem 16. How close do they come to the calculated distances?

18. If the ship sails 5 miles from its initial point in Problem 15, calculate the angle to the path at which the captain must look to see the buoy.

19. The ship sails 2 miles beyond the closest point of approach to the buoy. To see the buoy now, the captain must look *back* along a line that is at an *obtuse* angle to the ship's path. Calculate the measure of this obtuse angle.

20. What did you learn as a result of taking this test that you did not know before?

Precalculus with Trigonometry: Assessment Resources
© 2007 Key Curriculum Press

Test 6, Chapter 2   Form A

Objective: Find trigonometric functions of angles, and work problems from right triangle trigonometry.

Part 1: No calculators allowed (1–8)

1. The figure shows an angle θ in standard position, with terminal side containing the point (−7, 4).

   • Mark the reference angle.

   • Write the six trigonometric functions of θ.

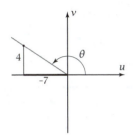

2. • Sketch an angle of 300° in standard position.

   • Mark the reference angle and find its measure.

   • Write the six trigonometric functions of 300°.

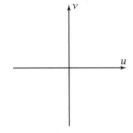

3. The figure shows an angle of 270° in standard position, with a point on the terminal side. A circle centered at the origin goes through this point. Explain why sin 270° = −1.

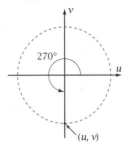

4. Explain why sec 270° is undefined.

5. Find the exact value of sin 225°.

6. The number of minutes it takes someone to run a mile depends on the speed at which he or she runs. Sketch a reasonable graph.

7. The time of sunset depends on the day of the year. Sketch a reasonable graph.

8. Only one of the functions in Problems 6 and 7 is periodic. Which one?

(Hand in this page to get the rest of the test.)

Part 2: Graphing calculators allowed (9–22)

9. Find sec 77°.

10. Find cot 158°.

11. Find csc (–190°).

12. Find $\cos^{-1} 0.3$. Explain the meaning of the answer.

13. For $\theta = 2812°$,
   - Find a coterminal angle between 0° and 360°.
   - Sketch the angle in standard position.
   - Mark the reference angle and find its measure.

14. Calculate the measure of side x.

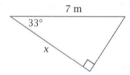

15. Calculate the measure of side y.

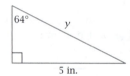

16. Calculate the measure of angle A.

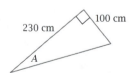

17. *Cable Car Problem:* One of the steeper streets in the United States is the 800 block of Powell Street in San Francisco, where cable cars run. Calvin measured on a brick wall 33 cm across and 5 cm down, as shown in the figure. Calculate the angle Powell Street makes with the horizontal.

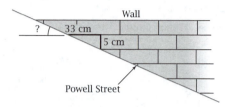

18. Here is the graph of $f(\theta) = \cos \theta$ (dashed). Function $g(\theta)$ (solid) is a horizontal translation and a vertical translation of function f. Write an equation for $g(\theta)$.

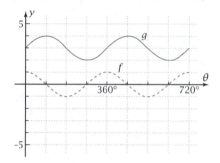

Building Height Problem (19-21): From a point in the parking lot, the angle of elevation to the top of an auditorium is 32°. From a point 30 ft closer to the auditorium, the angle of elevation is 47°.

19. Construct accurately the two angles and distance described. Use 1 cm for each 20 ft.

20. By measuring on your figure, estimate the height of the auditorium.

21. Calculate the height of the auditorium from the given information. Does the measured height in Problem 20 agree with the calculated height?

22. What did you learn as a result of taking this test that you did not know before?

Precalculus with Trigonometry: Assessment Resources
© 2007 Key Curriculum Press

Objective: Find trigonometric functions of angles, and work problems from right triangle trigonometry.

Part 1: No calculators allowed (1–8)

1. The figure shows an angle θ in standard position, with terminal side containing the point (4, −3).

   • Mark the reference angle.

   • Write the six trigonometric functions of θ.

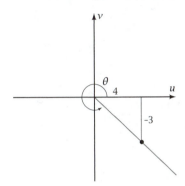

2. • Sketch an angle of 120° in standard position.

   • Mark the reference angle and find its measure.

   • Write the six trigonometric functions of 120°.

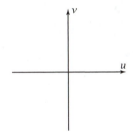

3. The figure shows an angle of 180° in standard position, with a point on the terminal side. A circle centered at the origin goes through this point. Explain why cos 180° = −1.

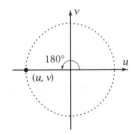

4. Explain why csc 180° is undefined.

5. Find the exact value of sin 315°.

6. The number of minutes it takes someone to hike a mile depends on the speed at which he or she hikes. Sketch a reasonable graph.

7. The pendulum in a clock swings back and forth. The distance from the end of the pendulum to the left side of the clock depends on time. Sketch a reasonable graph.

8. Only one of the functions in Problems 6 and 7 is periodic. Which one?

(Hand in this page to get the rest of the test.)

Part 2: Graphing calculators allowed (9–22)

9. Find csc 33°.

10. Find cot 122°.

11. Find sec (−130°).

12. Find $\tan^{-1}$ (0.7). Explain the meaning of the answer.

13. For $\theta = 3025°$,
    - Find a coterminal angle between 0° and 360°.
    - Sketch the angle in standard position.
    - Mark the reference angle and find its measure.

14. Calculate the measure of side x.

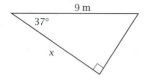

15. Calculate the measure of side y.

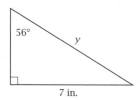

16. Calculate the measure of angle A.

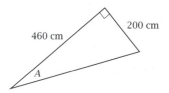

17. *Cable Car Problem:* One of the steeper streets in the United States is the 800 block of Powell Street in San Francisco, where cable cars run. Calvin measured on a brick wall 66 cm across and 10 cm down, as shown in the figure. Calculate the angle Powell Street makes with the horizontal.

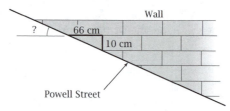

18. Here is the graph of $f(\theta) = \sin \theta$ (dashed). Function $g(\theta)$ (solid) is a horizontal translation and a vertical translation of function f. Write an equation for $g(\theta)$.

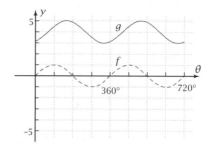

Building Height Problem (19-21): From a point in the parking lot, the angle of elevation to the top of an auditorium is 25°. From a point 30 ft closer to the auditorium, the angle of elevation is 40°.

19. Construct accurately the two angles and distance described. Use 1 cm for each 10 ft.

20. By measuring on your figure, estimate the height of the auditorium.

21. Calculate the height of the auditorium from the given information. Does the measured height in Problem 20 agree with the calculated height?

22. What did you learn as a result of taking this test that you did not know before?

Test 7, Sections 3-1 to 3-3

Form A

Objective: Draw graphs of sinusoids and of tangent and secant functions.

Part 1: No calculators allowed (1–9)

1. Darken exactly one cycle of this sinusoid.

2. Show the period of this sinusoid.

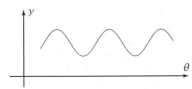

3. Show a critical point. Show a point of inflection. Identify which is which.

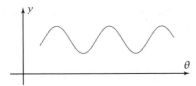

4. Show the phase displacement (for cosine).

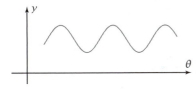

5. At the point shown, is this graph concave up or concave down?

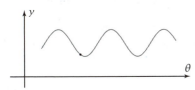

6. What is the period of $y = 2 + 3 \sin 6(\theta - 4°)$?

7. The dashed graph shows $y = \cos \theta$. Use this graph and the fact that $\sec \theta = \frac{1}{\cos \theta}$ to sketch the graph of $y = \sec \theta$.

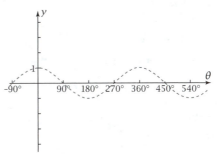

8. The dashed graph is $y = \cos \theta$ and the solid graph is $y = \sin \theta$. Use these graphs and the quotient property to draw the asymptotes and θ-intercepts of $y = \cot \theta$. (You don't need to draw the graph.)

$$\cot \theta = \frac{\cos \theta}{\sin \theta} \text{ (quotient property)}$$

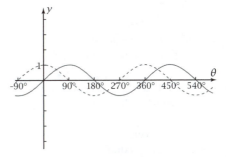

9. Sketch: $y = 5 + 2 \cos 4(\theta - 20°)$

Show units on the two axes.

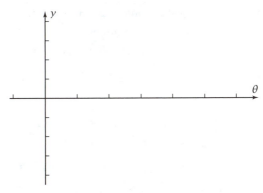

(Hand in this page to get the rest of the test.)

Test 7, Sections 3-1 to 3-3 continued   Form A

Part 2: Graphing calculators allowed (10–24)

10. For $y = -7 + 3 \cos 5(\theta - 13°)$, identify the
   - Vertical dilation
   - Vertical translation
   - Horizontal dilation
   - Horizontal translation

11. For the sinusoid in Problem 10, identify the
   - Amplitude
   - Period
   - Phase displacement (for cosine)
   - Sinusoidal axis location

12. The graph shows a half-cycle of a sinusoid. Sketch at least one complete cycle of the sinusoid.

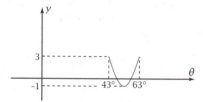

13. Write a particular equation of the sinusoid in Problem 12 using the cosine function.

14. For the sinusoid in Problem 12, write another particular equation using the sine function.

15. If the sinusoid in Problem 12 were extended to $\theta = 5461°$, what would y equal?

16. For $y = \tan \theta$, in the figure,
   - Darken one complete cycle.
   - Draw all vertical asymptotes in this window.
   - Write the θ-value at the rightmost θ-intercept.
   - Mark a point where the graph is concave down.

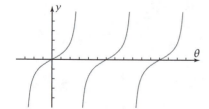

17. For $y = \csc \theta$, in the figure,
   - Darken one complete cycle.
   - Draw all vertical asymptotes in this window.
   - Mark a critical point.
   - Give the y-value at the critical point you marked.

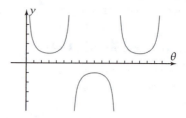

18. The tangent function can have a vertical dilation, such as

   $y = 3 \tan \theta$

   But the tangent function does not have an amplitude. Explain why not.

Ferris Wheel Problem (19–23): Ella Vader (Darth's other daughter) rides a Ferris wheel. As the wheel turns, her distance, y, from the ground, measured in feet, varies sinusoidally with time, t, measured in seconds, according to the equation

   $y = 25 + 20 \sin 18(t + 3)$

Angle θ, in degrees, shown in the figure, is equal to the argument of the sine function, $\theta = 18(t + 3)$.

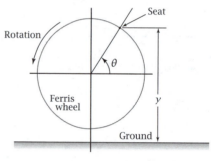

19. The last seat was filled, and the Ferris wheel started rotating at time $t = 0$ s. What was θ at this time? How high above the ground was Ella at this time?

20. When $t = 1$ s, what was θ? By how many degrees did the Ferris wheel rotate in this 1 s? Where do you find this number of degrees per second in the equation for y?

21. How high above the ground was Ella at $t = 1$ s?

22. What is the period of the sinusoid? That is, how long does it take for the Ferris wheel to make a complete 360° revolution?

23. Sketch two cycles of the sinusoid of y as a function of t. Put enough numbers on the axes so that your instructor can tell that you understand the meanings of the 25, the 20, and the 3 in the equation and the period of the sinusoid.

24. What did you learn as a result of taking this test that you did not know before?

Precalculus with Trigonometry: Assessment Resources
© 2007 Key Curriculum Press

Test 7, Sections 3-1 to 3-3   Form B

Objective: Draw graphs of sinusoids and of tangent and secant functions.

Part 1: No calculators allowed (1–9)

1. What is represented by the darkened portion of this sinusoid graph?

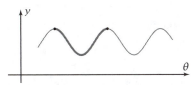

2. What is represented by the vertical lines on this sinusoid graph?

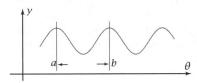

3. Point *A* on the sinusoid graph below is called

   a(n) _____

   Point *B* on the sinusoid graph below is called

   a(n) _____

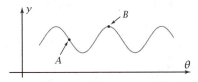

4. What is shown by the horizontal arrow on the cosine graph below?

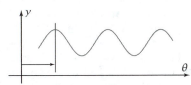

5. At the point shown, is this graph concave up or concave down?

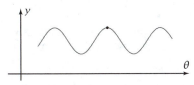

6. What is the period of $y = 1 + 2 \sin 4(\theta - 30°)$?

7. The dashed graph shows $y = \sin \theta$. Use this graph and the fact that $\csc \theta = \frac{1}{\sin \theta}$ to sketch the graph of $y = \csc \theta$.

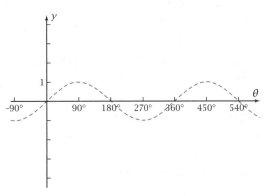

8. The dashed graph is $y = \cos \theta$ and the solid graph is $y = \sin \theta$. Use these graphs and the quotient property to draw the asymptotes and θ-intercepts of $y = \tan \theta$. (You don't need to draw the graph.)

$$\tan \theta = \frac{\sin \theta}{\cos \theta} \text{ (quotient property)}$$

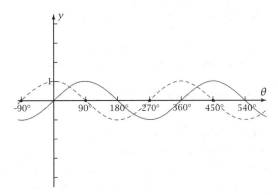

9. Sketch: $y = -5 + 3 \cos 6(\theta - 30°)$

   Show units on the two axes.

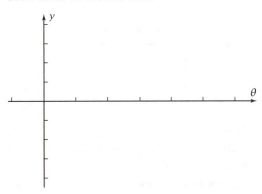

(Hand in this page to get the rest of the test.)

Test 7, Sections 3-1 to 3-3 continued   Form B

Part 2: Graphing calculators allowed (10–24)

10. For $y = 3 + 7 \cos 4(\theta - 20°)$, identify the
    - Vertical dilation
    - Vertical translation
    - Horizontal dilation
    - Horizontal translation

11. For the sinusoid in Problem 10, identify the
    - Amplitude
    - Period
    - Phase displacement (for cosine)
    - Sinusoidal axis location

12. The graph shows a half-cycle of a sinusoid. Sketch at least one complete cycle of the sinusoid.

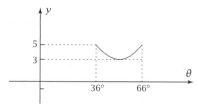

13. Write a particular equation of the sinusoid in Problem 12 using the cosine function.

14. For the sinusoid in Problem 12, write another particular equation using the sine function.

15. If the sinusoid in Problem 12 were extended to $\theta = 3628°$, what would y equal?

16. For $y = \cot \theta$, in the figure,
    - Darken one complete cycle.
    - Draw all vertical asymptotes in this window.
    - Write the θ-value at the rightmost θ-intercept.
    - Mark a point where the graph is concave down.

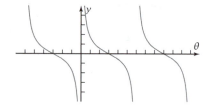

17. For $y = \sec \theta$, in the figure,
    - Darken one complete cycle.
    - Draw all vertical asymptotes in this window.
    - Mark a critical point.
    - Give the y-value at the critical point you marked.

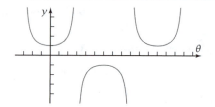

18. The cotangent function can have a vertical dilation, such as

    $$y = 2 \cot \theta$$

    But the cotangent function does not have an amplitude. Explain why not.

Ferris Wheel Problem (19–23): Ella Vader (Darth's other daughter) rides a Ferris wheel. As the wheel turns, her distance, y, from the ground, measured in feet, varies sinusoidally with time, t, measured in seconds, according to the equation

$$y = 30 + 25 \sin 15(t + 3)$$

Angle θ, in degrees, shown in the figure, is equal to the argument of the sine function, $\theta = 15(t + 3)$.

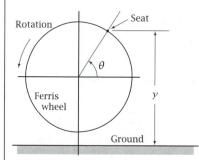

19. The last seat was filled, and the Ferris wheel started rotating at time $t = 0$ s. What was θ at this time? How high above the ground was Ella at this time?

20. When $t = 1$ s, what was θ? By how many degrees did the Ferris wheel rotate in this 1 s? Where do you find this number of degrees per second in the equation for y?

21. How high above the ground was Ella at $t = 1$ s?

22. What is the period of the sinusoid? That is, how long does it take for the Ferris wheel to make a complete 360° revolution?

23. Sketch two cycles of the sinusoid of y as a function of t. Put enough numbers on the axes so that your instructor can tell that you understand the meanings of the 30, the 25, and the 3 in the equation and the period of the sinusoid.

24. What did you learn as a result of taking this test that you did not know before?

Test 8, Sections 3-4 to 3-8

Form A

Objective: Convert between radians and degrees, and draw graphs of circular functions.

Part 1: No calculators allowed (1–8)

1. Sketch the parent circular sinusoid $y = \sin x$. Show scales on the two axes.

2. Sketch the parent circular sinusoid $y = \cos x$. Show scales on the two axes.

3. Find the number of degrees in $\frac{\pi}{3}$ radians.

4. Find the number of radians in 120°.

5. Write the general solution for arccos 0.3 in terms of $\cos^{-1} 0.3$.

6. The figure represents a circle of radius 10 ft.
   - On the circle, darken an arc of length 13 ft.
   - Sketch the central angle that subtends the arc.
   - Give the radian measure of the central angle.

7. The graph shows a circular function sinusoid. Find the

   Period _____

   Horizontal dilation _____

   Amplitude _____

   Vertical translation _____

   Phase displacement (for cosine) _____

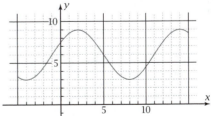

8. Write a particular equation of the sinusoid in Problem 7 using the cosine function.

(Hand in this page to get the rest of the test.)

Part 2: Graphing calculators allowed (9–18)

For Problems 9–14, the figure shows a sinusoid.

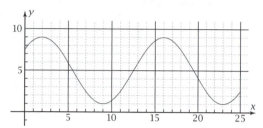

9. Draw a line at $y = 6$. Estimate from the graph the three values of x at $y = 6$ for the line you drew.

10. The particular equation of the sinusoid is

$$y = 5 + 4 \cos \frac{\pi}{7}(x - 2)$$

Plot this function and the line $y = 6$ on the same screen. Use the intersect feature to find the first two values of x shown in the figure for which $y = 6$. Round to three decimal places.

11. Starting at the leftmost value of x in Problem 10, write the values of x that are larger by $n = 1, 2,$ and 3 periods. Show that the value of x for $n = 1$ agrees with the graph.

12. Starting with the middle value of x in Problem 10, write the values of x that are larger by $n = 1, 2,$ and 3 periods.

13. Show how to use the technique of Problems 11 and 12 to find the value of x just to the left of the y-axis for which $y = 6$.

14. Solve the equation

$$5 + 4 \cos \frac{\pi}{7}(x - 2) = 6$$

algebraically, using the arccos relation, to find the first three values of x for which $y = 6$. Show that the answers agree with the numerical ones you found in Problems 10, 11, and 12.

Iridium Layer Problem (15–17): Sixty-five million years ago, a meteor is believed to have landed in the Gulf of Mexico. The materials thrown up into the atmosphere as a result are believed to have been responsible for the extinction of the dinosaurs and other species. A thin layer of material rich in the element iridium covered most of Earth. Since then, the iridium layer has been covered with other materials and warped into wavy shapes, parts have been eroded away by rivers, and so forth. The figure shows a part of the iridium layer in the cliff on the left bank of a river. From measurements on this layer, geologists figure that the layer is sinusoidal, with equation

$$y = 60 + 20 \cos \frac{\pi}{110}(x + 140)$$

where x and y are in feet in the coordinates shown.

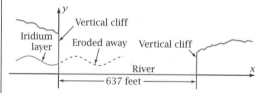

15. What are the x- and y-coordinates of the high point to the left of the left vertical cliff?

16. What is the period of the sinusoid?

17. Geologists want to find the iridium layer in the face of the vertical cliff on the right side of the river. Based on the sinusoidal model, how high above the river should they look on this cliff face to find the iridium layer? How do you find this number?

18. What did you learn as a result of taking this test that you did not know before?

Precalculus with Trigonometry: Assessment Resources
© 2007 Key Curriculum Press

Test 8, Sections 3-4 to 3-8   Form B

Objective: Convert between radians and degrees, and draw graphs of circular functions.

Part 1: No calculators allowed (1–8)

1. Sketch the parent circular sinusoid $y = \sin x$. Show scales on the two axes.

2. Sketch the parent circular sinusoid $y = \cos x$. Show scales on the two axes.

3. Find the number of degrees in $\frac{\pi}{6}$ radians.

4. Find the number of radians in 420°.

5. Write the general solution for arccos 0.7 in terms of $\cos^{-1} 0.7$.

6. The figure represents a circle of radius 20 ft.
   - On the circle, darken an arc of length 30 ft.
   - Sketch the central angle that subtends the arc.
   - Give the radian measure of the central angle.

7. The graph shows a circular function sinusoid. Find the

   Period _____

   Horizontal dilation _____

   Amplitude _____

   Vertical translation _____

   Phase displacement (for cosine) _____

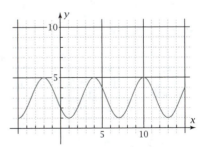

8. Write a particular equation of the sinusoid in Problem 7 using the cosine function.

(Hand in this page to get the rest of the test.)

Test 8, Sections 3-4 to 3-8 continued   Form B

Part 2: Graphing calculators allowed (9–18)

For Problems 9–14, the figure shows a sinusoid.

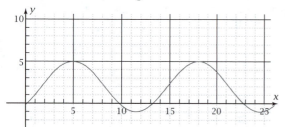

9. Draw a line at $y = 1$. Estimate from the graph the three values of x at $y = 1$ for the line you drew.

10. The particular equation of the sinusoid is

$$y = 2 + 3 \cos\frac{2\pi}{13}(x - 5)$$

Plot this function and the line $y = 1$ on the same screen. Use the intersect feature to find the first two values of x shown in the figure for which $y = 1$. Round to three decimal places.

11. Starting at the leftmost value of x in Problem 10, write the values of x that are larger by $n = 1, 2,$ and 3 periods. Show that the value of x for $n = 1$ agrees with the graph.

12. Starting with the middle value of x in Problem 10, write the values of x that are larger by $n = 1, 2,$ and 3 periods.

13. Show how to use the technique of Problems 11 and 12 to find the value of x just to the left of the y-axis for which $y = 6$.

14. Solve the equation

$$y = 2 + 3 \cos\frac{2\pi}{13}(x - 5) = 1$$

algebraically, using the arccos relation, to find the first three values of x for which $y = 6$. Show that the answers agree with the numerical ones you found in Problems 10, 11, and 12.

Sound Wave Problem (15–17): The hum you hear on some radios when they are not tuned to a station is a sound wave of 60 cycles per second.

15. Is the 60 cycles per second the period, or is it the frequency? If it is the period, find the frequency. If it is the frequency, find the period.

16. The wavelength of a sound wave is defined as the distance the wave travels in a time equal to one period. If sound travels at 1100 ft/s, find the wavelength of the 60-cycle-per-second hum.

17. The lowest musical note the human ear can hear is about 16 cycles per second. In order to play such a note, the pipe on an organ must be half as long as the wavelength. What length of organ pipe would be needed to generate a 16-cycle-per-second note?

18. What did you learn as a result of taking this test that you did not know before?

Precalculus with Trigonometry: Assessment Resources
© 2007 Key Curriculum Press

Test 9, Chapter 3

Form A

Objective: Analyze sinusoids.

Part 1: No calculators allowed (1–11)

1. The figure shows an *x*-axis drawn tangent to a unit circle in a *uv*-coordinate system. If the number line is wrapped around the unit circle, show where the point *x* = 2.7 on the line maps onto the circle.

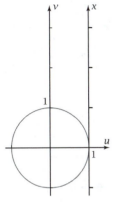

2. On the figure in Problem 1, sketch an angle of 2.7 radians in standard position.

3. What steps are needed to find a decimal approximation for the degree measure of an angle of 2.7 radians? In which quadrant will the angle terminate?

4. Find the exact radian measure of 30°.

5. Find the degree measure of $-\frac{2\pi}{3}$ radians.

6. Draw a sketch illustrating the angle $\cos^{-1} \frac{-3}{5}$.

7. $\cos^{-1} \frac{-3}{5}$ is one value of arccos $\frac{-3}{5}$. On your sketch in Problem 6, show another angle equal to arccos $\frac{-3}{5}$ terminating in a different quadrant.

8. Write the general solution for arccos $\frac{-3}{5}$ in terms of $\cos^{-1} \frac{-3}{5}$.

9. Sketch the graph of the parent trigonometric function $y = \sin \theta$. Show scales on both axes.

10. Sketch the graph of the parent circular function $y = \cos x$. Show scales on both axes.

11. Sketch the graph of $y = 4 + 3 \cos \frac{\pi}{8}(x - 5)$.

(Hand in this page to get the rest of the test.)

Part 2: Graphing calculators allowed (12–24)

12. Draw a sketch representing a circle of radius 5 ft. Sketch a central angle subtending an arc of 7 ft. What is the radian measure of this angle?

13. Find the degree measure of 3.5 radians.

14. Plot the graph of $y = \sec x$ using the window shown in this figure. Sketch the graph here, showing the vertical asymptotes.

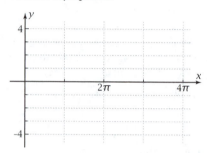

15. Plot the graph of $y = \cot x$ on your grapher using the same window as in Problem 14. Sketch the graph here.

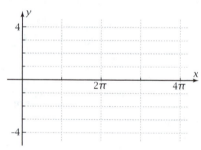

16. Based on the relationship between cotangent and tangent, explain why the cotangent function has vertical asymptotes where it does.

17. For this sinusoid, write the particular equation using cosine.

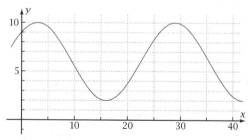

18. Write the particular equation of the sinusoid in Problem 17 using the sine function.

Earth and Mars Problem (19–23): The distance between Earth and Mars is a periodic function of time. Assume that the function is sinusoidal and that its particular equation is

$$y = 141 + 93 \cos\frac{\pi}{390}(x - 140)$$

where x is in days after today and y is in millions of miles. The figure shows the graph of this function.

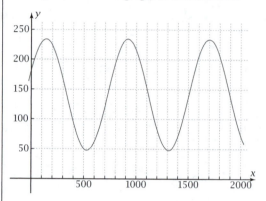

19. Identify the
    - Horizontal dilation
    - Period
    - Amplitude
    - Phase displacement
    - Vertical translation

20. Based on the equation, on what day will Earth and Mars first be closest to each other? Show how you find the answer.

21. There are intervals of time when Earth and Mars are within 100 million miles of each other. Estimate on the given graph the first such time interval.

22. Find the time interval in Problem 21 numerically. You may use either the solver or the intersect feature on your grapher.

23. Find the time interval in Problem 21 algebraically. Show that your answer agrees with Problem 22.

24. What did you learn as a result of taking this test that you did not know before?

Objective: Analyze sinusoids.

Part 1: No calculators allowed (1–11)

1. The figure shows an x-axis drawn tangent to a unit circle in a uv-coordinate system. If the number line is wrapped around the unit circle, show where the point $x = 1.8$ on the line maps onto the circle.

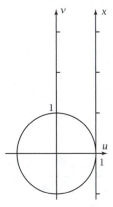

2. On the figure in Problem 1, sketch an angle of 1.8 radians in standard position.

3. What steps are needed to find a decimal approximation for the degree measure of an angle of 1.8 radians? In which quadrant will the angle terminate?

4. Find the exact radian measure of 240°.

5. Find the degree measure of $-\frac{5\pi}{6}$ radians.

6. Draw a sketch illustrating the angle $\cos^{-1} -\frac{2}{3}$.

7. $\cos^{-1} -\frac{2}{3}$ is one value of arccos $-\frac{2}{3}$. On your sketch in Problem 6, show another angle equal to arccos $-\frac{2}{3}$ terminating in a different quadrant.

8. Write the general solution for arccos $-\frac{2}{3}$ in terms of $\cos^{-1} -\frac{2}{3}$.

9. Sketch the graph of the parent trigonometric function $y = \sin \theta$. Show scales on both axes.

10. Sketch the graph of the parent circular function $y = \cos x$. Show scales on both axes.

11. Sketch the graph of $y = -2 + 4 \cos \frac{\pi}{12} (x + 3)$.

(Hand in this page to get the rest of the test.)

Part 2: Graphing calculators allowed (12–24)

12. Draw a sketch representing a circle of radius 6 ft. Sketch a central angle subtending an arc of 8 ft. What is the radian measure of this angle?

13. Find the degree measure of 4.8 radians.

14. Plot the graph of $y = \csc x$ using the window shown in this figure. Sketch the graph here, showing the vertical asymptotes.

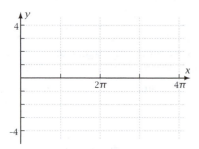

15. Plot the graph of $y = \cot x$ on your grapher using the same window as in Problem 14. Sketch the graph here.

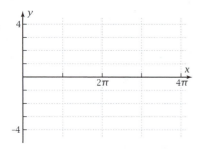

16. Based on the relationship between cosecant and sine, explain why the cosecant function has vertical asymptotes where it does.

17. For this sinusoid, write the particular equation using cosine.

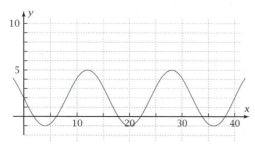

18. Write the particular equation of the sinusoid in Problem 17 using the sine function.

Tide Problem (19–23): The (average) depth of the water at a particular point on the beach varies sinusoidally with time due to the motion of the tides. The figure shows the depth, y, measured in feet, at such a point as a function of x, measured in hours after midnight at the beginning of January 1. The particular equation of the sinusoid is

$$y = 3 + 4 \cos \frac{\pi}{5.8}(x - 1)$$

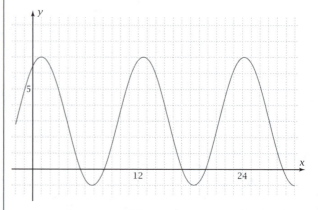

19. Identify the
    • Horizontal dilation
    • Period
    • Amplitude
    • Phase displacement
    • Vertical translation

20. Calculate the depth of the water at 4:00 p.m. on January 1. Show that the answer agrees with the graph.

21. There is a high tide close to midnight at the beginning of January 2 ($x = 24$). Is this high point on January 1 or on January 2? Show calculations to justify your answer.

22. Find graphically the first interval of times on January 1 for which the water is completely gone.

23. Calculate algebraically the first time on January 3 (in other words, $x \geq 48$) at which the depth of the water is exactly zero.

24. What did you learn as a result of taking this test that you did not know before?

Precalculus with Trigonometry: Assessment Resources
© 2007 Key Curriculum Press

Test 10, Sections 4-1 to 4-3

Form A

Objective: Transform trigonometric expressions and prove identities.

Part 1: No calculators allowed (1–6)

1. Write the three reciprocal properties.

2. Write the two quotient properties.

3. Write the three Pythagorean properties.

For Problems 4–6, Calvin must prove that this equation is an identity.

$$\cot \theta = \frac{\sec \theta}{\sin \theta} - \frac{\sin \theta}{\cos \theta}$$

4. Tell Calvin why you would recommend starting with the right side of the equation.

5. What should Calvin's thought process be in executing the first transformation of the right side?

6. Show Calvin how to do the proof.

(Hand in this page to get the rest of the test.)

Part 2: Graphing calculators allowed (7–15)

7. Transform: $\cot x + \tan x$ to $\csc x \sec x$

8. Show graphically that the equation

$$(1 + 2 \cos x)(1 - 2 \cos x) = 4 \sin^2 x - 3$$

is an identity. Use the window shown here. Sketch the result. Explain how the graphs confirm that the equation is an identity.

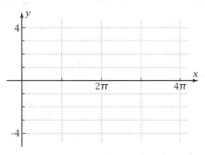

9. Prove algebraically that the equation in Problem 8 is an identity.

10. Plot the graph of $y = \cot x$ on your grapher using the window shown here. Sketch the result.

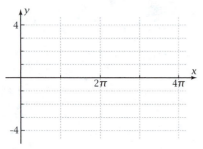

11. Based on the quotient property for cotangent, explain why the cotangent graph in Problem 10 has vertical asymptotes where it does.

For Problems 12–14, prove algebraically that the equation is an identity.

12. $\cos^3 A \sin^2 A = \cos^3 A - \cos^5 A$

13. $\dfrac{1}{1 - \cos B} + \dfrac{1}{1 + \cos B} = 2 \csc^2 B$

14. $(5 \cos C - 2 \sin C)^2 + (2 \cos C + 5 \sin C)^2 = 29$

15. What did you learn as a result of taking this test that you did not know before?

Precalculus with Trigonometry: Assessment Resources
© 2007 Key Curriculum Press

Name: ______________________________ Date: ______________

Test 10, Sections 4-1 to 4-3 — Form B

Objective: Transform trigonometric expressions and prove identities.

Part 1: No calculators allowed (1–6)

1. Complete the following reciprocal properties.

   sec x = ______________________

   csc x = ______________________

   cot x = ______________________

2. Complete the two quotient properties.

   tan x = ______________________

   cot x = ______________________

3. Write the three Pythagorean properties.

For Problems 4–6, Calvin must prove that this equation is an identity.

$$\tan\theta = \frac{1}{\sin\theta\cos\theta} - \frac{\cos\theta}{\sin\theta}$$

4. Tell Calvin why you would recommend starting with the right side of the equation.

5. What should Calvin's thought process be in executing the first transformation of the right side?

6. Show Calvin how to do the proof.

(Hand in this page to get the rest of the test.)

Test 10, Sections 4-1 to 4-3 continued

Form B

Part 2: Graphing calculators allowed (7–15)

7. Transform: $\csc x - \sin x$ to $\cot x \cos x$.

8. Show graphically that the equation

$$(3 - 4 \sin x)(3 + 4 \sin x) = 16 \cos^2 x - 7$$

is an identity. Use the window shown here. Sketch the result. Explain how the graphs confirm that the equation is an identity.

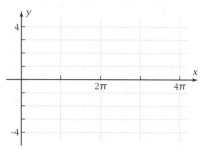

9. Prove algebraically that the equation in Problem 8 is an identity.

10. Plot the graph of $y = \tan x$ on your grapher using the window shown here. Sketch the result.

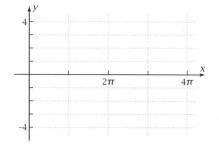

11. Based on the quotient property for tangent, explain why the tangent graph in Problem 10 has vertical asymptotes where it does.

For Problems 12–14, prove algebraically that the equation is an identity.

12. $\csc^2 A + \cot^2 A \csc^2 A = \csc^4 A$

13. $\dfrac{1}{1 + \sin B} + \dfrac{1}{1 - \sin B} = 2 \sec^2 B$

14. $(3 \cos x + 4 \sin x)^2 + (3 \cos x - 4 \sin x)^2 = 25$

15. What did you learn as a result of taking this test that you did not know before?

Test 11, Section 4-4

Form A

Objective: Find values of arcsine, arccosine, and arctangent, and use them to solve trigonometric equations.

Part 1: No calculators allowed (1–6)

1. If $\theta = \sin^{-1} A = -50°$,
   - Sketch θ in the *uv*-coordinate system shown.
   - Show another angle in a different quadrant equal to arcsin A. Mark this other angle with an appropriate arc.
   - Write the measure of this other angle.
   - Write the general solution for arcsin A.

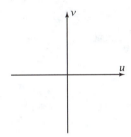

2. If $\theta = \tan^{-1} A = 20°$,
   - Sketch θ in the *uv*-coordinate system shown.
   - Show another angle in a different quadrant equal to arctan A. Mark this other angle with an appropriate arc.
   - Write the measure of this other angle.
   - Write the general solution for arctan A.

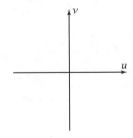

3. If $x = \cos^{-1} A = 2$,
   - Sketch θ in the *uv*-coordinate system shown.
   - Show another angle in a different quadrant equal to arccos A. Mark this other angle with an appropriate arc.
   - Write the measure of this other angle.
   - Write the general solution for arccos A.

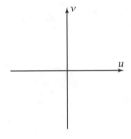

4. If $x = \sin^{-1} A = 1$ radian, write the general solution for arcsin A.

5. Amos Take is solving a trigonometric equation. He writes

   $$\theta - 30° = \pm 40° + 360n°$$

   $$\theta = \pm 70° + 360n°$$

   What should he have written for the second line?

6. Mae Danerror is solving a trigonometric equation. She writes

   $$2x = 1.8 + 2\pi n$$

   $$x = 0.9 + 2\pi n$$

   What should she have written for the second line?

(Hand in this page to get the rest of the test.)

Test 11, Section 4-4 continued   Form A

Part 2: Graphing calculators allowed (7–11)

7. Solve algebraically:

   $2 \cos (\theta - 13°) = \sqrt{3}$, $\theta \in [0°, 720°]$

8. Solve algebraically:

   $\tan^2 x - 3 \tan x - 4 = 0$, $\theta \in [0, 3\pi]$

9. Solve algebraically:

   $5 - 7 \sin \theta = 2 \cos^2 \theta$, $\theta \in [-360°, 450°]$

10. The axes here present the graphs of

    $y_1 = 5 - 7 \sin \theta$

    $y_2 = 2 \cos^2 \theta$

    Show on the graph that all of your answers in Problem 9 are correct.

    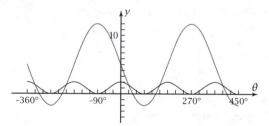

11. What did you learn as a result of taking this test that you did not know before?

Precalculus with Trigonometry: Assessment Resources
© 2007 Key Curriculum Press

Test 11, Section 4-4

Objective: Find values of arcsine, arccosine, and arctangent, and use them to solve trigonometric equations.

Part 1: No calculators allowed (1–6)

1. If $\theta = \sin^{-1} A = -20°$,
   - Sketch θ in the *uv*-coordinate system shown.
   - Show another angle in a different quadrant equal to arcsin A. Mark this other angle with an appropriate arc.
   - Write the measure of this other angle.
   - Write the general solution for arcsin A.

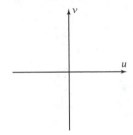

2. If $\theta = \tan^{-1} A = 35°$,
   - Sketch θ in the *uv*-coordinate system shown.
   - Show another angle in a different quadrant equal to arctan A. Mark this other angle with an appropriate arc.
   - Write the measure of this other angle.
   - Write the general solution for arctan A.

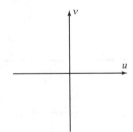

3. If $x = \cos^{-1} A = 1$,
   - Sketch θ in the *uv*-coordinate system shown.
   - Show another angle in a different quadrant equal to arccos A. Mark this other angle with an appropriate arc.
   - Write the measure of this other angle.
   - Write the general solution for arccos A.

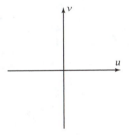

4. If $x = \sin^{-1} A = 2$ radian, write the general solution for arcsin A.

5. Amos Take is solving a trigonometric equation. He writes

   $$\theta - 70° = \pm 20° + 360n°$$

   $$\theta = \pm 90° + 360n°$$

   What should he have written for the second line?

6. Mae Danerror is solving a trigonometric equation. She writes

   $$4x = 2.4 + 2\pi n$$

   $$x = 0.6 + 2\pi n$$

   What should she have written for the second line?

(Hand in this page to get the rest of the test.)

Test 11, Section 4-4 continued

Form B

Part 2: Graphing calculators allowed (7–11)

7. Solve algebraically:

$$2 \sin(\theta + 21°) = \sqrt{3}, \ \theta \in [0°, 720°]$$

8. Solve algebraically:

$$\tan^2 x - 2 \tan x - 3 = 0, \ \theta \in [0, 3\pi]$$

9. Solve algebraically:

$$1 + 3 \cos \theta = \sin^2 \theta, \ \theta \in [-360°, 450°]$$

10. The axes here present the graphs of

$$y_1 = 1 + 3 \cos \theta$$

$$y_2 = \sin^2 \theta$$

Show on the graph that all of your answers in Problem 9 are correct.

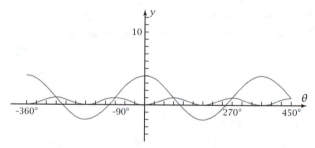

11. What did you learn as a result of taking this test that you did not know before?

Precalculus with Trigonometry: Assessment Resources
© 2007 Key Curriculum Press

Test 12, Chapter 4 Form A

Objective: Transform expressions, solve equations, and analyze parametric and inverse trigonometric relations.

Part 1: No calculators allowed (1–8)

1. Write the reciprocal property for cosecant.

2. Write the quotient property for tangent.

3. Write the Pythagorean property involving cosine and sine.

4. Explain why this is a conditional equation,

$$1 - \tan^2 x = \sec^2 x$$

but this is an identity,

$$1 + \tan^2 x = \sec^2 x$$

5. In proving that the equation

$$\cot \theta = \frac{\sec \theta}{\sin \theta} - \frac{\sin \theta}{\cos \theta}$$

is an identity, you first pick one side with which to start. Describe the second step.

6. If $\theta = \sin^{-1} y = 50°$, sketch the 50° angle and the value of θ in another quadrant, and write the general solution for θ.

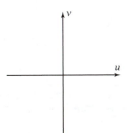

7. Write parametric equations for this ellipse.

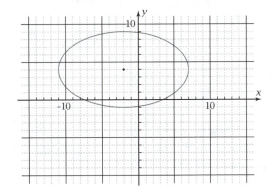

8. The figure shows the graph of $y = \arccos x$.
   • Darken the graph of $y = \cos^{-1} x$.
   • Give the range of $y = \cos^{-1} x$.
   • Give any three of the criteria that go into selecting the range.

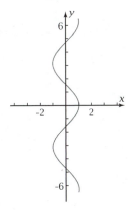

(Hand in this page to get the rest of the test.)

Test 12, Chapter 4 continued

Form A

Part 2: Graphing calculators allowed (9–19)

9. Transform $\cos A (\sec A - \cos A)$ to $\sin^2 A$.

10. Prove that $\dfrac{\cos^2 \theta}{1 + \sin \theta} = 1 - \sin \theta$ is an identity.

11. The graph shows both sides of the equation

$$2 + \sin \theta = 2 \cos^2 \theta$$

From the graph, estimate the solutions in the domain $\theta \in [0°, 720°]$.

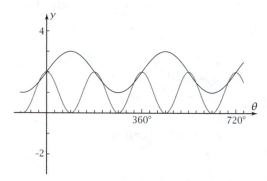

12. Solve the equation in Problem 11 algebraically. Show that all of the solutions agree with the graph.

13. Explain why your calculator gives an error message when you press $\sin^{-1} 1.2$.

Problems 14–17 refer to this hyperbola whose parametric equations are

$$x = 2 + 5 \tan t$$
$$y = 1 + 3 \sec t$$

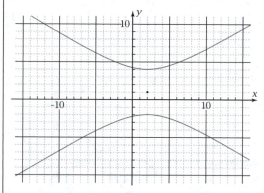

14. Plot this graph on your grapher. You will find that the reciprocal property you wrote in Problem 1 will help in entering the equations. Use degree mode, with a t-range of $[0°, 720°]$, a t-step of $5°$, and x- and y-windows as shown in the figure. Trace to $t = 60°$, write the values of x and y, and show that the point is on the graph.

15. Trace to $t = 420°$. How do you explain the fact that the values of x and y are the same as in Problem 14?

16. By performing appropriate operations on the parametric equations, eliminate the parameter and get a Cartesian equation relating x and y. You should find that one of the Pythagorean properties will help.

17. How does the Cartesian equation in Problem 16 confirm that the graph really is a hyperbola?

18. The figure shows the graph of the inverse trigonometric relation $y = \arctan x$. Duplicate this graph on your grapher. Describe how you did it.

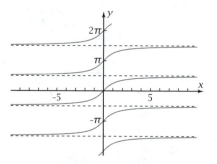

19. What did you learn as a result of taking this test that you did not know before?

Test 12, Chapter 4

Form B

Objective: Transform expressions, solve equations, and analyze parametric and inverse trigonometric relations.

Part 1: No calculators allowed (1–8)

1. Write the reciprocal property for secant.

2. Write the quotient property for cotangent.

3. Write the Pythagorean property involving cosine and sine.

4. Explain why this is a conditional equation,

   $$\sec^2 x + \tan^2 x = 1$$

   but this is an identity,

   $$\sec^2 x - \tan^2 x = 1$$

5. In proving that the equation

   $$\frac{\sin \theta}{\csc \theta} + \frac{\cos \theta}{\sec \theta} = 1$$

   is an identity, you first pick one side with which to start. Describe the second step.

6. If $\theta = \sin^{-1} y = 70°$, sketch the 70° angle and the value of θ in another quadrant, and write the general solution for θ.

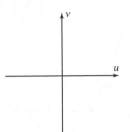

7. Write parametric equations for this ellipse.

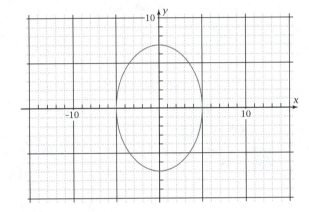

8. The figure shows the graph of $y = \arcsin x$.
   - Darken the graph of $y = \sin^{-1} x$.
   - Give the range of $y = \sin^{-1} x$.
   - Give any three of the criteria that go into selecting the range.

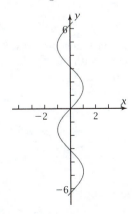

(Hand in this page to get the rest of the test.)

Part 2: Graphing calculators allowed (9–19)

9. Transform $\tan A \, (\cot A \cos A + \sin A)$ to $\sec A$.

10. Prove that $\dfrac{\sin \theta}{\csc \theta - 1} - \dfrac{\sin \theta}{\cot^2 \theta} = \tan^2 \theta$ is an identity.

11. The graph shows both sides of the equation

    $$2 + \cos \theta = 2 \sin^2 \theta$$

    From the graph, estimate the solutions in the domain $\theta \in [0°, 720°]$.

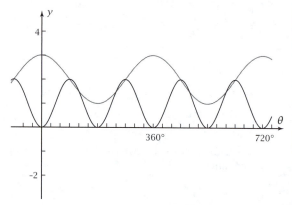

12. Solve the equation in Problem 11 algebraically. Show that all of the solutions agree with the graph.

13. Explain why your grapher gives an error message when you press $\cos^{-1} 1.2$.

Problems 14–17 refer to this hyperbola whose parametric equations are

$$x = 1 + 3 \tan t$$
$$y = 2 + 5 \sec t$$

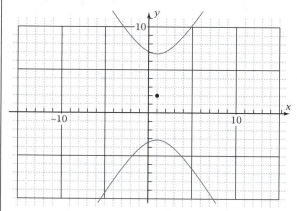

14. Plot this graph on your grapher. You will find that the reciprocal property you wrote in Problem 1 will help in entering the equations. Use degree mode, with a t-range of $[0°, 720°]$, a t-step of 5°, and x- and y-windows as shown in the figure. Trace to $t = 60°$, write the values of x and y, and show that the point is on the graph.

15. Trace to $t = 420°$. How do you explain the fact that the values of x and y are the same as in Problem 14?

16. By performing appropriate operations on the parametric equations, eliminate the parameter and get a Cartesian equation relating x and y. You should find that one of the Pythagorean properties will help.

17. How does the Cartesian equation in Problem 16 confirm that the graph really is a hyperbola?

18. The figure shows the graph of the inverse trigonometric relation $y = \text{arccot } x$. Duplicate this graph on your grapher. Describe how you did it.

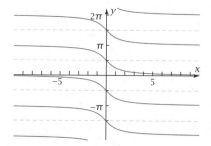

19. What did you learn as a result of taking this test that you did not know before?

Precalculus with Trigonometry: Assessment Resources
© 2007 Key Curriculum Press

Test 13, Sections 5-1 to 5-3   Form A

Objective: Use the composite argument properties for cosine and sine.

Part 1: No calculators allowed (1–8)

1. State these composite argument properties.

   $\cos(A - B) =$ _____

   $\cos(A + B) =$ _____

   $\sin(A - B) =$ _____

   $\sin(A + B) =$ _____

2. State verbally the first property in Problem 1.

3. Write these function values.

   $\cos 90° =$ _____

   $\sin 90° =$ _____

   $\cos 0° =$ _____

   $\sin 0° =$ _____

4. State these cofunction properties.

   $\cos(90° - B) =$ _____

   $\sin(90° - B) =$ _____

5. Substitute 90° for A in the third property in Problem 1. Then substitute the values of $\sin 90°$ and $\cos 90°$ on the right side of the equation to prove that the cofunction property you wrote in Problem 4 for $\sin(90° - B)$ really is correct.

6. Substitute 0° for A in the third property in Problem 1. Then substitute the values for $\sin 0°$ and $\cos 0°$ on the right side of the equation, and simplify. How does the result prove that sine is an odd function?

7. Write the equation expressing the fact that cosine is an even function.

8. The graph of $y = \cos(x - 1.3)$ is a sinusoid with a phase displacement of 1.3 radians. Given that $\cos 1.3 \approx 0.27$ and $\sin 1.3 \approx 0.96$, write y as a linear combination of $\cos x$ and $\sin x$.

(Hand in this page to get the rest of the test.)

Part 2: Graphing calculators allowed (9–20)

9. Show numerically that the composite argument property for $\cos(A - B)$ is correct by substituting $37°$ for A and $21°$ for B and showing that you get the same answer for both sides of the equation.

10. Suppose that $\cos A = 0.6$ and $\sin A = 0.8$. Suppose that $\cos B = 0.96$ and $\sin B = 0.28$. Use the composite argument property to find $\cos(A + B)$.

11. Show that both $\cos^{-1} 0.6$ and $\sin^{-1} 0.8$ give the same degree measure for angle A in Problem 10. Store the measure of A without round-off.

12. Show that both $\cos^{-1} 0.96$ and $\sin^{-1} 0.28$ give the same degree measure for angle B in Problem 10. Store the measure of B without round-off.

13. By adding the measures of A and B from Problems 11 and 12, find the measure of angle $(A + B)$. Then find directly the value of $\cos(A + B)$. Does it agree with your answer to Problem 10?

14. Draw an appropriate sketch and use it to write $y = 4 \cos \theta + 3 \sin \theta$ as a cosine with a phase displacement.

15. Draw an appropriate sketch and use it to write $y = -2 \cos \theta + 5 \sin \theta$ as a cosine with a phase displacement.

16. Draw an appropriate sketch and use it to write $y = -3 \cos \theta - 1 \sin \theta$ as a cosine with a phase displacement.

17. Draw an appropriate sketch and use it to write $y = 8 \cos \theta - 15 \sin \theta$ as a cosine with a phase displacement.

18. Use the composite argument property to write $y = 7 \cos(\theta - 20°)$ as a linear combination of $\cos \theta$ and $\sin \theta$.

19. Solve algebraically for $\theta \in [0°, 360°]$:

   $8 \cos \theta - 15 \sin \theta = 10$

20. What did you learn as a result of taking this test that you did not know before?

Precalculus with Trigonometry: Assessment Resources
© 2007 Key Curriculum Press

Test 13, Sections 5-1 to 5-3   Form B

Objective: Use the composite argument properties for cosine and sine.

Part 1: No calculators allowed (1–8)

1. State these composite argument properties.

   $\cos A \cos B + \sin A \sin B =$ _____

   $\cos A \cos B - \sin A \sin B =$ _____

   $\sin A \cos B - \cos A \sin B =$ _____

   $\sin A \cos B + \cos A \sin B =$ _____

2. State verbally the first property in Problem 1.

3. Write these function values.

   $\cos 90° =$ _____

   $\sin 90° =$ _____

   $\cos 0° =$ _____

   $\sin 0° =$ _____

4. State these cofunction properties.

   $\cos (90° - B) =$ _____

   $\sin (90° - B) =$ _____

5. Substitute 90° for A in the first property in Problem 1. Then substitute the values of sin 90° and cos 90° on the right side of the equation to prove that the cofunction property you wrote in Problem 4 for cos (90° − B) really is correct.

6. Substitute 0° for A in the right side of the first property in Problem 1. Then substitute the values for sin 0° and cos 0° on the left side of the equation, and simplify. How does the result prove that cosine is an even function?

7. Write the equation expressing the fact that sine is an odd function.

8. The graph of $y = \sin (x - 1.3)$ is a sinusoid with a phase displacement of 1.3 radians. Given that cos 1.3 ≈ 0.27 and sin 1.3 ≈ 0.96, write y as a linear combination of cos x and sin x.

(Hand in this page to get the rest of the test.)

Test 13, Sections 5-1 to 5-3 continued

Part 2: Graphing calculators allowed (9–20)

9. Show numerically that the composite argument property for cos $(A + B)$ is correct by substituting 37° for A and 21° for B and showing that you get the same answer for both sides of the equation.

10. Suppose that cos $A = 0.6$ and sin $A = 0.8$. Suppose that cos $B = 0.96$ and sin $B = 0.28$. Use the composite argument property to find cos $(A − B)$.

11. Show that both $\cos^{-1} 0.6$ and $\sin^{-1} 0.8$ give the same degree measure for angle A in Problem 10. Store the measure of A without round-off.

12. Show that both $\cos^{-1} 0.96$ and $\sin^{-1} 0.28$ give the same degree measure for angle B in Problem 10. Store the measure of B without round-off.

13. By subtracting the measures of A and B from Problems 11 and 12, find the measure of angle $(A − B)$. Then find directly the value of cos $(A − B)$. Does it agree with your answer to Problem 10?

14. Draw an appropriate sketch and use it to write $y = −4 \cos \theta + 3 \sin \theta$ as a cosine with a phase displacement.

15. Draw an appropriate sketch and use it to write $y = 2 \cos \theta − 5 \sin \theta$ as a cosine with a phase displacement.

16. Draw an appropriate sketch and use it to write $y = 3 \cos \theta + 1 \sin \theta$ as a cosine with a phase displacement.

17. Draw an appropriate sketch and use it to write $y = −8 \cos \theta − 15 \sin \theta$ as a cosine with a phase displacement.

18. Use the composite argument property to write $y = 9 \cos (\theta − 40°)$ as a linear combination of cos θ and sin θ.

19. Solve algebraically for $\theta \in [0°, 360°]$:

$$-8 \cos \theta − 15 \sin \theta = 4$$

20. What did you learn as a result of taking this test that you did not know before?

Test 14, Section 5-4

Form A

Objective: Composition of ordinates and harmonic analysis.

Part 1: No calculators allowed (1–8)

1. The figure shows two functions, one a sinusoid and the other not. Draw the graph of the function composed by **multiplying** the ordinates. Use all values of x in the domain [0, 20].

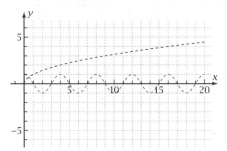

2. The graph shows the two functions in Problem 1. Draw the graph of the function composed by **adding** the ordinates. Use all values of x in the domain [0, 20].

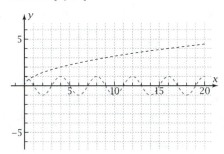

3. What is the name of the process used to draw the graphs in Problems 1 and 2?

4. What is the name of the process used to find the equation of a graph that was formed by adding or multiplying two sinusoids?

5. If two sinusoids with much different periods are combined to form a periodic function with a varying sinusoidal axis, which operation was used?

6. If two sinusoids with much different periods are combined to form a periodic function with a varying amplitude, which operation was used?

7. The solid graph is a product of a sine function (dashed) and another function (not shown). Which is the other function, a sine or a cosine?

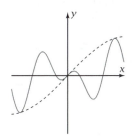

8. The solid graph is a product of a sine function (dashed) and another function (not shown). Which is the other function, a sine or a cosine?

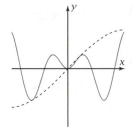

(Hand in this page to get the rest of the test.)

Test 14, Section 5-4 continued

Form A

Part 2: Graphing calculators allowed (9–21)

9. Write an equation for this graph.

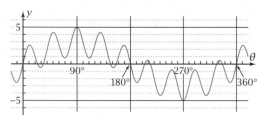

10. Write an equation for this graph.

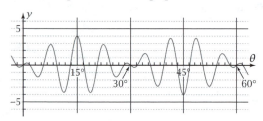

11. For the "envelope" sinusoid in Problem 10, give the
   • Amplitude
   • Period
   • Horizontal dilation

12. Write an equation for this graph.

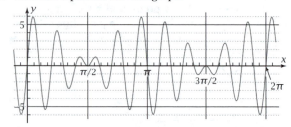

13. Write an equation for this graph.

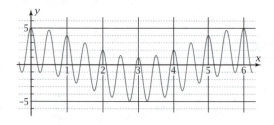

14. For the "sinusoidal axis" curve in Problem 13, give the
   • Amplitude
   • Period
   • Horizontal dilation

Submarine Sonar Problem (15-18): The sonar on a ship picks up sound being generated by equipment on a submarine. By performing harmonic analysis on the sound wave, it may be possible to identify the nationality of the submarine.

15. The sound wave has the following pattern, where x is time, in seconds. Write an equation for this graph. Observe that the longer wave sinusoidal axis completes *three* cycles before the wave pattern starts repeating itself.

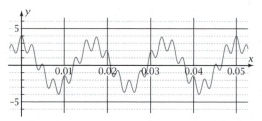

16. What is the period of the longer sinusoid? What is the period of the shorter sinusoid?

17. The **frequency** of a sinusoid is the reciprocal of the period. What are the frequencies of the two sinusoids in Problem 16?

18. U.S. submarines have some electrical generators that rotate at 60 cycles per second and other electrical generators that rotate at 400 cycles per second. Based on your results in Problems 15–17, could the sound have been coming from the generators on a U.S. submarine?

19. Plot on your grapher

   $y_1 = \cos 6\theta + \cos 4\theta$

   $y_2 = 2 \cos 5\theta \cdot \cos \theta$ (thick style)

   Use a θ window of $[0°, 360°]$. Do you agree that the graphs coincide?

20. Prove algebraically that

   $\cos 6\theta + \cos 4\theta = 2 \cos 5\theta \cdot \cos \theta$

   Start with the left side of the equation and write 6θ as $(5\theta + \theta)$ and 4θ as $(5\theta - \theta)$. You should find that the composite argument properties are helpful.

21. What did you learn as a result of taking this test that you did not know before?

Precalculus with Trigonometry: Assessment Resources
© 2007 Key Curriculum Press

Test 14, Section 5-4   Form B

Objective: Composition of ordinates and harmonic analysis.

Part 1: No calculators allowed (1–8)

1. The figure shows two functions, one a sinusoid and the other not. Draw the graph of the function composed by **multiplying** the ordinates. Use all values of x in the domain [0, 20].

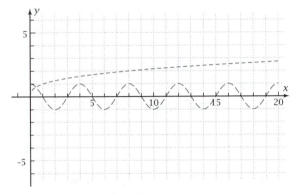

2. The graph shows the two functions in Problem 1. Draw the graph of the function composed by **adding** the ordinates. Use all values of x in the domain [0, 20].

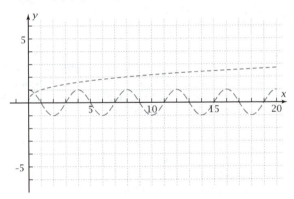

3. What is the name of the process used to draw the graphs in Problems 1 and 2?

4. What is the name of the process used to find the equation of a graph that was formed by adding or multiplying two sinusoids?

5. If two sinusoids with much different periods are combined to form a periodic function with a varying sinusoidal axis, which operation was used?

6. If two sinusoids with much different periods are combined to form a periodic function with a varying amplitude, which operation was used?

7. The solid graph is a product of a cosine function (dashed) and another function (not shown). Which is the other function, a sine or a cosine?

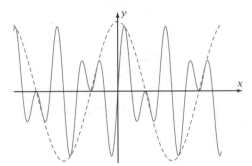

8. The solid graph is a product of a sine function (dashed) and another function (not shown). Which is the other function, a sine or a cosine?

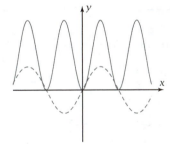

(Hand in this page to get the rest of the test.)

Test 14, Section 5-4 continued

Form B

Part 2: Graphing calculators allowed (9–21)

9. Write an equation for this graph.

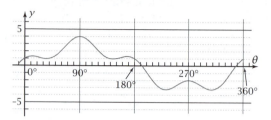

10. Write an equation for this graph.

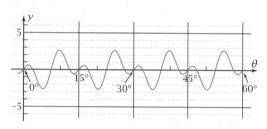

11. For the "envelope" sinusoid in Problem 10, give the
   • Amplitude
   • Period
   • Horizontal dilation

12. Write an equation for this graph.

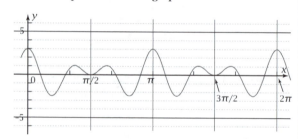

13. Write an equation for this graph.

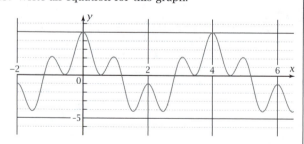

14. For the "sinusoidal axis" curve in Problem 13, give the
   • Amplitude
   • Period
   • Horizontal dilation

Submarine Sonar Problem (15–18): The sonar on a ship picks up sound being generated by equipment on a submarine. By performing harmonic analysis on the sound wave, it may be possible to identify the nationality of the submarine.

15. The sound wave has the following pattern, where x is time, in seconds. Write an equation for this graph. Observe that the longer wave sinusoidal axis completes *three* cycles before the wave pattern starts repeating itself.

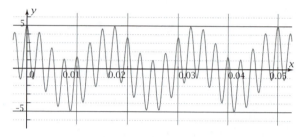

16. What is the period of the longer sinusoid? What is the period of the shorter sinusoid?

17. The **frequency** of a sinusoid is the reciprocal of the period. What are the frequencies of the two sinusoids in Problem 16?

18. U.S. submarines have some electrical generators that rotate at 60 cycles per second and other electrical generators that rotate at 400 cycles per second. Based on your results in Problems 15-17, could the sound have been coming from the generators on a U.S. submarine?

19. Plot on your grapher

   $y_1 = \cos 5\theta + \cos 3\theta$

   $y_2 = 2 \cos 3\theta \cdot \cos \theta$ (thick style)

   Use a θ window of [0°, 360°]. Do you agree that the graphs coincide?

20. Prove algebraically that

   $$\cos 5\theta + \cos 3\theta = 2 \cos 4\theta \cdot \cos \theta$$

   Start with the left side of the equation and write 5θ as $(4\theta + \theta)$ and 3θ as $(4\theta - \theta)$. You should find that the composite argument properties are helpful.

21. What did you learn as a result of taking this test that you did not know before?

Precalculus with Trigonometry: Assessment Resources
© 2007 Key Curriculum Press

Objective: Use properties of trigonometric functions of more than one argument to transform expressions and solve equations.

Part 1: No calculators allowed (1–7)

1. Write the composite argument property.

   $\cos(x - y) =$ _____

2. Write the double argument property for $\sin A$.

   $\sin 2A =$ _____

3. Write the three forms of the double argument property for $\cos 2A$.

   Both cosine and sine:

   　$\cos 2A =$ _____

   Cosine only:

   　$\cos 2A =$ _____

   Sine only:

   　$\cos 2A =$ _____

4. The half-argument property for sine is

   $$\sin\frac{1}{2}x = \pm\sqrt{\frac{1}{2}(1 - \cos x)}$$

   To find $\sin 200°$ using the value of $\cos 400°$, which would you use, the + sign or the − sign? Draw a graph showing how you decide.

5. Sketch the graph of the sum of these two sinusoids.

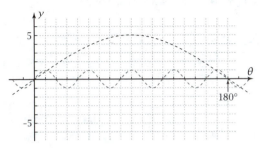

6. Use this figure to help you explain graphically why $\cos \theta = \sin(90° - \theta)$.

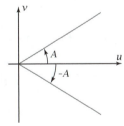

7. Use this figure to help you explain graphically why sine is an odd function.

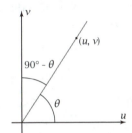

(Hand in this page to get the rest of the test.)

Part 2: Graphing calculators allowed (8–22)

8. Show numerically that

$$\cos(70° - 23°) \neq \cos 70° - \cos 23°$$

9. Show numerically that

$$\cos(70° - 23°) = \cos 70° \cos 23° + \sin 70° \sin 23°$$

10. Use the composite argument property for cosine to transform $y = 7 \cos(\theta - 30°)$ to a linear combination of $\cos \theta$ and $\sin \theta$.

11. Transform this linear combination of $\cos \theta$ and $\sin \theta$ to the form $y = A \cos(\theta - D)$.

$$y = -15 \cos \theta + 8 \sin \theta$$

12. Use the composite argument property for sine and the values of $\sin 90°$ and $\cos 90°$ to prove algebraically that $\cos \theta = \sin(90° - \theta)$.

13. The figures show angles A and B. Use the composite argument property for sine to find the *exact* value (no decimals) of $\sin(A + B)$.

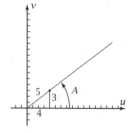
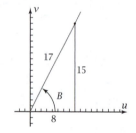

14. Find the measure of angle $(A + B)$ in Problem 13. Without round-off, find $\sin(A + B)$. Show that the answer agrees with the answer in Problem 13.

15. Find the particular equation of this function that is composed of two sinusoids.

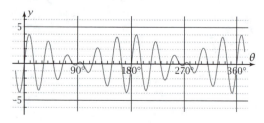

16. What is the name of the process used to find the equation of a graph that was formed by adding or multiplying two sinusoids as in Problem 15?

17. Show how you can combine the composite argument properties for $\cos(A + B)$ and $\cos(A - B)$ to give the sum and product property,

$$\cos(A + B) + \cos(A - B) = 2 \cos A \cos B$$

18. Use the sum and product property in Problem 17 to show how you can transform this product of two sinusoids with much different periods into a sum of two sinusoids with almost equal periods.

$$y = 2 \cos 32x \cos x$$

19. Use similar reasoning to that in Problem 17 to express $\cos 75° - \cos 71°$ as a product of two sines. Check your answer numerically by evaluating the given expression and your answer.

20. Use the double argument property,

$$\cos 2x = 1 - 2 \sin^2 x$$

to express $\cos 60°$ in terms of $\sin 30°$. Check your answer by evaluating it and comparing it to the actual value of $\cos 60°$.

21. Use the double argument property in Problem 20 and appropriate algebra to write $\sin 200°$ in terms of $\cos 400°$. Check your answer numerically.

22. What did you learn as a result of taking this test that you did not know before?

Objective: Use properties of trigonometric functions of more than one argument to transform expressions and solve equations.

Part 1: No calculators allowed (1–7)

1. Write the composite argument property.

   $\cos(x + y) =$ _____

2. Write the double argument property for sin A.

   $\sin 2A =$ _____

3. Write the three forms of the double argument property for cos $2A$.

   Both cosine and sine:

   $\cos 2A =$ _____

   Cosine only:

   $\cos 2A =$ _____

   Sine only:

   $\cos 2A =$ _____

4. The half-argument property for sine is

   $$\sin\frac{1}{2}x = \pm\sqrt{\frac{1}{2}(1 - \cos x)}$$

   To find sin 100° using the value of cos 200°, which would you use, the + sign or the − sign? Draw a graph showing how you decide.

5. Sketch the graph of the sum of these two sinusoids.

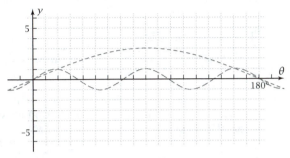

6. Use this figure to help you explain graphically why $\sin \theta = \cos(90° - \theta)$.

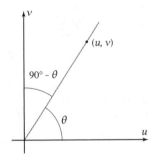

7. Use this figure to help you explain graphically why cosine is an even function.

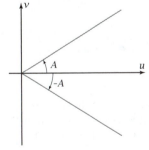

(Hand in this page to get the rest of the test.)

Part 2: Graphing calculators allowed (8–22)

8. Show numerically that

$$\cos(50° - 17°) \neq \cos 50° - \cos 17°$$

9. Show numerically that

$$\cos(50° - 17°) = \cos 50° \cos 17° + \sin 50° \sin 17°$$

10. Use the composite argument property for cosine to transform $y = 4 \cos(\theta - 60°)$ to a linear combination of $\cos \theta$ and $\sin \theta$.

11. Transform this linear combination of $\cos \theta$ and $\sin \theta$ to the form $y = A \cos(\theta - D)$.

$$y = -7 \cos \theta + 2 \sin \theta$$

12. Use the composite argument property for sine and the values of $\sin 90°$ and $\cos 90°$ to prove algebraically that $\sin \theta = \cos(90° - \theta)$.

13. The figures show angles A and B. Use the composite argument property for sine to find the *exact* value (no decimals) of $\cos(A + B)$.

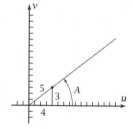
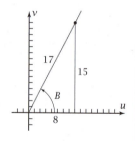

14. Find the measure of angle $(A + B)$ in Problem 13. Without round-off, find $\cos(A + B)$. Show that the answer agrees with the answer in Problem 13.

15. Find the particular equation of this function that is composed of two sinusoids.

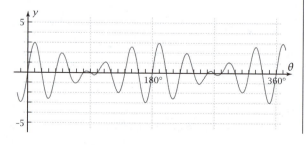

16. What is the name of the process used to find the equation of a graph that was formed by adding or multiplying two sinusoids as in Problem 15?

17. Show how you can combine the composite argument properties for $\cos(A + B)$ and $\cos(A - B)$ to give the sum and product property,

$$\cos(A + B) + \cos(A - B) = 2 \cos A \cos B$$

18. Use the sum and product property in Problem 17 to show how you can transform this product of two sinusoids with much different periods into a sum of two sinusoids with almost equal periods.

$$y = 2 \cos 19x \cos x$$

19. Use similar reasoning to that in Problem 17 to express $\cos 65° - \cos 61°$ as a product of two sines. Check your answer numerically by evaluating the given expression and your answer.

20. Use the double argument property,

$$\cos 2x = 1 - 2 \sin^2 x$$

to express $\cos 120°$ in terms of $\sin 60°$. Check your answer by evaluating it and comparing it to the actual value of $\cos 120°$.

21. Use the double argument property in Problem 20 and appropriate algebra to write $\sin 100°$ in terms of $\cos 200°$. Check your answer numerically.

22. What did you learn as a result of taking this test that you did not know before?

Precalculus with Trigonometry: Assessment Resources
© 2007 Key Curriculum Press

Test 16, Sections 6-1 to 6-4   Form A

Objective: Solve oblique triangle problems.

Part 1: No calculators allowed (1–11)

Problems 1-6 refer to $\triangle XYZ$.

1. Sketch $\triangle XYZ$. Label the angles and the corresponding sides.

2. Write the law of cosines for finding side x in $\triangle XYZ$.

3. Write the law of sines for $\triangle XYZ$.

4. Write the area formula for $\triangle XYZ$ that involves angle X.

5. Write a formula for the semiperimeter, s, of $\triangle XYZ$.

6. Write Hero's formula for $\triangle XYZ$.

Problems 7-9 refer to $\triangle ABC$.

7. Sketch $\triangle ABC$ if $a = 3$, $b = 5$, and $c = 7$.

8. Based on the side lengths from Problem 7, which angle is the largest: A, B, or C? What property from geometry allows you to tell this quickly?

9. Write the law of cosines for $\triangle ABC$ that involves the largest angle. Then perform a calculation that will tell whether the largest angle is acute or obtuse.

Problems 10 and 11 refer to $\triangle DEF$.

10. Side $d = 4$ and side $e = 6$. If $\sin F = 0.2$, find the area of the triangle.

11. Is angle F acute or obtuse? How do you know?

(Hand in this page to get the rest of the test.)

Part 2: Graphing calculators allowed (12–24)

Problems 12–14 refer to a triangle that has two sides of 50 ft and 70 ft and an included angle 57°.

12. Sketch the triangle.

13. Find the length of the third side of the triangle.

14. Find the area of the triangle.

15. *Roof Problem:* The figure shows a 20-foot-wide building that is to be built with an asymmetrical roof. Solar panels will be placed on the face adjacent to the 23° angle. What is the maximum length of solar panel that can be placed from the eaves to the ridge, perpendicular to both, without hanging over either one?

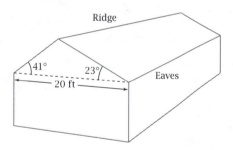

Surveying Problem (16–18): Surveyors measure a triangular field and find that the sides have lengths 250 ft, 300 ft, and 500 ft.

16. Find the measure of the largest angle of the triangle. Store the answer without rounding.

17. Find the area of the field using the area formula and the angle you calculated.

18. Find the area of the field directly, using Hero's formula. Show that the answer agrees with the area in Problem 16.

19. *Impossible Triangle Problem:* Phoebe is asked to sketch a triangle with sides 3 cm, 4 cm, and 8 cm. Show her that it is impossible, by attempting to find the measure of the largest angle using the law of cosines.

Variable Angle Problem (20–23): Calvin is asked to find the area of a triangle with sides 50 cm and 60 cm and a variable included angle A.

20. Calvin finds that the area for $A = 2°$ is about double the area for $A = 1°$. Show him that this is correct.

21. Show Calvin that the area for $A = 160°$ is *not* double the area for $A = 80°$.

22. The statement "The area varies directly with the measure of the angle" is false. Describe to Calvin properly how the area varies with the angle.

23. If the area of the triangle is 150 cm², find the *two* possible values of A.

24. What did you learn as a result of doing this test that you did not know before?

Precalculus with Trigonometry: Assessment Resources
© 2007 Key Curriculum Press

Test 16, Sections 6-1 to 6-4   Form B

Objective: Solve oblique triangle problems.

Part 1: No calculators allowed (1–11)

Problems 1-6 refer to $\triangle ABC$.

1. Sketch $\triangle ABC$. Label the angles and the corresponding sides.

2. Write the law of cosines for finding side b in $\triangle ABC$.

3. Write the law of sines for $\triangle ABC$.

4. Write the area formula for $\triangle ABC$ that involves angle A.

5. Write a formula for the semiperimeter, s, of $\triangle ABC$.

6. Write Hero's formula for $\triangle ABC$.

Problems 7–9 refer to $\triangle XYZ$.

7. Sketch $\triangle XYZ$ if $x = 5$, $y = 7$, and $z = 9$.

8. Based on the side lengths from Problem 7, which angle is the largest: X, Y, or Z? What property from geometry allows you to tell this quickly?

9. Write the law of cosines for $\triangle XYZ$ that involves the largest angle. Then perform a calculation that will tell whether the largest angle is acute or obtuse.

Problems 10 and 11 refer to $\triangle DEF$.

10. Side $d = 3$ and side $e = 5$. If $\sin F = 0.4$, find the area of the triangle.

11. Is angle F acute or obtuse? How do you know?

(Hand in this page to get the rest of the test.)

Part 2: Graphing calculators allowed (12–24)

Problems 12–14 refer to a triangle that has two sides of 40 ft and 60 ft and an included angle 47°.

12. Sketch the triangle.

13. Find the length of the third side of the triangle.

14. Find the area of the triangle.

15. *Roof Problem:* The figure shows a 23-foot-wide building that is to be built with an asymmetrical roof. Solar panels will be placed on the face adjacent to the 22° angle. What is the maximum length of solar panel that can be placed from the eaves to the ridge, perpendicular to both, without hanging over either one?

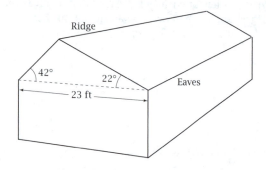

Surveying Problem (16–18): Surveyors measure a triangular field and find that the sides have lengths 500 ft, 600 ft, and 1000 ft.

16. Find the measure of the largest angle of the triangle. Store the answer without rounding.

17. Find the area of the field using the area formula and the angle you calculated.

18. Find the area of the field directly, using Hero's formula. Show that the answer agrees with the area in Problem 16.

19. *Impossible Triangle Problem:* Phoebe is asked to sketch a triangle with sides 3 cm, 7 cm, and 11 cm. Show her that it is impossible, by attempting to find the measure of the largest angle using the law of cosines.

Variable Angle Problem (20–23): Calvin is asked to find the area of a triangle with sides 45 cm and 55 cm and a variable included angle A.

20. Calvin finds that the area for $A = 2°$ is about double the area for $A = 1°$. Show him that this is correct.

21. Show Calvin that the area for $A = 160°$ is *not* double the area for $A = 80°$.

22. The statement "The area varies directly with the measure of the angle" is false. Describe to Calvin properly how the area varies with the angle.

23. If the area of the triangle is 160 cm², find the *two* possible values of A.

24. What did you learn as a result of doing this test that you did not know before?

Precalculus with Trigonometry: Assessment Resources
© 2007 Key Curriculum Press

Test 17, Chapter 6   Form A

Objective: Find unknown parts of oblique triangles.

Part 1: No calculators allowed (1–9)

Problems 1–3 refer to △*FGH*, shown here.

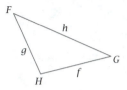

1. Write the part of the law of sines involving sides *f* and *g*.

2. Write the law of cosines involving angle *G*.

3. Write the area formula involving angle *G*.

4. Explain why you *cannot* use the law of cosines for this triangle.

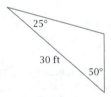

5. Explain why you *cannot* use the law of sines for this triangle.

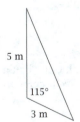

6. Explain why there is *no* triangle with the given side measurements.

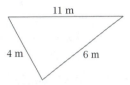

7. In the interior of this triangle, shade a second triangle, not congruent to this one, that has the same given side and angle measurements but is not congruent to it.

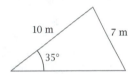

8. Sketch the resultant of these two vectors.

9. Write this vector in terms of its *x*- and *y*-components.

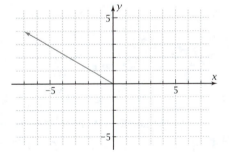

(Hand in this page to get the rest of the test.)

Test 17, Chapter 6 continued

Form A

Part 2: Graphing calculators allowed (10–21)

10. Construct a triangle with sides 5 cm and 4 cm and included angle 27°. Measure the third side.

11. Use the appropriate technique to calculate the length of the third side in Problem 10. Does it check?

12. Sketch a triangle with base 5 in. and the two base angles 20° and 130°. Find the measure of the third angle.

13. Calculate the length of the longest side of the triangle in Problem 12.

14. Sketch a triangle with sides 4 cm, 6 cm, and 9 cm. Find the measure of the largest angle. Store it without round-off.

15. Find the area of the triangle in Problem 14 using the formula

$$\text{Area} = \frac{1}{2}(\text{side})(\text{side}) \sin (\text{included angle})$$

16. Use Hero's formula,

$$\text{Area} = \sqrt{s(s - a)(s - b)(s - c)}$$

to find the area of the triangle in Problem 14 directly. Does the answer agree with your answer to Problem 15?

17. An airplane is flying on a bearing of 70° at a speed of 200 mi/h with respect to the air. The air is moving on a bearing of 10° at a speed of 50 mi/h with respect to the ground. What is the plane's velocity vector (bearing and speed) with respect to the ground?

Chris's Golf Problem (18–20): Chris Sollars hits his tee shot. The ball winds up exactly 100 yd from the hole. On his second shot, the ball winds up exactly 50 yd from the hole, somewhere on the circle shown in the figure.

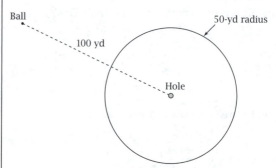

18. If Chris's second shot went on a line 17° to the right of the line to the hole, sketch on the figure the two possible places the ball could be. Calculate the two possible distances the shot could have gone.

19. If Chris's second shot had gone on a line 35° to the right of the line to the hole, show by calculation that it could not have been within 50 yd of the hole. Sketch the path of the ball, illustrating your answer.

20. What is the maximum angle at which Chris could have hit his second shot and still have it come to rest 50 yd from the hole?

21. What did you learn as a result of taking this test that you did not know before?

Test 17, Chapter 6

Form B

Objective: Find unknown parts of oblique triangles.

Part 1: No calculators allowed (1–9)

Problems 1–3 refer to △*ABC*, shown here.

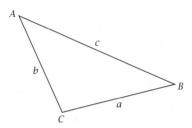

1. Write the part of the law of sines involving sides *a* and *b*.

2. Write the law of cosines involving angle *B*.

3. Write the area formula involving angle *B*.

4. Explain why you *cannot* use the law of cosines for this triangle.

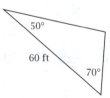

5. Explain why you *cannot* use the law of sines for this triangle.

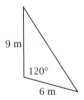

6. Explain why there is *no* triangle with the given side measurements.

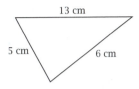

7. In the interior of this triangle, shade a second triangle, not congruent to this one, that has the same given side and angle measurements but is not congruent to it.

8. Sketch the resultant of these two vectors.

9. Write this vector in terms of its *x*- and *y*-components.

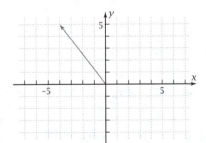

(Hand in this page to get the rest of the test.)

Test 17, Chapter 6 continued

Form B

Part 2: Graphing calculators allowed (10–21)

10. Construct a triangle with sides 5 cm and 6 cm and included angle 93°. Measure the third side.

11. Use the appropriate technique to calculate the length of the third side in Problem 10. Does it check?

12. Sketch a triangle with base 4 cm and the two base angles 40° and 120°. Find the measure of the third angle.

13. Calculate the length of the longest side of the triangle in Problem 12.

14. Sketch a triangle with sides 6 cm, 9 cm, and 11 cm. Find the measure of the largest angle. Store it without round-off.

15. Find the area of the triangle in Problem 14 using the formula

$$\text{Area} = \frac{1}{2}(\text{side})(\text{side}) \sin (\text{included angle})$$

16. Use Hero's formula,

$$\text{Area} = \sqrt{s(s-a)(s-b)(s-c)}$$

to find the area of the triangle in Problem 14 directly. Does the answer agree with your answer to Problem 15?

17. An airplane is flying on a bearing of 65° at a speed of 190 mi/h with respect to the air. The air is moving on a bearing of 15° at a speed of 60 mi/h with respect to the ground. What is the plane's velocity vector (bearing and speed) with respect to the ground?

Rocket Problem (18–20): An observer 2 km from the launching pad observes a rocket ascending vertically. At one instant, the angle of elevation is 20°. Four seconds later, the angle has increased to 35°.

18. Draw a diagram of this situation. How far did the rocket travel during the 4-s interval?

19. What was its average speed during this interval?

20. If the rocket keeps going vertically at the same average speed, what will be the angle of elevation 15 s after the *first* sighting?

21. What did you learn as a result of taking this test that you did not know before?

Test 18, Cumulative Test, Chapters 1–6 (Two hours)   Form A

Objective: Apply trigonometric and circular functions to periodic functions and triangle problems.

Part 1: No calculators allowed (1–11)

You started the course by **transforming** parent functions by **dilation** and **translation.**

1. Describe verbally and algebraically what transformation was applied to the dashed graph, f, to get the solid graph, g.

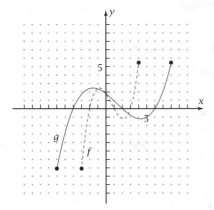

Words: _____

Equation: _____

2. In precalculus you have used angles to measure **rotation,** so the angles can be greater than 180° or negative. Sketch an angle of 210° in **standard position** in a uv-coordinate system. Mark the **reference angle** and write its measure. Write the *exact* value (no decimals!) of cos 210°.

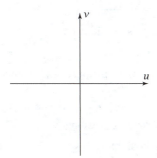

3. You apply transformations to a **sinusoid,** an example of a **periodic function.** Sketch one **cycle** of this sinusoid. Show coordinates of high and low points and **upper** and **lower bounds.**

$$y = 5 + 2 \cos 3(\theta - 20°)$$

4. Use the appropriate property to find tan x if sin $x = -0.6$ and cos $x = 0.8$.

5. Use the appropriate property to find sec x if sin $x = -0.6$ and cos $x = 0.8$.

6. Write the **Pythagorean property** involving cosine and sine.

7. Write the **composite argument property** for $\cos(A - B)$.

8. Is sine an **odd function** or an **even function**? Write an equation expressing this property.

9. By the **cofunction property,**

$$\cos 33° = \sin \underline{\hspace{2cm}}$$

10. For $\triangle RST$, write the **law of cosines** involving angle R.

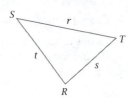

11. For $\triangle RST$ in Problem 10, write the **law of sines** involving angles R and S.

(Hand in this page to get the rest of the test.)

Test 18, Cumulative Test, Chapters 1–6 (Two hours) continued   Form A

Part 2: Graphing calculators allowed (12–44)

To apply sinusoids to real-world problems, you defined **circular functions,** with the help of **radians.**

12. Show how the x-axis is wrapped around the unit circle to define an angle of 2 radians.

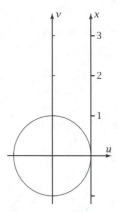

13. How many degrees are there in 2 radians?

14. Write the exact number (no decimals!) of radians in 90°.

15. Making a **mathematical model** involves finding the particular equation. Find an equation for the sinusoid for which a half-cycle is shown here.

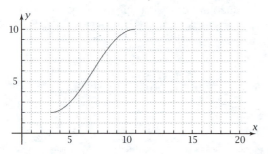

16. Dilations and translations have special names when applied to sinusoids. For the graph in Problem 15, give the:

- **Amplitude**
- **Phase displacement** (for cosine)
- **Period**
- **Sinusoidal axis** location

Tide Problem (17–20): The depth of water at the seacoast is a periodic function of time due to the motion of the tides. Suppose that the depth y, in feet, is given by

$$y = 3 + 4 \cos \frac{\pi}{5.7}(x - 2)$$

where x is time in hours after midnight last night.

17. At what time did the first high tide occur today? How deep was the water at that time?

18. What is the period of this function?

19. When does the second high tide occur today?

20. The tide is completely "out" when the depth calculated for the water is zero or less. Between what two times is the tide first completely out today? Show how you get your answer.

You can find x or θ for a given value of y algebraically by finding values of **inverse circular** or **inverse trigonometric relations.**

21. Write the general solution for $\theta = \arcsin 0.3$.

22. Write the general solution for $x = \arccos(-0.9)$.

23. Find the first three positive values of $\theta = \arctan 3$.

24. Explain why arcsin 3 is undefined.

25. The figure shows the **principal branch** of the tangent function. On this figure, sketch the **inverse tangent function,** $y = \tan^{-1} x$. Show how the two graphs are related to the line $y = x$.

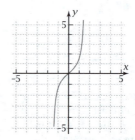

You can use properties of trigonometric and circular functions to **transform expressions.**

26. Transform $\cot x + \tan x$ to $\frac{1}{\cos x \sin x}$.

27. Prove that this equation is an **identity.**

$$\cos x(\sec x - \cos x) = \sin^2 x$$

28. Use the **composite argument property** for cosine to prove that $\cos(90° - \theta) = \sin \theta$.

Trigonometric functions are given that name because they are used in the measurement of triangles.

29. Recall that the **law of cosines** states

side² + side² − 2(side)(side) cosine of included angle = (third side)²

Use the law of cosines to find the third side of a triangle if two sides are 20 cm and 30 cm and the included angle is 140°.

30. Recall that the **area formula** for a triangle is

$$\text{Area} = \frac{1}{2}(\text{side})(\text{side}) \sin \text{ of included angle}$$

Find the area of the triangle in Problem 29.

(Next page.)

31. A triangular tract of land has sides 50 ft, 70 ft, and 100 ft. Find the measure of the largest angle.

32. Recall that **Hero's formula** states

$$\text{Area} = \sqrt{s(s-a)(s-b)(s-c)}$$

Use Hero's formula to find the area of the tract of land in Problem 31.

33. The triangle shown here is an example of the **case SSA.** Show that you understand why this is called the **ambiguous case** by sketching another triangle on this figure that has the same given sides and angles but is not congruent to the given triangle. Shade the interior of the new triangle.

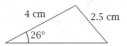

34. Calculate the two possible measures of the third side of the triangle in Problem 33.

35. You can analyze **vectors** by trigonometry. Find the resultant of these two vectors, using the angle the shorter vector makes with the longer vector when they are placed tail-to-tail.

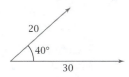

36. Recall that a **linear combination** of cosine and sine with equal periods is a sinusoid with the same period but with a different amplitude and a phase displacement. For example, you can write

$$y = -6 \cos \theta + 5 \sin \theta$$

as

$$y = A \cos(\theta - D)$$

On this *uv*-diagram, show how to calculate the constants A and D.

37. Plot $y_1 = -6 \cos \theta + 5 \sin \theta$ from Problem 36. Plot $y_2 = A \cos(\theta - D)$ from Problem 36. Explain what you see on the screen.

Problems 38–40 involve the **composite function** $f(g(x))$, where

$$f(x) = 0.5x + 1.5 \quad \text{for } 1 \le x \le 5$$
$$g(x) = 8 - x \quad \text{for } 2 \le x \le 4$$

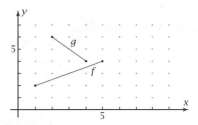

38. Explain why $f(g(2))$ is undefined even though both $f(2)$ and $g(2)$ are defined.

39. Plot $y = f(g(x))$ on your grapher. Sketch the result on the given figure.

40. From the graph, give the domain of function $f \circ g$.

41. By **composition of ordinates,** draw the graph of the product of these two sinusoids.

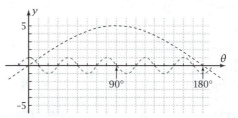

42. **Harmonic analysis** reverses the process of composition of ordinates. Write a particular equation for this graph.

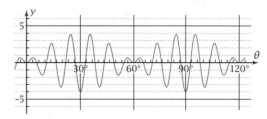

43. Write a particular equation for this graph.

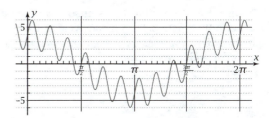

44. What is the one most important thing you have learned as a result of taking this test?

Test 18, Cumulative Test, Chapters 1–6 (Two hours)   Form B

Objective: Apply trigonometric and circular functions to periodic functions and triangle problems.

Part 1: No calculators allowed (1–11)

You started the course by **transforming** parent functions by **dilation** and **translation.**

1. Describe verbally and algebraically what transformation was applied to the dashed graph, *f,* to get the solid graph, *g.*

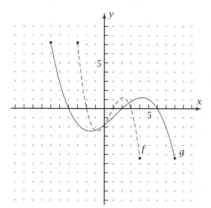

   Words: _____

   Equation: _____

2. In precalculus you have used angles to measure **rotation,** so the angles can be greater than 180° or negative. Sketch an angle of 300° in **standard position** in a *uv*-coordinate system. Mark the **reference angle** and write its measure. Write the *exact* value (no decimals!) of cos 300°.

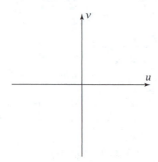

3. You apply transformations to a **sinusoid,** an example of a **periodic function.** Sketch one **cycle** of this sinusoid. Show coordinates of high and low points and **upper** and **lower bounds.**

   $y = 2 + 3 \cos 2(\theta - 30°)$

4. Use the appropriate property to find cot *x* if sin *x* = −0.6 and cos *x* = 0.8.

5. Use the appropriate property to find csc *x* if sin *x* = −0.6 and cos *x* = 0.8.

6. Write the **Pythagorean property** involving cosine and sine.

7. Write the **composite argument property** for cos (*A* + *B*).

8. Is cosine an **odd function** or an **even function**? Write an equation expressing this property.

9. By the **cofunction property,**

   sin 20° = cos _____

10. For △*ABC*, write the **law of cosines** involving angle *A.*

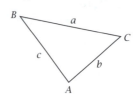

11. For △*ABC* in Problem 10, write the **law of sines** involving angles *A* and *B.*

(Hand in this page to get the rest of the test.)

Test 18, Cumulative Test, Chapters 1–6 (Two hours) continued   Form B

Part 2: Graphing calculators allowed (12–44)

To apply sinusoids to real-world problems, you defined **circular functions,** with the help of **radians.**

12. Show how the *x*-axis is wrapped around the unit circle to define an angle of 1 radian.

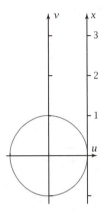

13. How many degrees are there in 2 radians?

14. Write the exact number (no decimals!) of radians in 45°.

15. Making a **mathematical model** involves finding the particular equation. Find an equation for the sinusoid for which a half-cycle is shown here.

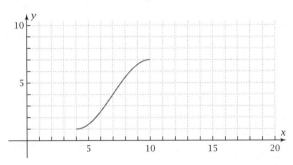

16. Dilations and translations have special names when applied to sinusoids. For the graph in Problem 15, give the:

 • **Amplitude**   • **Phase displacement** (for cosine)
 • **Period**   • **Sinusoidal axis** location

Tide Problem (17–20): The depth of water at the seacoast is a periodic function of time due to the motion of the tides. Suppose that the depth *y*, in feet, is given by

$$y = 2 + 3 \cos \frac{\pi}{4.8}(x - 5)$$

where *x* is time in hours after midnight last night.

17. At what time did the first high tide occur today? How deep was the water at that time?

18. What is the period of this function?

19. When does the second high tide occur today?

20. The tide is completely "out" when the depth calculated for the water is zero or less. Between what two times is the tide first completely out today? Show how you get your answer.

You can find *x* or θ for a given value of *y* algebraically by finding values of **inverse circular** or **inverse trigonometric relations.**

21. Write the general solution for $\theta = \arccos 0.3$.

22. Write the general solution for $x = \arcsin(-0.9)$.

23. Find the first three positive values of $\theta = \arctan 2$.

24. Explain why arcsin 4 is undefined.

25. The figure shows the **principal branch** of the tangent function. On this figure, sketch the **inverse tangent function,** $y = \tan^{-1} x$. Show how the two graphs are related to the line $y = x$.

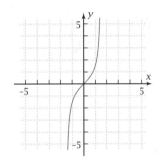

You can use properties of trigonometric and circular functions to **transform expressions.**

26. Transform csc *x* – sin *x* to cot *x* cos *x*.

27. Prove that this equation is an **identity.**

$$\sin x(\csc x - \sin x) = \cos^2 x$$

28. Use the **composite argument property** for cosine to prove that $\cos(90° - \theta) = \sin \theta$.

Trigonometric functions are given that name because they are used in the measurement of triangles.

29. Recall that the **law of cosines** states

$$\text{side}^2 + \text{side}^2 - 2(\text{side})(\text{side}) \text{ cosine of included}$$
$$\text{angle} = (\text{third side})^2$$

Use the law of cosines to find the third side of a triangle if two sides are 25 cm and 35 cm and the included angle is 145°.

30. Recall that the **area formula** for a triangle is

$$\text{Area} = \frac{1}{2}(\text{side})(\text{side}) \sin \text{ of included angle}$$

Find the area of the triangle in Problem 29.

(Next page.)

31. A triangular tract of land has sides 40 ft, 60 ft, and 90 ft. Find the measure of the largest angle.

32. Recall that **Hero's formula** states

$$\text{Area} = \sqrt{s(s-a)(s-b)(s-c)}$$

Use Hero's formula to find the area of the tract of land in Problem 31.

33. The triangle shown here is an example of the **case SSA.** Show that you understand why this is called the **ambiguous case** by sketching another triangle on this figure that has the same given sides and angles but is not congruent to the given triangle. Shade the interior of the new triangle.

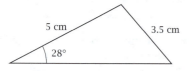

34. Calculate the two possible measures of the third side of the triangle in Problem 33.

35. You can analyze **vectors** by trigonometry. Find the resultant of these two vectors, using the angle it makes with the longer vector when they are placed tail-to-tail.

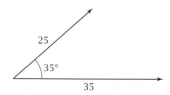

36. Recall that a **linear combination** of cosine and sine with equal periods is a sinusoid with the same period but with a different amplitude and a phase displacement. For example, you can write

$$y = -5 \cos \theta + 6 \sin \theta$$

as

$$y = A \cos(\theta - D)$$

On this *uv*-diagram, show how to calculate the constants A and D.

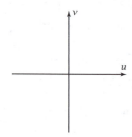

37. Plot $y_1 = -5 \cos \theta + 6 \sin \theta$ from Problem 36. Plot $y_2 = A \cos(\theta - D)$ from Problem 36. Explain what you see on the screen.

Problems 38–40 involve the **composite function** $f(g(x))$, where

$$f(x) = -0.5x + 5.5 \quad \text{for } 1 \le x \le 7$$
$$g(x) = 4 + x \quad \text{for } 2 \le x \le 4$$

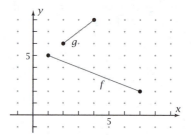

38. Explain why $f(g(4))$ is undefined even though both $f(4)$ and $g(4)$ are defined.

39. Plot $y = f(g(x))$ on your grapher. Sketch the result on the given figure.

40. From the graph, give the domain of function $f \circ g$.

41. By **composition of ordinates,** draw the graph of the product of these two sinusoids.

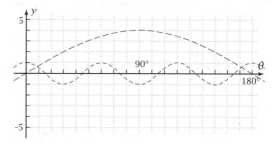

42. **Harmonic analysis** reverses the process of composition of ordinates. Write a particular equation for this graph.

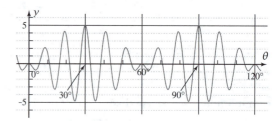

43. Write a particular equation for this graph.

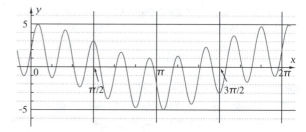

44. What is the one most important thing you have learned as a result of taking this test?

Precalculus with Trigonometry: Assessment Resources
© 2007 Key Curriculum Press

Test 19, Sections 7-1 to 7-3   Form A

Objective: Fit functions to graphs and data.

Part 1: No calculators allowed (1–11)

For Problems 1–4, describe what type of function could have the given graph, whether the function is increasing or decreasing, and which way the graph is concave.

1. Type of function: _____

    Increasing or decreasing: _____

    Concave: _____

2. Type of function: _____

    Increasing or decreasing: _____

    Concave: _____

3. Type of function: _____

    Increasing or decreasing: _____

    Concave: _____

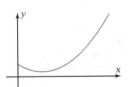

4. Type of function: _____

    Increasing or decreasing: _____

    Concave: _____

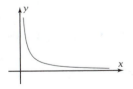

Snake Problem (5–7): The weights, W, of similarly shaped snakes are directly proportional to the cube of the length, L.

5. Write the general equation expressing W as a function of L.

6. A boa constrictor is five times as long as a rattlesnake. How does the weight of a boa constrictor compare to the weight of a rattlesnake?

7. The skin area of a snake is directly proportional to the square of the length. If the rattlesnake in Problem 6 has 2 square feet of skin, how much skin does a boa constrictor have?

8. Which type of function has the multiply-multiply property?

9. Which type of function has the add-multiply property?

10. Which type of function would fit these points? How can you tell?

x	$f(x)$
3	1600
6	400
9	100
12	25

11. For the points in Problem 10, find $f(15)$.

(Hand in this page to get the rest of the test.)

Part 2: Graphing calculators allowed (12–25)

Model Rocket (12–14): A precalculus class launches a model rocket on the football field. The rocket fires for two seconds. Each second thereafter they measure its altitude, finding these values.

t (s)	h (ft)
2	166
3	216
4	234
5	220
6	174

12. Show that the second differences in the h data are constant.

13. Show how matrices are used to find the particular equation of the function algebraically.

14. At what time t do you predict the rocket will hit the ground? Show your method.

Hose Flow Problem (15–19): The rate at which water flows out of a hose is a function of the water pressure at the faucet. Suppose that these flow rates have been measured (*psi* is "pounds per square inch").

x (psi)	y (gal/min)
4	5.0
9	7.5
16	10.0
25	12.5
36	15.0

15. Based on physical considerations, the flow rate is expected to be a power function of the pressure. Use the first and second data points to find the particular equation of the power function.

16. Plot the given points and the equation on the same screen. Sketch the results. How well does the equation fit the other three points?

17. Predict the flow rate if the pressure is increased to 100 psi. Which do you use, extrapolation or interpolation?

18. What pressure would be required to attain a flow rate of 20 gal/min? Show how you get the answer. Which do you use, extrapolation or interpolation?

19. This set of points has the multiply-multiply property that multiplying x by 4 multiplies y by 2. Show two instances in the table where this is true.

Function from Pattern Problem (20–22): These are values of a particular function f.

x	f(x)
3	1600
6	400
9	100
12	25

20. By observing the pattern in the x- and $f(x)$-values, state which type of function f is.

21. Use the first and last data points to find the particular equation of the exponential function algebraically.

22. Show that the equation in Problem 21 gives the correct value for $f(6)$.

23. *Concavity Problem:* The function graphed here is increasing, and the graph is concave down. What do these facts tell you about the rate at which y is increasing as x increases?

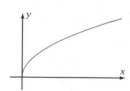

24. Power functions have the multiply-multiply property. Prove:

For $y = ax^n$, if $x_2 = cx_1$, then $y_2 = ky_1$.

25. What did you learn as a result of doing this test that you did not know before?

Test 19, Sections 7-1 to 7-3   Form B

Objective: Fit functions to graphs and data.

Part 1: No calculators allowed (1–11)

For Problems 1–4, describe what type of function could have the given graph, whether the function is increasing or decreasing, and which way the graph is concave.

1. Type of function: _____

   Increasing or decreasing: _____

   Concave: _____

   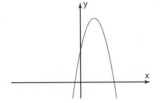

2. Type of function: _____

   Increasing or decreasing: _____

   Concave: _____

   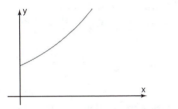

3. Type of function: _____

   Increasing or decreasing: _____

   Concave: _____

   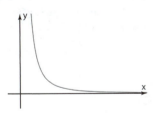

4. Type of function: _____

   Increasing or decreasing: _____

   Concave: _____

   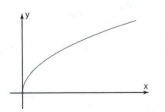

Shark Problem (5–7): The weights, *W*, of similarly shaped great white sharks are directly proportional to the cube of the length, *L*.

5. Write the general equation expressing *W* as a function of *L*.

6. A 15-foot-long great white shark caught off Catalina Island weighed 200 pounds. How much would a 5-foot-long juvenile shark weigh?

7. The girth of a shark is the circumferece around its middle at its widest point. If the girth of the 15-foot-long shark is 9 feet, what is the girth of the 5-foot-long shark?

8. Which type of function has the multiply–multiply property?

9. Which type of function has the add–multiply property?

10. Which type of function would fit these points? How can you tell?

x	f(x)
4	2000
8	400
12	80
16	16

11. For the points in Problem 10, find $f(20)$.

(Hand in this page to get the rest of the test.)

Test 19, Sections 7-1 to 7-3 continued

Form B

Part 2: Graphing calculators allowed (12–25)

Model Rocket (12–14): A precalculus class launches a model rocket on the football field. The rocket fires for one second. Every two seconds thereafter, they measure its altitude, finding these values.

t (s)	h (ft)
1	84
3	216
5	220
7	96

12. Show that the second differences in the h data are constant.

13. Show how matrices are used to find the particular equation of the function algebraically.

14. At what time t do you predict the rocket will hit the ground? Show your method.

Pendulum Problem (15–19): The period of a pendulum (the length of time it takes to make one complete swing) is a function of the length of the pendulum. By experiment, you find the periods (y) for the lengths in meters (x) as shown in the table.

x (m)	y (s)
0.5	0.709
1	1.004
2	1.420
2.5	1.588
8	2.84

15. Based on physical considerations, the period is expected to be a power function of the length. Use the first and second data points to find the particular equation of the power function.

16. Plot the given points and the equation on the same screen. Sketch the results. How well does the equation fit the other three points?

17. Predict the period of a pendulum 4 m long. Which do you use, extrapolation or interpolation?

18. What length pendulum would be required to attain a period of 4 s? Show how you get the answer. Which do you use, extrapolation or interpolation?

19. This set of points has the multiply-multiply property that multiplying x by 2 multiplies y by 1.41. Show two instances in the table where this is true.

Function from Pattern Problem (20–22): These are values of a particular function f.

x	$f(x)$
4	2000
8	400
12	80
16	16

20. By observing the pattern in the x- and $f(x)$-values, state which type of function f is.

21. Use the first and last data points to find the particular equation of the exponential function algebraically.

22. Show that the equation in Problem 21 gives the correct value for $f(8)$.

23. *Concavity Problem:* The function graphed here is increasing, and the graph is concave down. What do these facts tell you about the *rate* at which y is increasing as x increases?

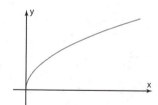

24. Power functions have the multiply-multiply property. Prove:

For $y = ax^n$, if $x_2 = cx_1$, then $y_2 = ky_1$.

25. What did you learn as a result of doing this test that you did not know before?

Objective: Analyze logarithmic and logistic functions.

Part 1: No calculators allowed (1–14)

1. The definition of logarithm states that $p = \log_m y$ if and only if —?—. What goes in the blank?

2. Use the definition of logarithm to write this equation in logarithmic form.

   $9^x = y$

3. Based on the definition of logarithm, explain why $\log_{10} 100 = 2$.

4. Write an equation stating the log of a product property.

5. Write an equation stating the log of a quotient property.

6. Write an equation stating the log of a power property.

7. Let $x = \log_5 13$. Use the definition of logarithm to write this equation in exponential form. Then take the natural logarithm of both sides. Use the answer to write $\log_5 13$ in terms of natural logarithms.

8. The answer to Problem 7 is an example of a property of logarithms. What is the name of that property?

9. $\log 2 + \log 4 = \log \underline{\hspace{1.5cm}}$

10. $\ln 24 - \ln 8 = \ln \underline{\hspace{1.5cm}}$

11. $\ln 7^5 = \underline{\hspace{1.5cm}} \ln 7$

12. $\log 28 - \log 2 + \log 3 = \log \underline{\hspace{1.5cm}}$

13. The figure shows the graph of the natural exponential function, $y = e^x$. On the figure, sketch the graph of the natural logarithmic function, $y = \ln x$, and state how it relates to the graphs of $y = x$.

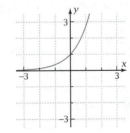

14. A logistic function has the equation

$$y = \frac{5}{1 + e^{-x}}$$

Explain why the graph has a horizontal asymptote at $y = 5$.

(Hand in this page to get the rest of the test.)

Test 20, Sections 7-4 to 7-6 continued   Form A

Part 2: Graphing calculators allowed (15–26)

For Problems 15–17, a logarithmic function contains these points.

x	y
2	13
10	17

15. Based on the pattern followed by points in a logarithmic function, write the x- and y-values for another ordered pair.

16. The general equation of the natural logarithmic function is $y = a + b \ln x$. Use the two given points to find the particular equation of this logarithmic function algebraically.

17. Show that your equation in Problem 16 gives the correct value for y when you substitute the value of x you found in Problem 15.

For Problems 18 and 19, use logarithms to solve the equation.

18. $e^{-3x} = 0.001$ (Use natural logarithms.)

19. $\log_6 (x - 1) + \log_6 (x + 4) = 2$

Spreading the News Problem (20–25): Josie and some friends heard from their principal that the school dance has been postponed. They start spreading the news. One student determines that the number of students, y, who have heard the news is given by this function of x, the number of minutes since Josie heard the news.

$$y = \frac{1200}{1 + 150e^{-0.5x}}$$

20. What kind of function is this?

21. Plot the graph for the first 20 min after Josie heard the news. Sketch the graph.

22. On your sketch, mark the point of inflection.

23. According to this mathematical model, about how many students heard the news at time zero?

24. About how many students had heard the news after 15 min? At that time was the rate at which students were hearing the news increasing or decreasing? How can you tell?

25. According to this mathematical model, how many students were at school that day, assuming that every student eventually hears the news? How can you tell?

26. What did you learn as a result of taking this test that you did not know before?

Precalculus with Trigonometry: Assessment Resources
© 2007 Key Curriculum Press

Test 20, Sections 7-4 to 7-6   Form B

Objective: Analyze logarithmic and logistic functions.

Part 1: No calculators allowed (1–14)

1. The definition of logarithm states that $b = \log_a y$ if and only if —?—. What goes in the blank?

2. Use the definition of logarithm to write this equation in logarithmic form.

    $16^x = y$

3. Based on the definition of logarithm, explain why $\log_8 64 = 2$.

4. Write an equation stating the log of a product property.

5. Write an equation stating the log of a quotient property.

6. Write an equation stating the log of a power property.

7. Let $x = \log_{13} 5$. Use the definition of logarithm to write this equation in exponential form. Then take the natural logarithm of both sides. Use the answer to write $\log_{13} 5$ in terms of natural logarithms.

8. The answer to Problem 7 is an example of a property of logarithms. What is the name of that property?

9. $\log 3 + \log 6 = \log$ _____

10. $\ln 36 - \ln 9 = \ln$ _____

11. $\ln 5^7 =$ _____ $\ln 5$

12. $\log 24 - \log 8 + \log 3 = \log$ _____

13. The figure shows the graph of the natural logarithmic function $y = \ln x$. On the figure, sketch the graph of the natural exponential function, $y = e^x$, and state how it relates to the graph of $y = x$.

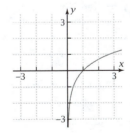

14. A logistic function has the equation

    $$y = \frac{3}{1 + e^{-x}}$$

    Explain why the graph has a horizontal asymptote at $y = 3$.

(Hand in this page to get the rest of the test.)

Test 20, Sections 7-4 to 7-6 continued   Form B

Part 2: Graphing calculators allowed (15–26)

For Problems 15–17, a logarithmic function contains these points.

x	y
5	14
10	18

15. Based on the pattern followed by points in a logarithmic function, write the x- and y-values for another ordered pair.

16. The general equation of the natural logarithmic function is $y = a + b \ln x$. Use the two given points to find the particular equation of this logarithmic function algebraically.

17. Show that your equation in Problem 16 gives the correct value for y when you substitute the value of x you found in Problem 15.

For Problems 18 and 19, use logarithms to solve the equation.

18. $e^{-3x} = 0.01$ (Use natural logarithms.)

19. $\log_6 (x + 1) + \log_6 (x - 4) = 1$

Spreading the News Problem (20–25): You arrive at school and meet your mathematics teacher, who tells you today's test has been canceled, and immediately you start spreading the news. One student determines that the number of students, y, who have heard the news is given by this function of x, the number of minutes since you heard the news.

$$y = \frac{1000}{1 + 100e^{-0.5x}}$$

20. What kind of function is this?

21. Plot the graph for the first 20 min after you heard the news. Sketch the graph.

22. On your sketch, mark the point of inflection.

23. According to this mathematical model, about how many students heard the news at time zero?

24. About how many students had heard the news after 15 min? At that time was the rate at which students were hearing the news increasing or decreasing? How can you tell?

25. According to this mathematical model, how many students were at school that day, assuming that every student eventually hears the news? How can you tell?

26. What did you learn as a result of taking this test that you did not know before?

Precalculus with Trigonometry: Assessment Resources
© 2007 Key Curriculum Press

Test 21, Chapter 7   Form A

Objective: Analyze functions from graphical and numerical patterns, and find particular equations.

Part 1: No calculators allowed (1–12)

1. Write the general equation of
   - An exponential function _____
   - A power function _____
   - A logarithmic function _____
   - A logistic function _____

2. Sketch the graph of a decreasing exponential function.

3. Sketch the graph of a power function that is concave down, if the exponent is positive.

4. Sketch the graph of a logistic function. Show the point of inflection.

5. Sketch the graph of the inverse of this logarithmic function. What is the base of the logarithm?

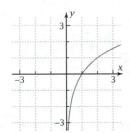

6. $\ln 5 + \ln 7 = \ln$ _____

7. $\log 42 - \log 6 = \log$ _____

8. $\ln 4^7 =$ _____ $\ln 4$

9. Write in logarithmic form: $p^n = j$

10. $g(x) = e^{(x-4)}$ is a horizontal translation by 4 units of the parent function $f(x) = e^x$. Explain why you can also write the transformed function $g(x) = ke^x$, where k stands for a constant. What does k equal in this case?

11. Describe the pattern followed by regularly spaced points for
    - A quadratic function _____
    - A power function _____
    - A logarithmic function _____

12. An exponential function has $f(8) = 13$ and $f(11) = 26$. Find another value of $f(x)$ using the pattern followed by regularly spaced points.

(Hand in this page to get the rest of the test.)

Test 21, Chapter 7 continued   Form A

Part 2: Graphing calculators allowed (13–25)

Gravity Problem (13-15): The acceleration acting on a falling object due to gravity varies inversely with the square of the object's distance from the center of Earth. At the surface of Earth, where $x = 1$ Earth radius, the acceleration is $y = 9.8$ m/s^2.

13. Use the multiply-multiply pattern of power functions to find the acceleration at 3 and 9 Earth radii from the center.

14. Find the particular equation expressing y as a function of x.

15. What is the acceleration due to Earth's gravity acting on someone standing on the Moon, 63 Earth radii away from Earth's center?

Quadratic Function Problem (16-19): A quadratic function f contains these points.

x	$f(x)$
3	36.7
5	27.5
7	20.7
9	16.3
11	14.3

16. Show that the given points have the characteristic pattern for quadratic functions with regularly spaced x-values.

17. Find the particular equation for $f(x)$ as a function of x.

18. Which way is the graph of f concave: up or down?

19. Find another value of x, besides $x = 3$, for which $f(x) = 36.7$.

Logarithmic Function Problem (20-21): A particular logarithmic function has the equation

$$L(x) = 2 + 5 \ln x$$

20. Find $L(1)$, $L(3)$, and $L(9)$. Show that these values have the multiply-add property of logarithmic functions.

21. Find algebraically the value of x for which $L(x) = 10$.

Hot Water Problem (22-24): Suppose that the water in a hot water heater is 70° Celsius above room temperature. When you first turn on the faucet, the water coming out is only 2° above room temperature. Ten seconds later it has warmed to 15° above room temperature.

22. Explain why a logistic function would be a reasonable mathematical model for the temperature, $T(x)$, at the faucet, x, in seconds, after you turn on the water.

23. The general equation for a logistic function is

$$T(x) = \frac{c}{1 + ae^{-bx}}$$

Use the three given values to find algebraically the particular equation of this function.

24. The point of inflection for a logistic function of this kind is halfway from the x-axis to the upper horizontal asymptote. What is the value of x at the point of inflection for this function?

25. What did you learn as a result of taking this test that you did not know before?

Test 21, Chapter 7   Form B

Objective: Analyze functions from graphical and numerical patterns, and find particular equations.

Part 1: No calculators allowed (1–12)

1. Write the general equation of
   - An exponential function _____
   - A power function _____
   - A logarithmic function _____
   - A logistic function _____

2. Sketch the graph of a decreasing exponential function.

3. Sketch the graph of a power function that is concave down, if the exponent is positive.

4. Sketch the graph of a logistic function. Show the point of inflection.

5. Sketch the graph of the inverse of this logarithmic function. What is the base of the logarithm?

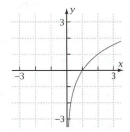

6. $\ln 3 + \ln 8 = \ln$ _____

7. $\log 56 - \log 8 = \log$ _____

8. $\ln 7^4 =$ _____ $\ln 7$

9. Write in logarithmic form: $q^m = r$

10. $g(x) = e^{(x-2)}$ is a horizontal translation by 2 units of the parent function $f(x) = e^x$. Explain why you can also write the transformed function $g(x) = ke^x$, where k stands for a constant. What does k equal in this case?

11. Describe the pattern followed by regularly spaced points for
    - A linear function _____
    - A power function _____
    - An exponential function _____

12. An exponential function has $f(5) = 44$ and $f(9) = 22$. Find another value of $f(x)$ using the pattern followed by regularly spaced points.

(Hand in this page to get the rest of the test.)

Test 21, Chapter 7 continued

Form B

Part 2: Graphing calculators allowed (13–25)

Sunlight Under the Water Problem (13-15): The intensity of sunlight under water decreases with depth. The table shows the depth, *y*, in feet, below the surface of the ocean you must go to reduce the intensity of the light to the given percentage, *x*, of what it was at the surface.

x (%)	Depth y (ft)
100	0
50	13

13. Use the multiply-add pattern of logarithmic functions to find the next two entries in the table.

14. Find the particular equation expressing *y* as a function of *x*. Use the common logarithm.

15. Based on this mathematical model, how deep do you have to go for the light to be reduced to 1% of its intensity at the surface?

Quadratic Function Problem (16-19): A quadratic function *f* contains these points.

x	f(x)
1	25
5	85
9	113
13	109
17	73

16. Show that the given points have the characteristic pattern for quadratic functions with regularly spaced *x*-values.

17. Find the particular equation for *f(x)* as a function of *x*.

18. Which way is the graph of *f* concave: up or down?

19. Find another value of *x*, besides *x* = 1, for which *f(x)* = 25.

Logarithmic Function Problem (20-21): A particular logarithmic function has the equation

$$L(x) = 5 + 2 \ln x$$

20. Find $L(1)$, $L(3)$, and $L(9)$. Show that these values have the multiply-add property of logarithmic functions.

21. Find algebraically the value of *x* for which $L(x) = 8$.

Population Problem (22-24): A small community is built on an island in the Gulf of Mexico. The population grows steadily, and the community has room for 460 residents. After 6 months, 75 people live in the community. After 12 months, 153 people live in the community.

22. Explain why a logistic function would be a reasonable mathematical model for the population, *P(x)*, of the island, as a function of time, *x*, in months.

23. The general equation for a logistic function is

$$P(x) = \frac{c}{1 + ae^{-bx}}$$

Use the three given values to find algebraically the particular equation of this function.

24. The point of inflection for a logistic function of this kind is halfway from the *x*-axis to the upper horizontal asymptote. What is the value of *x* at the point of inflection for this function?

25. What did you learn as a result of taking this test that you did not know before?

Test 22, Chapter 8   Form A

Objective: Fit linear, quadratic, logarithmic, exponential, power, or logistic functions to data.

Part 1: No calculators allowed (1–11)

1. Write the general equation of
   - A quadratic function _____
   - A power function _____

2. Name the kind of function.
   - $f(x) = \dfrac{300}{1 + 25e^{-0.3x}}$ _____
   - $g(x) = 3 + 7 \ln x$ _____

3. Name the numerical pattern followed by regularly spaced points in
   - An exponential function _____
   - A quadratic function _____

4. Which type of function listed in this test's objective has a graph like the one shown here?

   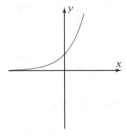

5. On the figure in Problem 4, sketch the graph of the inverse of the function.

6. The table shows x- and y-values measured from a real-world situation. The regression equation for the best-fitting linear function is

   $$\hat{y} = -2x + 19.5$$

   In the table, write the value of $\hat{y}$, the residual, and the square of the residual for each point. Calculate SS_{res}, the sum of the squares of the residuals.

x	y	$\hat{y}$	Residual	Residual^2
1	16			
3	16			
5	9			
7	5			

   $SS_{res} =$ _____

7. If you found SS_{res} for the data in Problem 6 using any other line besides $\hat{y} = -2x + 19.5$, how would the value of SS_{res} compare with the value you calculated in Problem 6?

8. The figure shows a scatter plot of the data in Problem 6 along with the regression line. The figure also shows a line plotted at $y = \bar{y}$, where $\bar{y} = 11.5$ is the average of the y-values. For the point where $x = 3$, show the deviation and the residual.

   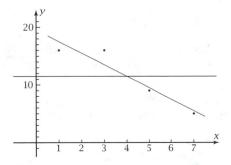

9. For the data in Problem 6, the sum of the squares of the deviations is $SS_{dev} = 89$. Use this information to write the coefficient of determination, r^2.

10. The correlation coefficient is the square root of the coefficient of determination. Which square root would you use for the data in Problem 6: the positive one or the negative one? Explain why.

11. The full name of "residual" is "residual deviation." What is the meaning of "residual" used in this context?

(Hand in this page to get the rest of the test.)

Test 22, Chapter 8 continued

Form A

Part 2: Graphing calculators allowed (12–28)

Exponential Function Problem (12–15): An exponential function contains these two points.

x	y
3	17
6	34

12. Without finding the equation, show how to calculate quickly the value of y when x = 12.

13. Find algebraically the particular equation of the exponential function by substituting the two given points into the general equation and finding the two coefficients.

14. Show that the equation in Problem 13 gives the value of y you calculated in Problem 12 at x = 12.

15. Use the equation in Problem 13 to find y when x = 4.7. Which does this calculation involve: interpolation or extrapolation? How can you tell?

Housing Problem (16–19): The table shows the number of houses in the new community of Scorpion Gulch at various numbers of years after the community was opened.

Year	Houses
0	13
1	15
2	18
3	25
4	34
5	42
6	50
7	55
8	58
9	60

16. Enter the data in two lists in your grapher and make a scatter plot. Give a reason why a logistic function would be appropriate based on
    • The pattern of the data
    • The endpoint behavior

17. Do logistic regression. Write the particular equation and paste it into the y= menu. Use the result to predict the number of houses at year 12.

18. Based on the logistic model, about how many houses will Scorpion Gulch ultimately have?

19. Use the regression equation and the given data in an appropriate way to calculate SS_{res}, the sum of the squares of the residuals.

Hot Water Problem (20–27): Calvin Butterball heats a pot of water. Here are its temperatures at various numbers of seconds since he started heating it.

Time (s)	Temperature (°C)
10	23.1
20	26.3
30	29.5
40	32.8
50	35.9
60	38.6
70	41.2
80	43.9
90	46.7
100	49.3

20. Find the best-fitting linear function for the data. Write the particular equation and the correlation coefficient. Store the equation as y_1.

21. How can you tell from the correlation coefficient that a linear function fits the data quite well?

22. Find SS_{res} for the data and the linear function.

23. Make a residual plot. What does the fact that the residuals follow a pattern tell you about how well a linear function fits the data?

24. Find the best-fitting quadratic function for the residuals. Write the equation. Store it as y_2.

25. Let $y_3 = y_1 + y_2$. Plot y_3 and the scatter plot of the original data on the same screen. Sketch the result.

26. Find SS_{res} for the function in y_3. How do you interpret the fact that it is smaller than SS_{res} in Problem 22 for the linear function?

27. Perform quadratic regression on the original data. Write the particular equation. Store it as y_4. Plot y_4 on the same screen as the plot in Problem 25. Use thick style. What do you notice about the resulting graph?

28. What did you learn as a result of taking this test that you did not know before?

Objective: Fit linear, quadratic, logarithmic, exponential, power, or logistic functions to data.

Part 1: No calculators allowed (1–11)

1. Write the general equation of
   - A logarithmic function _____
   - An exponential function _____

2. Name the kind of function.
   - $f(x) = \dfrac{300}{1 + 25e^{-0.3x}}$ _____
   - $g(x) = -4x^2 + 25x + 55$ _____

3. Name the numerical pattern followed by regularly spaced points in
   - A power function _____
   - An exponential function _____

4. Which type of function listed in this test's objective has a graph like the one shown here?

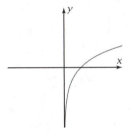

5. On the figure in Problem 4, sketch the graph of the inverse of the function.

6. The table shows x- and y-values measured from a real-world situation. The regression equation for the best-fitting linear function is

   $$\hat{y} = 1.95x + 4$$

   In the table, write the value of $\hat{y}$, the residual, and the square of the residual for each point. Calculate SS_{res}, the sum of the squares of the residuals.

x	y	$\hat{y}$	Residual	Residual^2
2	8			
4	10			
6	19			
8	18			

   $SS_{res} =$ _____

7. If you found SS_{res} for the data in Problem 6 using any other line besides $\hat{y} = 1.95x + 4$, how would the value of SS_{res} compare with the value you calculated in Problem 6?

8. The figure shows a scatter plot of the data in Problem 6 along with the regression line. The figure also shows a line plotted at $y = \bar{y}$, where $\bar{y} = 13.75$ is the average of the y-values. For the point where $x = 8$, show the deviation. For the point where $x = 6$, show the residual.

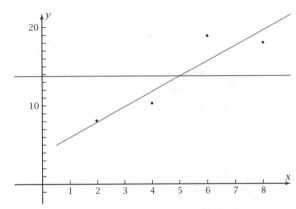

9. For the data in Problem 6, the sum of the squares of the deviations is $SS_{dev} = 92.75$. Use this information to write the coefficient of determination, r^2.

10. The correlation coefficient is the square root of the coefficient of determination. Which square root would you use for the data in Problem 6: the positive one or the negative one? Explain why.

11. The full name of "residual" is "residual deviation." What is the meaning of "residual" used in this context?

(Hand in this page to get the rest of the test.)

Test 22, Chapter 8 continued

Part 2: Graphing calculators allowed (12–28)

Exponential Function Problem (12–15): An exponential function contains these two points.

x	y
4	12
8	18

12. Without finding the equation, show how to calculate quickly the value of y when $x = 12$.

13. Find algebraically the particular equation of the exponential function by substituting the two given points into the general equation and finding the two coefficients.

14. Show that the equation in Problem 13 gives the value of y you calculated in Problem 12 at $x = 12$.

15. Use the equation in Problem 13 to find y when $x = 5.2$. Which does this calculation involve: interpolation or extrapolation? How can you tell?

Rabbits Problem (16–19): The table shows the number of rabbits in a particular woods as a function of time, x, in years.

Year	Rabbits
0	100
1	232
2	451
3	691
4	858
5	943
6	978
7	992
8	997
9	999

16. Enter the data in two lists in your grapher and make a scatter plot. Give a reason why a logistic function would be appropriate based on
    - The pattern of the data
    - The endpoint behavior

17. Do logistic regression. Write the particular equation and paste it into the $y =$ menu. Use the result to predict the number of rabbits at year 12.

18. Based on the logistic model, about how many rabbits will these woods ultimately have?

19. Use the regression equation and the given data in an appropriate way to calculate SS_{res}, the sum of the squares of the residuals.

Hot Water Problem (20–27): Calvin Butterball heats a pot of water. Here are its temperatures at various numbers of seconds since he started heating it.

Time (s)	Temperature (°C)
15	21
25	24.2
35	27.4
45	30.7
55	33.8
65	36.5
75	39.1
85	41.8
95	44.6
105	47.2

20. Find the best-fitting linear function for the data. Write the particular equation and the correlation coefficient. Store the equation as y_1.

21. How can you tell from the correlation coefficient that a linear function fits the data quite well?

22. Find SS_{res} for the data and the linear function.

23. Make a residual plot. What does the fact that the residuals follow a pattern tell you about how well a linear function fits the data?

24. Find the best-fitting quadratic function for the residuals. Write the equation. Store it as y_2.

25. Let $y_3 = y_1 + y_2$. Plot y_3 and the scatter plot of the original data on the same screen. Sketch the result.

26. Find SS_{res} for the function in y_3. How do you interpret the fact that it is smaller than SS_{res} in Problem 22 for the linear function?

27. Perform quadratic regression on the original data. Write the particular equation. Store it as y_4. Plot y_4 on the same screen as the plot in Problem 25. Use thick style. What do you notice about the resulting graph?

28. What did you learn as a result of taking this test that you did not know before?

Test 23, Sections 9-1 to 9-5

Form A

Objective: Find probabilities of certain events, some involving permutations and combinations.

Part 1: No calculators allowed (1–9)

Dice Problem (1–6): Two dice are rolled, a red one and a green one.

1. What special name is given to an act such as rolling dice in which there is no way of telling beforehand how the result will come out?

2. The table shows all 36 ways the dice could come out (red, green). What special name is given to this set of outcomes?

   (1, 1) (1, 2) (1, 3) (1, 4) (1, 5) (1, 6)
   (2, 1) (2, 2) (2, 3) (2, 4) (2, 5) (2, 6)
   (3, 1) (3, 2) (3, 3) (3, 4) (3, 5) (3, 6)
   (4, 1) (4, 2) (4, 3) (4, 4) (4, 5) (4, 6)
   (5, 1) (5, 2) (5, 3) (5, 4) (5, 5) (5, 6)
   (6, 1) (6, 2) (6, 3) (6, 4) (6, 5) (6, 6)

3. What is the probability that the red die has a 3 and the green die has a 2?

4. What is the probability that the red die has a 3 or the green die has a 2?

5. Which is more probable, that the total on the dice is 6 or that you roll a "double" (same on each die)? Show numbers to support your answer.

6. The probability of getting a certain total on the dice, such as 2, 3, 4, 5, . . . , 12, is a function of that total. The total, *x*, is called a **random variable.** Plot the probability as a function of *x*.

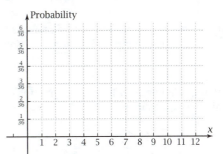

Calvin's Snack Problem (7–9): Calvin Butterball comes home from school and finds a plate with 20 pieces of candy and 13 cookies.

7. In how many different ways could he select a cookie or a piece of candy to eat?

8. In how many different ways could Calvin select a cookie and then a piece of candy to eat?

9. In how many different ways could Calvin select a cookie and then another cookie to eat?

(Hand in this page to get the rest of the test.)

Test 23, Sections 9-1 to 9-5 continued

Form A

Part 2: Graphing calculators allowed (10–24)

10. What is the difference between a **permutation** of the elements from a set and a **combination** of the elements from a set?

11. Calculate the number of different permutations that can be made of 50 elements taken three at a time.

12. Calculate the number of different combinations that can be made of 50 elements taken three at a time.

13. Explain the real-world meaning of the fact that $_{50}C_3$ and $_{50}C_{47}$ are equal to each other.

Playground Problem (14–19): Ten first-graders are playing on the playground.

14. In how many different ways could they arrange themselves in a straight line?

15. In how many different ways could the first-graders form a line containing exactly three of them?

16. How many different groups of the three first-graders could be formed (without regard to the order in which they are arranged)?

17. Six of the first-graders are girls and four are boys. In how many ways could you select a group consisting of exactly three girls and two boys?

18. In how many ways could you select a group of five of the ten first-graders without regard to whether they are boys or girls?

19. If a group of five of the ten first-graders is selected at random, what is the probability that three are girls and two are boys?

20. Suppose there are ten cars on a car dealer's lot, three of which are the same model and color and are considered to be identical. So there are fewer different permutations because rearranging the three identical cars does not form a new permutation. To find out how many different permutations could be made, consider two events.

Event *A:* Select a permutation, $n(A) = x$ ways

Event *B:* Arrange the three identical cars, $n(B) = 3! = 6$ ways

In terms of x, find $n(A$ and then $B)$.

21. The answer to Problem 20 has to equal 10!, the total number of permutations that could be made if all of the cars were considered to be different. Use this information to calculate x.

22. Use what you learned in Problems 20 and 21 to find the number of different permutations of the letters in ASSESSING, realizing that interchanging S's does not form a different permutation.

23. Calculate the number of different permutations of the letters in MISSISSIPPI.

24. What did you learn as a result of taking this test that you did not know before?

Test 23, Sections 9-1 to 9-5   Form B

Objective: Find probabilities of certain events, some involving permutations and combinations.

Part 1: No calculators allowed (1–9)

Dice Problem (1–6): Two dice are rolled, a red one and a green one.

1. What special name is given to an act such as drawing a card or rolling dice in which there is no way of telling beforehand how the result will come out?

2. The table shows all 36 ways the dice could come out (red, green). What special name is given to this set of outcomes?

   (1, 1) (1, 2) (1, 3) (1, 4) (1, 5) (1, 6)
   (2, 1) (2, 2) (2, 3) (2, 4) (2, 5) (2, 6)
   (3, 1) (3, 2) (3, 3) (3, 4) (3, 5) (3, 6)
   (4, 1) (4, 2) (4, 3) (4, 4) (4, 5) (4, 6)
   (5, 1) (5, 2) (5, 3) (5, 4) (5, 5) (5, 6)
   (6, 1) (6, 2) (6, 3) (6, 4) (6, 5) (6, 6)

3. What is the probability that the red die has a 3 and the green die has a 3?

4. What is the probability that the red die has a 4 or the green die has a 3?

5. Which is more probable, that the total on the dice is 6 or that you roll a "double" (same on each die)? Show numbers to support your answer.

6. The probability of getting a certain total on the dice, such as 2, 3, 4, 5, . . . , 12, is a function of that total. The total, x, is called a **random variable.** Plot the probability as a function of x.

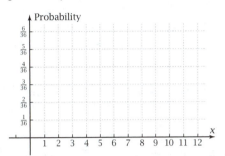

Calvin's Recreation Problem (7–9): Calvin Butterball comes home from school and looks at his shelf, which contains 15 video games and 30 movies.

7. In how many different ways could he select a game or a movie?

8. In how many different ways could Calvin select a game and then a movie?

9. In how many different ways could Calvin select a movie and then another movie?

(Hand in this page to get the rest of the test.)

Test 23, Sections 9-1 to 9-5 continued

Form B

Part 2: Graphing calculators allowed (10–24)

10. What is the difference between a **permutation** of the elements from a set and a **combination** of the elements from a set?

11. Calculate the number of different permutations that can be made of 40 elements taken five at a time.

12. Calculate the number of different combinations that can be made of 40 elements taken five at a time.

13. Explain the real-world meaning of the fact that $_{40}C_5$ and $_{40}C_{35}$ are equal to each other.

Marching Band Practice Problem (14–19): Twelve members of the marching band are on the football field.

14. In how many different ways could they arrange themselves in a straight line?

15. In how many different ways could the band members form a line containing exactly seven of them?

16. How many different groups of the seven band members could be formed without regard to the order in which they are arranged?

17. Eight of the band members are flutists and four are drummers. In how many ways could you select a group consisting of exactly three flutists and two drummers?

18. In how many ways could you select a group of five of the twelve band members without regard to whether they are flutists or drummers?

19. If a group of five of the twelve band members is selected at random, what is the probability that three are flutists and two are drummers?

20. Suppose there are nine books on a library's shelf, four of which are the same title, author, and edition and are considered to be identical. So there are fewer different permutations because rearranging the four identical books does not form a new permutation. To find out how many different permutations could be made, consider two events.

Event *A*: Select a permutation, $n(A) = x$ ways

Event *B*: Arrange the four identical books, $n(B) = 4! = 6$ ways

In terms of *x*, find $n(A$ and then $B)$.

21. The answer to Problem 20 has to equal 9!, the total number of permutations that could be made if all of the books were considered to be different. Use this information to calculate *x*.

22. Use what you learned in Problems 20 and 21 to find the number of different permutations of the letters in ASSESSING, realizing that interchanging S's does not form a different permutation.

23. Calculate the number of different permutations of the letters in TENNESSEE.

24. What did you learn as a result of taking this test that you did not know before?

Test 24, Chapter 9   Form A

Objective: Find probabilities and mathematical expectations for functions of a random variable.

Part 1: No calculators allowed (1–10)

1. Calculate the number of permutations of six objects taken four at a time. Show your method.

2. Write the number of combinations of ten objects taken seven at a time using factorials.

3. If you calculate the number of different groups of 5 that can be made from a class of 31 students, is this a number of combinations or a number of permutations? How can you tell?

4. If you calculate the number of different ways five of the students could be chosen to put Problems 1, 2, 3, 4, and 5 on the board, is this a number of combinations or a number of permutations? How can you tell?

5. Given X and Y are independent events and $P(X) = 0.6$ and $P(Y) = 0.7$, find $P(X \text{ and } Y)$.

6. Given X and Y are independent events and $P(X) = 0.6$ and $P(Y) = 0.7$, find $P(X \text{ or } Y)$.

7. If the probability of rain on a particular day is 60%, what is the probability of no rain on that day?

8. If the probability of rain is 60% on each of three consecutive days, find
   - The probability that it rains on all three days

   - The probability that it rains on exactly two of the three days

9. What is the relationship between the answers to Problem 8 and the binomial expansion of $(0.4 + 0.6)^3$?

10. The table shows the probabilities and payoffs for the three possible outcomes of a random experiment. Find the mathematical expectation. Explain the significance of the fact that the expectation is negative.

Event	Probability	Payoff
A	0.02	$100
B	0.08	$2
C	0.90	−$3

(Hand in this page to get the rest of the test.)

Test 24, Chapter 9 continued

Form A

Part 2: Graphing calculators allowed (11–28)

Sales Incentive Problem (11 and 12): Luis is a salesperson specializing in televisions at an electronics store. This table shows the probability of his selling various sizes of televisions.

TV Sales	Probability
30″	0.1
25″	0.4
19″	0.3
13″ (smallest)	0.15

11. What is the probability of his selling a larger television than the ones listed? Show how you got your answer.

12. Luis's manager offers him a selling incentive. He agrees to give Luis $25 for every 30″ television sold, $10 for every 25″ television, $10 for every 19″ television, and nothing for every 13″ television. If Luis sells a larger television, the manager agrees to give him $50. What is the mathematical expectation for this payment plan?

Rain Problem (13–16): Suppose there is a 70% probability of rain on Thursday and a 60% probability of rain on Friday. Find the probabilities of these events.

13. It rains both days.

14. It rains either Thursday or Friday.

15. It rains Thursday but not Friday.

16. It rains neither day.

Interrelated Problems (17–20): These problems have a relationship to each other.

17. Find the number of combinations of seven things taken three at a time.

18. Find the term in the binomial series from $(a + b)^7$ that has b^3.

19. Find the number of different permutations of the letters YYYNNNN.

20. What is the relationship among Problems 17–19?

Traffic Light Problem (21–27): As you drive north on Broadway, you have a 40% probability of having to stop at the traffic light at the intersection with Nacogdoches Road.

21. What is the probability you will not have to stop on any one such drive?

22. If you drive north on Broadway every day for a week, what is the probability you will have to stop all seven times?

23. What is the probability you will have to stop none of the seven times?

24. Show how you calculate the probability you will have to stop exactly three of the seven times.

25. Use your binomial distribution program to calculate $P(0)$ through $P(7)$, the probabilities of being stopped zero through seven times. Write the probabilities in a table.

26. Plot the graph of the probability distribution in Problem 25.

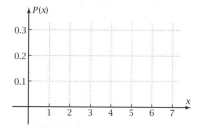

27. You are "pleased" if you are stopped just a few times and "displeased" if you are stopped many times. Suppose you get a "payoff" of 100 units of pleasure if you must stop no times and −100 units of pleasure if you must stop all seven times. The payoffs in terms of pleasure units are shown here.

Number	Pleasure Units
0	100
1	90
2	60
3	10
4	−20
5	−50
6	−70
7	−100

In this table, show how you calculate the mathematically expected number of pleasure units for the whole week. You may do the actual calculations by appropriate use of tables on your grapher.

28. What did you learn as a result of taking this test that you did not know before?

Test 24, Chapter 9

Objective: Find probabilities and mathematical expectations for functions of a random variable.

Part 1: No calculators allowed (1–10)

1. Calculate the number of permutations of five objects taken three at a time. Show your method.

2. Write the number of combinations of eleven objects taken six at a time using factorials.

3. If you calculate the number of different groups of 6 that can be made from a class of 30 students, is this a number of combinations or a number of permutations? How can you tell?

4. If you calculate the number of different ways six of the students could be chosen to put Problems 1, 2, 3, 4, 5, and 6 on the board, is this a number of combinations or a number of permutations? How can you tell?

5. Given X and Y are independent events and $P(X) = 0.4$ and $P(Y) = 0.3$, find $P(X \text{ and } Y)$.

6. Given X and Y are independent events and $P(X) = 0.4$ and $P(Y) = 0.3$, find $P(X \text{ or } Y)$.

7. If the probability of taking a test on a particular day is 30%, what is the probability of no test on that day?

8. If the probability of taking a test is 30% on each of three consecutive days, find
   - The probability that you take a test on all three days
   - The probability that you take a test on exactly two of the three days

9. What is the relationship between the answers to Problem 8 and the binomial expansion of $(0.3 + 0.7)^3$?

10. The table shows the probabilities and payoffs for the three possible outcomes of a random experiment. Find the mathematical expectation. Explain the significance of the fact that the expectation is negative.

Event	Probability	Payoff
A	0.04	$100
B	0.06	$4
C	0.90	−$5

(Hand in this page to get the rest of the test.)

Test 24, Chapter 9 continued

Form B

Part 2: Graphing calculators allowed (11–28)

Sales Incentive Problem (11 and 12): Luisa is a salesperson specializing in video players at an electronics store. This table shows the probability of her selling various types of video players.

Player Sales	Probability
DVD player	0.4
DVD/VCR player	0.25
VCR player	0.1
Portable DVD player	0.15

11. What is the probability of her selling a DVD player/recorder, which is not one of the types of players listed? Show how you got your answer.

12. Luisa's manager offers her a selling incentive. He agrees to give Luisa $20 for every DVD player sold, $25 for every DVD/VCR player sold, $30 for every portable DVD player sold, and nothing for every VCR player sold. If Luisa sells a DVD player/recorder, the manager agrees to give her $50. What is the mathematical expectation for this payment plan?

Snow Problem (13-16): Suppose there is a 30% probability of snow on Thursday and a 40% probability of snow on Friday. Find the probabilities of these events.

13. It snows both days.

14. It snows either Thursday or Friday.

15. It snows Thursday but not Friday.

16. It snows neither day.

Interrelated Problems (17-20): These problems have a relationship to each other.

17. Find the number of combinations of six things taken four at a time.

18. Find the term in the binomial series from $(a + b)^6$ that has b^4.

19. Find the number of different permutations of the letters YYNNNN.

20. What is the relationship among Problems 17-19?

Grade A Problem (21-27): The probability that you will make an A in any of your courses is 70%.

21. What is the probability you will not make an A in any one of your courses?

22. What is the probability you will make an A in all six of your courses?

23. What is the probability you will not make an A in any of your six courses?

24. Show how you calculate the probability you will make an A in exactly four of the six courses.

25. Use your binomial distribution program to calculate $P(0)$ through $P(6)$, the probabilities of making zero A's through six A's. Write the probabilities in a table.

26. Plot the graph of the probability distribution in Problem 25.

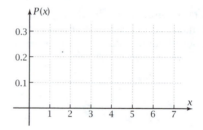

27. Your parents offer you a deal for making grades of A, as shown in the following table.

Number of A's	Money Earned ($)
0	−100
1	50
2	60
3	70
4	80
5	90
6	100

In this table, show how you calculate the mathematically expected monetary reward from your parents. You may do the actual calculations by appropriate use of tables on your grapher.

28. What did you learn as a result of taking this test that you did not know before?

Test 25, Cumulative Test, Chapters 7–9 (Two hours)   Form A

Objective: Fit functions to data and find probabilities for random experiments.

Part 1: No calculators allowed (1–12)

1. Write the general equation for
   - An exponential function _____
   - A power function _____
   - A logarithmic function _____

2. Sketch the graph of a
   - Logistic function

   - Quadratic function

3. Name the pattern followed by the y-values of functions with regularly spaced x-values for
   - Exponential functions _____
   - Power functions _____

For Problems 4, 5, and 6, the figure shows a set of points with a dashed line drawn across at $y = \bar{y}$, the average of the y-values.

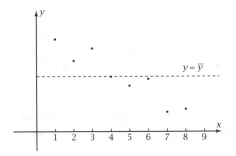

4. Sketch the deviation from the average for the point at $x = 3$.

5. Find $\bar{x}$, the average of the x-values, and show on the figure the average-average point, $(\bar{x}, \bar{y})$.

6. Sketch what you think is the best-fitting linear function, taking into account your answer to Problem 5. Show the residual for the point at $x = 3$. How does the size of the residual compare with the size of the deviation?

7. Suppose that the regression equation for a set of data is $\hat{y} = -2x + 13$. What does the residual equal for the data point $(3, 5)$?

8. Suppose that for a regression line, $SS_{res} = 19$. What is true about the sum of the squares of the residuals for any other linear function?

9. Suppose that the sum of the squares of the deviations is $SS_{dev} = 100$ and that $SS_{res} = 19$. What does the coefficient of determination, r^2, equal?

10. Suppose that a computer software company has 30 programmers. Use factorials to write the number of different ways they could select a group of 6 of the programmers to work on a particular project.

11. Given A and B are independent events with probabilities $P(A) = 0.9$ and $P(B) = 0.8$, find the probability that A or B occurs.

12. Given that the probability of event C is 0.3 and the payoff is $10 if C occurs and $-2 if C does not occur, find
    - $P(\text{not } C)$ _____
    - The mathematical expectation

(Hand in this page to get the rest of the test.)

Test 25, Cumulative Test, Chapters 7–9 (Two hours) continued   Form A

Part 2: Graphing calculators allowed (13–40)

Dog's Weight Problem (13–16): As dogs of a particular breed grow, their weight is a function of their length. Suppose these lengths and weights have been measured.

x (in.)	y (lb)
6	2
12	14
24	98
29	170
34	260
37	330

13. What pattern do the first three data points follow? What type of function has this pattern?

14. Find the particular equation for the function in Problem 13 algebraically by substituting the second and third points into the general equation. Show that the equation gives values for the last three points close to the values in the table.

15. Use the appropriate kind of regression to find the function of the type in Problem 13 that best fits all six data points. Write the correlation coefficient, and explain how it indicates that the function fits the data quite well.

16. Use the regression equation from Problem 15 to predict the weight of a newborn puppy 4 inches long. Which do you use, interpolation or extrapolation, to find this? How can you decide?

Weight-lifting Problem (17–20): Emma Strong starts an exercise routine to build up her muscles. She measures her progress at the end of each week, x, by the number of pounds, y, she can lift (see the table and graph).

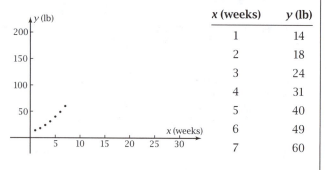

x (weeks)	y (lb)
1	14
2	18
3	24
4	31
5	40
6	49
7	60

17. What graphical evidence is there that an exponential function might fit the points? Based on endpoint behavior, why would a logistic function be more reasonable?

18. Write the particular equation of the best-fitting logistic function. Use the equation to predict the weight she can lift after week 15.

19. Plot the logistic function. Sketch the result on the given figure. Show the upper horizontal asymptote and the point of inflection.

20. What limit does the number of pounds approach?

Flower Pot Problem (21–24): A precalculus class reasons that the height, h, in centimeters, of a stack of flower pots should be a linear function of the number of pots, p, in the stack. They measure the data shown in the table and point plot.

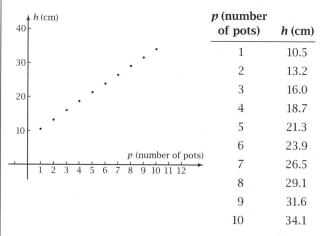

p (number of pots)	h (cm)
1	10.5
2	13.2
3	16.0
4	18.7
5	21.3
6	23.9
7	26.5
8	29.1
9	31.6
10	34.1

21. Write the linear regression equation, and give numerical evidence from the regression result that a linear function fits very well.

22. Use the regression equation to predict the height of a stack of 20 pots. Why is this not twice the height of a stack of 10 pots?

23. Put a list in your grapher to calculate the residuals. Make a residual plot and sketch the result. What information do you get from the residual plot concerning how well the linear function fits the data?

(Next page.)

24. Based on the residual plot, is the graph of h versus p concave up or concave down? What information does this fact give you about the rate at which the height increases as p gets larger? What real-world reason can you think of that would explain this behavior?

Logarithmic Function Problems (25–28):

25. Use the definition of logarithm to evaluate $y = \log_7 41$.

26. Use the log of a power property to solve this exponential equation: $5^{2x} = 157$

27. Use the change-of-base property to evaluate $\log_8 91$ using natural logarithms.

28. Plot the graph of $f(x) = \ln x$. Sketch the result. Explain why $f(1) = 0$. Give numerical evidence to show how $f(4)$ and $f(6)$ are related to $f(24)$.

Rainfall Probability Problems (29–33): Suppose that the probability of rain on each of several consecutive days is 30%.

29. What is the probability that it does not rain on a particular day?

30. Let x be the number of days. Let $P_1(x)$ be the probability that it rains on exactly x of five consecutive days. Show how you calculate $P_1(2)$.

31. Calculate $P_1(x)$ for $x = 0$ to $x = 5$. Plot the probability distribution on this graph paper.

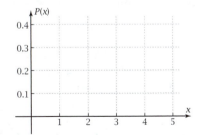

32. Let $P_2(x)$ be the probability that it rains at least once during the first x days. Find $P_2(x)$ for $x = 1$ to $x = 5$. To do this, you can subtract from 1 the probability that it rains on none of the first x days.

33. Plot the graph of the probability distribution P_2. Sketch the result, showing a dashed curve to indicate what the distribution looks like as x gets larger.

34. *Permutations Problem:* Show how the number of permutations of 68 objects taken five at a time is computed. Write the answer.

Croquet Probability Problem (35–39): Lowe High School has two varsity croquet teams. The A team has an 80% probability of winning this weekend, and the B team has a 60% probability of winning.

35. Find the probability that both teams win.

36. Find the probability that either the A team or the B team wins.

37. The probability that A wins and B does not is 0.32. Show how this number is calculated.

38. Find the probability that B wins and A does not.

39. If both teams win, the athletic department gets a prize of $200. If exactly one team wins, the department gets a plaque worth $30. If neither team wins, the department must pay the $100 fee for rental of the bus to the croquet match. What is the department's mathematical expectation for this weekend?

40. What did you learn as a result of taking this test that you did not know before?

Test 25, Cumulative Test, Chapters 7–9 (Two hours)　　　　Form B

Objective: Fit functions to data and find probabilities for random experiments.

Part 1: No calculators allowed (1–12)

1. Write the general equation for
   - A quadratic function _____
   - An exponential function _____
   - A logarithmic function _____

2. Sketch the graph of a
   - Power function

   - Logistic function

3. Name the pattern followed by the y-values of functions with regularly spaced x-values for
   - Logarithmic functions _____
   - Power functions _____

For Problems 4, 5, and 6, the figure shows a set of points with a dashed line drawn across at $y = \bar{y}$, the average of the y-values.

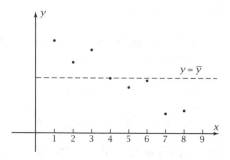

4. Sketch the deviation from the average for the point at $x = 3$.

5. Find $\bar{x}$, the average of the x-values, and show on the figure the average-average point, $(\bar{x}, \bar{y})$.

6. Sketch what you think is the best-fitting linear function, taking into account your answer to Problem 5. Show the residual for the point at $x = 3$. How does the size of the residual compare with the size of the deviation?

7. Suppose that the regression equation for a set of data is $\hat{y} = -2x + 13$. What does the residual equal for the data point (3, 5)?

8. Suppose that for a regression line, $SS_{\text{res}} = 19$. What is true about the sum of the squares of the residuals for any other linear function?

9. Suppose that the sum of the squares of the deviations is $SS_{\text{dev}} = 100$ and that $SS_{\text{res}} = 19$. What does the coefficient of determination, r^2, equal?

10. Suppose that a cleaning company has 20 workers. Use factorials to write the number of different ways they could select a group of 5 of the workers to work on a particular project.

11. Given A and B are independent events with probabilities $P(A) = 0.7$ and $P(B) = 0.8$, find the probability that A or B occurs.

12. Given that the probability of event C is 0.4 and the payoff is $20 if C occurs and −$4 if C does not occur, find
   - $P(\text{not } C)$ _____
   - The mathematical expectation

(Hand in this page to get the rest of the test.)

Precalculus with Trigonometry: Assessment Resources
© 2007 Key Curriculum Press

Test 25, Cumulative Test, Chapters 7–9 (Two hours) continued   Form B

Part 2: Graphing calculators allowed (13–40)

Shark Problem (13–16): Suppose that based on great white sharks caught in the past, this data regarding weights and lengths has been gathered.

x (ft)	y (lb)
5	75
10	600
20	4800
25	9340
30	16,100
35	25,600

13. What pattern do the first three data points follow? What type of function has this pattern?

14. Find the particular equation for the function in Problem 13 algebraically by substituting the second and third points into the general equation. Show that the equation gives values for the last three points close to the values in the table.

15. Use the appropriate kind of regression to find the function of the type in Problem 13 that best fits all six data points. Write the correlation coefficient, and explain how it indicates that the function fits the data quite well.

16. Use the regression equation from Problem 15 to predict the weight of a shark 32 feet long. Which do you use, interpolation or extrapolation, to find this? How can you decide?

Weight-lifting Problem (17–20): Emma Strong starts an exercise routine to build up her muscles. She measures her progress at the end of each week, *x*, by the number of pounds, *y*, she can lift (see the table and graph).

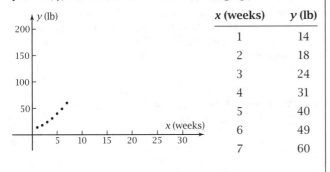

x (weeks)	y (lb)
1	14
2	18
3	24
4	31
5	40
6	49
7	60

17. What graphical evidence is there that an exponential function might fit the points? Based on endpoint behavior, why would a logistic function be more reasonable?

18. Write the particular equation of the best-fitting logistic function. Use the equation to predict the weight she can lift after week 15.

19. Plot the logistic function. Sketch the result on the given figure. Show the upper horizontal asymptote and the point of inflection.

20. What limit does the number of pounds approach?

Plastic Cup Problem (21–24): A precalculus class reasons that the height, *h*, in centimeters, of a stack of plastic cups should be a linear function of the number of cups, *c*, in the stack. They measure the data shown in the table and point plot.

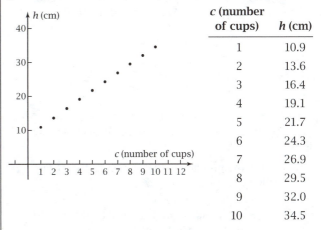

c (number of cups)	h (cm)
1	10.9
2	13.6
3	16.4
4	19.1
5	21.7
6	24.3
7	26.9
8	29.5
9	32.0
10	34.5

21. Write the linear regression equation, and give numerical evidence from the regression result that a linear function fits very well.

22. Use the regression equation to predict the height of a stack of 20 cups. Why is this not twice the height of a stack of 10 cups?

23. Put a list in your grapher to calculate the residuals. Make a residual plot and sketch the result. What information do you get from the residual plot concerning how well the linear function fits the data?

(Next page.)

24. Based on the residual plot, is the graph of h versus c concave up or concave down? What information does this fact give you about the rate at which the height increases as c gets larger? What real-world reason can you think of that would explain this behavior?

Logarithmic Function Problems (25–28):

25. Use the definition of logarithm to evaluate $y = \log_6 35$.

26. Use the log of a power property to solve this exponential equation: $4^{3x} = 291$

27. Use the change-of-base property to evaluate $\log_9 78$ using natural logarithms.

28. Plot the graph of $f(x) = \ln x$. Sketch the result. Explain why $f(1) = 0$. Give numerical evidence to show how $f(2)$ and $f(5)$ are related to $f(10)$.

Sleet Probability Problems (29–33): Suppose that the probability of sleet on each of several consecutive days is 80%.

29. What is the probability that it does not sleet on a particular day?

30. Let x be the number of days. Let $P_1(x)$ be the probability that it sleets on exactly x of five consecutive days. Show how you calculate $P_1(2)$.

31. Calculate $P_1(x)$ for $x = 0$ to $x = 5$. Plot the probability distribution on this graph paper.

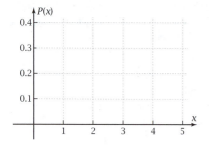

32. Let $P_2(x)$ be the probability that it sleets at least once during the first x days. Find $P_2(x)$ for $x = 1$ to $x = 5$. To do this, you can subtract from 1 the probability that it sleets on none of the first x days.

33. Plot the graph of the probability distribution P_2. Sketch the result, showing a dashed curve to indicate what the distribution looks like as x gets larger.

34. *Permutations Problem:* Show how the number of permutations of 58 objects taken four at a time is computed. Write the answer.

Squash Probability Problem (35–39): Lowe High School has two varsity squash teams. The A team has a 70% probability of winning this weekend, and the B team has a 50% probability of winning.

35. Find the probability that both teams win.

36. Find the probability that either the A team or the B team wins.

37. The probability that A wins and B does not is 0.35. Show how this number is calculated.

38. Find the probability that B wins and A does not.

39. If both teams win, the athletic department gets a prize of $200. If exactly one team wins, the department gets a plaque worth $30. If neither team wins, the department must pay the $100 fee for rental of the bus to the squash match. What is the department's mathematical expectation for this weekend?

40. What did you learn as a result of taking this test that you did not know before?

Test 26, Sections 10-1 to 10-4   Form A

Objective: Find and use sums, differences, and dot products of three-dimensional vectors.

Part 1: No calculators allowed (1–9)

1. Draw $\vec{v} = 5\vec{i} + 7\vec{j} + 10\vec{k}$ as a position vector in three-dimensional coordinates. Show the "box" that makes the vector look three-dimensional.

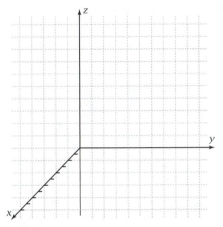

2. Show that you know what the three unit vectors $\vec{i}, \vec{j},$ and $\vec{k}$ mean by sketching them starting from the origin in Problem 1.

3. The figure shows two vectors, $\vec{a}$ and $\vec{b}$. By appropriate translation of the vectors, show the vector sum, $\vec{a} + \vec{b}$.

4. The figure shows $\vec{a}$ and $\vec{b}$ from Problem 3 translated so they are tail-to-tail. Draw the vector difference, $\vec{a} - \vec{b}$.

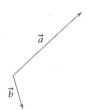

5. If $\vec{a}$ is 5 units long, the magnitude of $\vec{b}$ is 2 units, and the cosine of the angle between the two vectors is −0.3 when they are placed tail-to-tail, what does the inner product of $\vec{a}$ and $\vec{b}$ equal?

6. Let
$$\vec{m} = 5\vec{i} + 3\vec{j} + 7\vec{k}$$
$$\vec{r} = 2\vec{i} - 8\vec{j} + 3\vec{k}$$

Find the scalar product of $\vec{m}$ and $\vec{r}$.

7. Draw the vector projection of $\vec{c}$ on $\vec{d}$.

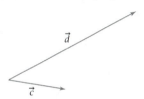

8. Draw the vector projection of $\vec{r}$ on $\vec{s}$.

9. If the scalar projection of $\vec{v}$ on unit vector $\vec{u}$ is $p = 10$ and $\vec{u} = \frac{1}{3}\vec{i} + \frac{2}{3}\vec{j} - \frac{2}{3}\vec{k}$, find $\vec{p}$, the vector projection of $\vec{v}$ on $\vec{u}$.

(Hand in this page to get the rest of the test.)

Part 2: Graphing calculators allowed (10–22)

For Problems 10–16, let

$$\vec{a} = 5\vec{i} + 3\vec{j} + 7\vec{k}$$
$$\vec{b} = 2\vec{i} - 8\vec{j} + 3\vec{k}$$

10. Find $|\vec{a}|$ and $|\vec{b}|$.

11. Find $\vec{a} \cdot \vec{b}$.

12. Use the definition of $\vec{a} \cdot \vec{b}$ and the answers to Problems 10 and 11 to find the angle θ between $\vec{a}$ and $\vec{b}$ when they are placed tail-to-tail.

13. Use the angle you found in Problem 12 and the definition of scalar projection to find the scalar projection, p, of $\vec{a}$ on $\vec{b}$.

14. Show that you get the same value for p using the shortcut $p = \frac{\vec{a} \cdot \vec{b}}{|\vec{b}|}$.

15. Write a unit vector in the direction of $\vec{b}$.

16. Write the vector projection, $\vec{p}$, of $\vec{a}$ on $\vec{b}$.

Spaceship Problem (17 and 18): A spaceship far from Earth is acted on by force vectors $\vec{e}$ from Earth's gravity and $\vec{m}$ from the Moon's gravity, where the forces are in pounds and

$$\vec{e} = -30\vec{i} - 40\vec{j} - 50\vec{k}$$
$$\vec{m} = 32\vec{i} + 38\vec{j} + 51\vec{k}$$

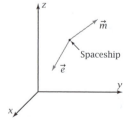

17. Find the resultant force vector $\vec{r}$ on the spaceship and how many pounds it is.

18. Quick! Will the angle between $\vec{r}$ and $\vec{m}$ be acute or obtuse? How can you tell?

Chandelier Problem (19–21): Two chandeliers are to be suspended from the ceiling in a hotel lobby. An *xyz*-coordinate system is set up with the *x*- and *y*-axes where two perpendicular walls meet the floor and the *z*-axis where the two walls intersect each other. The chandeliers are at the points $A(37, 50, 18)$ and $B(80, 19, 22)$, with dimensions in feet.

19. The figure shows A and B (not to scale). Sketch position vectors $\vec{a}$ and $\vec{b}$ to the two chandeliers.

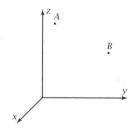

20. Sketch the displacement vector, $\vec{d}$, from A to B on the figure in Problem 19. Find $\vec{d}$ in terms of its components.

21. A wire is to go from A to B, and a light is to be placed on the wire 60% of the way from A to B. Show the position vector $\vec{v}$ to this light on the figure in Problem 19. Find $\vec{v}$ in terms of its components.

22. What did you learn as a result of taking this test that you did not know before?

Precalculus with Trigonometry: Assessment Resources
© 2007 Key Curriculum Press

Test 26, Sections 10-1 to 10-4   Form B

Objective: Find and use sums, differences, and dot products of three-dimensional vectors.

Part 1: No calculators allowed (1–9)

1. Draw $\vec{v} = 7\vec{i} + 6\vec{j} + 10\vec{k}$ as a position vector in three-dimensional coordinates. Show the "box" that makes the vector look three-dimensional.

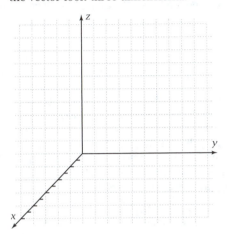

2. Show that you know what the three unit vectors $\vec{i}, \vec{j}$, and $\vec{k}$ mean by sketching them starting from the origin in Problem 1.

3. The figure shows two vectors, $\vec{a}$ and $\vec{b}$. By appropriate translation of the vectors, show the vector sum, $\vec{a} + \vec{b}$.

4. The figure shows $\vec{a}$ and $\vec{b}$ from Problem 3 translated so they are tail-to-tail. Draw the vector difference, $\vec{a} - \vec{b}$.

5. If $\vec{a}$ is 7 units long, the magnitude of $\vec{b}$ is 3 units, and the cosine of the angle between the two vectors is −0.4 when they are placed tail-to-tail, what does the inner product of $\vec{a}$ and $\vec{b}$ equal?

6. Let

$$\vec{m} = 4\vec{i} + 3\vec{j} + 7\vec{k}$$
$$\vec{r} = 5\vec{i} - 6\vec{j} + 1\vec{k}$$

Find the scalar product of $\vec{m}$ and $\vec{r}$.

7. Draw the vector projection of $\vec{c}$ on $\vec{d}$.

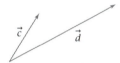

8. Draw the vector projection of $\vec{r}$ on $\vec{s}$.

9. If the scalar projection of $\vec{v}$ on unit vector $\vec{u}$ is $p = 12$ and $\vec{u} = \frac{2}{3}\vec{i} + \frac{1}{3}\vec{j} - \frac{2}{3}\vec{k}$, find $\vec{p}$, the vector projection of $\vec{v}$ on $\vec{u}$.

(Hand in this page to get the rest of the test.)

Test 26, Sections 10-1 to 10-4 continued   Form B

Part 2: Graphing calculators allowed (10–22)

For Problems 10–16, let

$\vec{a} = 4\vec{i} + 6\vec{j} + 5\vec{k}$

$\vec{b} = 3\vec{i} - 10\vec{j} + 7\vec{k}$

10. Find $|\vec{a}|$ and $|\vec{b}|$.

11. Find $\vec{a} \cdot \vec{b}$.

12. Use the definition of $\vec{a} \cdot \vec{b}$ and the answers to Problems 10 and 11 to find the angle θ between $\vec{a}$ and $\vec{b}$ when they are placed tail-to-tail.

13. Use the angle you found in Problem 12 and the definition of scalar projection to find the scalar projection, p, of $\vec{a}$ on $\vec{b}$.

14. Show that you get the same value for p using the shortcut $p = \frac{\vec{a} \cdot \vec{b}}{|\vec{b}|}$.

15. Write a unit vector in the direction of $\vec{b}$.

16. Write the vector projection, $\vec{p}$, of $\vec{a}$ on $\vec{b}$.

Spaceship Problem (17 and 18): A spaceship far from Earth is acted on by force vectors $\vec{e}$ from Earth's gravity and $\vec{m}$ from the Moon's gravity, where the forces are in pounds and

$\vec{e} = -30\vec{i} - 40\vec{j} - 50\vec{k}$

$\vec{m} = 32\vec{i} + 38\vec{j} + 51\vec{k}$

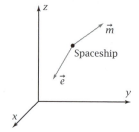

17. Find the resultant force vector $\vec{r}$ on the spaceship and how many pounds it is.

18. Quick! Will the angle between $\vec{r}$ and $\vec{m}$ be acute or obtuse? How can you tell?

Chandelier Problem (19–21): Two chandeliers are to be suspended from the ceiling in a hotel lobby. An *xyz*-coordinate system is set up with the *x*- and *y*-axes where two perpendicular walls meet the floor and the *z*-axis where the two walls intersect each other. The chandeliers are at the points $A(35, 55, 20)$ and $B(75, 18, 24)$, with dimensions in feet.

19. The figure shows A and B (not to scale). Sketch position vectors $\vec{a}$ and $\vec{b}$ to the two chandeliers.

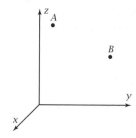

20. Sketch the displacement vector, $\vec{d}$, from A to B on the figure in Problem 19. Find $\vec{d}$ in terms of its components.

21. A wire is to go from A to B, and a light is to be placed on the wire 60% of the way from A to B. Show the position vector $\vec{v}$ to this light on the figure in Problem 19. Find $\vec{v}$ in terms of its components.

22. What did you learn as a result of taking this test that you did not know before?

Precalculus with Trigonometry: Assessment Resources
© 2007 Key Curriculum Press

Test 27, Sections 10-4 to 10-6   Form A

Objective: Find and use dot products and cross products of vectors.

Part 1: No calculators allowed (1–7)

1. Write the definition of dot product, $\vec{a} \cdot \vec{b}$.

2. Write the definition of cross product, $\vec{a} \times \vec{b}$.

3. Write the other names of dot product and cross product that allow you to identify what kind of quantity the answer is.

4. Explain why $\vec{i} \cdot \vec{i} = 1$ but $\vec{i} \cdot \vec{j} = 0$.

5. Explain why $\vec{i} \times \vec{i}$ is the zero vector but $\vec{i} \times \vec{j} = \vec{k}$.

6. If $\vec{a} = 1\vec{i} + 2\vec{j} + 3\vec{k}$ and $\vec{b} = 6\vec{i} + 5\vec{j} + 4\vec{k}$, find $\vec{a} \cdot \vec{b}$ by dotting each component of $\vec{a}$ with each component of $\vec{b}$. Arrange the nine terms in such a way that you can explain why the dot product is also called the *inner product*.

7. Find the particular equation of the plane normal to vector $\vec{a}$ in Problem 6 that contains the point (9, 8, 7).

(Hand in this page to get the rest of the test.)

Part 2: Graphing calculators allowed (8–21)

Exhibit Problem (8–20): The figure shows a canvas cover to be made over an exhibit area at a trade show and the shadow it will cast on the floor in the *xy*-plane. Dimensions are in feet.

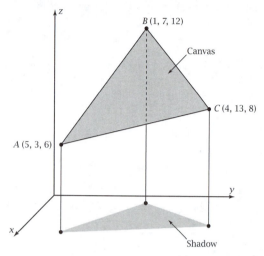

8. Draw the displacement vectors $\vec{v}_1$ from point A to point B and $\vec{v}_2$ from A to C. Write these two vectors in terms of their components.

9. Find the magnitude of $\vec{v}_1$.

10. Find the absolute value of $\vec{v}_2$.

11. Find the scalar product of $\vec{v}_1$ and $\vec{v}_2$.

12. Find the cross product $\vec{v}_1 \times \vec{v}_2$.

13. Find the angle at vertex A at which the canvas must be cut. Store this angle without rounding.

14. Show numerically that $|\vec{v}_1 \times \vec{v}_2| = |\vec{v}_1||\vec{v}_2| \sin A$, in accordance with the definition of cross product.

15. Show by appropriate computation that $\vec{v}_1$ really is perpendicular to $\vec{v}_1 \times \vec{v}_2$, in accordance with the definition of cross product.

16. Find the area of the canvas cover.

17. Quick! Write a vector normal to the plane of the canvas.

18. Find a particular equation of the plane of the canvas.

19. A vertical pole is to be placed at point $(3, 8, 0)$ in the shadow on the floor, reaching up until it just touches the canvas. How long must the pole be?

20. If the plane of the canvas were extended far enough, where would it cross the *y*-axis?

21. What did you learn as a result of taking this test that you did not know before?

Precalculus with Trigonometry: Assessment Resources
© 2007 Key Curriculum Press

Test 27, Sections 10-4 to 10-6 — Form B

Objective: Find and use dot products and cross products of vectors.

Part 1: No calculators allowed (1–7)

1. Write the definition of dot product, $\vec{a} \cdot \vec{b}$.

2. Write the definition of cross product, $\vec{a} \times \vec{b}$.

3. Write the other names of dot product and cross product that allow you to identify what kind of quantity the answer is.

4. Explain why $\vec{i} \cdot \vec{i} = 1$ but $\vec{i} \cdot \vec{j} = 0$.

5. Explain why $\vec{j} \times \vec{j}$ is the zero vector but $\vec{j} \times \vec{k} = \vec{i}$.

6. If $\vec{a} = 4\vec{i} + 5\vec{j} + 6\vec{k}$ and $\vec{b} = 3\vec{i} + 2\vec{j} + 1\vec{k}$, find $\vec{a} \cdot \vec{b}$ by dotting each component of $\vec{a}$ with each component of $\vec{b}$. Arrange the nine terms in such a way that you can explain why the dot product is also called the *inner product*.

7. Find the particular equation of the plane normal to vector $\vec{a}$ in Problem 6 that contains the point (1, 2, 3).

(Hand in this page to get the rest of the test.)

Test 27, Sections 10-4 to 10-6 continued   Form B

Part 2: Graphing calculators allowed (8–21)

Exhibit Problem (8–20): The figure shows a canvas cover to be made over an exhibit area at a trade show and the shadow it will cast on the floor in the *xy*-plane. Dimensions are in feet.

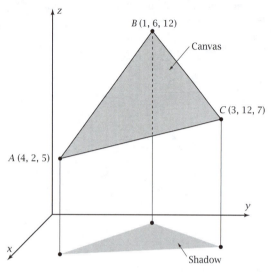

8. Draw the displacement vectors $\vec{v}_1$ from point A to point B and $\vec{v}_2$ from A to C. Write these two vectors in terms of their components.

9. Find the magnitude of $\vec{v}_1$.

10. Find the absolute value of $\vec{v}_2$.

11. Find the scalar product of $\vec{v}_1$ and $\vec{v}_2$.

12. Find the cross product $\vec{v}_1 \times \vec{v}_2$.

13. Find the angle at vertex A at which the canvas must be cut. Store this angle without rounding.

14. Show numerically that $|\vec{v}_1 \times \vec{v}_2| = |\vec{v}_1||\vec{v}_2| \sin A$, in accordance with the definition of cross product.

15. Show by appropriate computation that $\vec{v}_1$ really is perpendicular to $\vec{v}_1 \times \vec{v}_2$, in accordance with the definition of cross product.

16. Find the area of the canvas cover.

17. Quick! Write a vector normal to the plane of the canvas.

18. Find a particular equation of the plane of the canvas.

19. A vertical pole is to be placed at point $(3, 8, 0)$ in the shadow on the floor, reaching up until it just touches the canvas. How long must the pole be?

20. If the plane of the canvas were extended far enough, where would it cross the *y*-axis?

21. What did you learn as a result of taking this test that you did not know before?

Precalculus with Trigonometry: Assessment Resources
© 2007 Key Curriculum Press

Test 28, Chapter 10   Form A

Objective: Operate with three-dimensional vectors.

Part 1: No calculators allowed (1–9)

1. How do you calculate an angle between $\vec{a}$ and $\vec{b}$ using the dot product?

2. How could you calculate the angle between $\vec{a}$ and $\vec{b}$ using the cross product? What difficulty might you encounter with this method that you would not encounter using the dot product?

3. How would you find a unit vector in the opposite direction from $\vec{b}$?

4. A plane in space has equation $3x + 4y + 5z = 60$.
   - Find a vector normal to the plane.

   - Find the y-intercept of the plane.

5. Sketch the vector projection of $\vec{c}$ on $\vec{d}$.

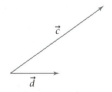

6. A line in space has the vector equation shown here. Find the position vector $\vec{v}$ to the fixed point on the line that appears in the equation.

$$\vec{r} = \left(5 + \frac{6}{11}d\right)\vec{i} + \left(3 + \frac{9}{11}d\right)\vec{j} + \left(7 + \frac{2}{11}d\right)\vec{k}$$

7. Write the coordinates of the point on the line that is 11 units in the positive d-direction away from the fixed point in Problem 6.

8. Sketch the direction angles for this position vector.

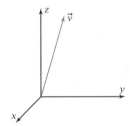

9. If α, β, and γ are direction angles for a vector in three dimensions and $\cos\alpha = 0.6$ and $\cos\beta = 0.7$, find $\cos\gamma$.

(Hand in this page to get the rest of the test.)

Part 2: Graphing calculators allowed (10–24)

For Problems 10-15, the figure represents this plane (not to scale).

$$3x + 2y + 5z = 54$$

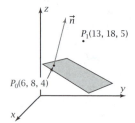

10. Show numerically that point $P_0(6, 8, 4)$ is on the plane and that point $P_1(13, 18, 5)$ is *not* on the plane.

11. Find $\vec{n}$, a vector normal to the plane.

12. Find vector $\vec{v}$ from P_0 to P_1.

13. Find the angle between $\vec{n}$ and $\vec{v}$.

14. On the figure, show the scalar projection, p, of $\vec{v}$ on $\vec{n}$. By suitable trigonometry, calculate p.

15. On the given figure, draw the perpendicular distance, d, from P_1 to the plane. Explain why d is equal to the scalar projection p in Problem 14.

For Problems 16-23, the figure represents this line (not to scale).

$$\vec{r} = \left(5 + \frac{6}{11}d\right)\vec{i} + \left(3 + \frac{9}{11}d\right)\vec{j} + \left(7 + \frac{2}{11}d\right)\vec{k}$$

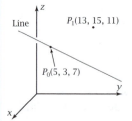

16. Show that $P_0(5, 3, 7)$ is on the line.

17. Find a unit vector, $\vec{u}$, in the direction of the line. Show that $\vec{u}$ really *is* a unit vector.

18. Find vector $\overrightarrow{P_0P_1}$ from P_0 to $P_1(13, 15, 11)$.

19. Find the angle between $\overrightarrow{P_0P_1}$ and $\vec{u}$.

20. On the figure, draw the perpendicular distance, p, from P_1 to the line. By suitable trigonometry, calculate p.

21. Find $\overrightarrow{P_0P_1} \times \vec{u}$.

22. Show that the distance p in Problem 20 is equal to the length of $\overrightarrow{P_0P_1} \times \vec{u}$.

23. Based on the definition of cross product and on your work in the previous problems, explain *why* the distance in Problem 20 is equal to the length of the cross product in Problem 22.

24. What did you learn as a result of taking this test that you did not know before?

Precalculus with Trigonometry: Assessment Resources
© 2007 Key Curriculum Press

Test 28, Chapter 10   Form B

Objective: Operate with three-dimensional vectors.

Part 1: No calculators allowed (1–9)

1. How do you calculate an angle between $\vec{a}$ and $\vec{b}$ using the dot product?

2. How could you calculate the angle between $\vec{a}$ and $\vec{b}$ using the cross product? What difficulty might you encounter with this method that you would not encounter using the dot product?

3. How would you find a unit vector in the opposite direction from $\vec{b}$?

4. A plane in space has equation $6x + 8y + 10z = 120$.
   • Find a vector normal to the plane.

   • Find the y-intercept of the plane.

5. Sketch the vector projection of $\vec{c}$ on $\vec{d}$.

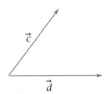

6. A line in space has the vector equation shown here. Find the position vector $\vec{v}$ to the fixed point on the line that appears in the equation.

$$\vec{r} = \left(1 + \frac{3}{7}d\right)\vec{i} + \left(2 + \frac{6}{7}d\right)\vec{j} + \left(3 + \frac{2}{7}d\right)\vec{k}$$

7. Write the coordinates of the point on the line that is 7 units in the positive d-direction away from the fixed point in Problem 6.

8. Sketch the direction angles for this position vector.

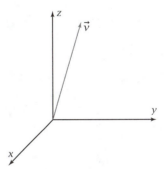

9. If α, β, and γ are direction angles for a vector in three dimensions and $\cos \alpha = 0.3$ and $\cos \beta = 0.6$, find $\cos \gamma$.

(Hand in this page to get the rest of the test.)

Test 28, Chapter 10 continued   Form B

Part 2: Graphing calculators allowed (10–24)

For Problems 10-15, the figure represents this plane (not to scale).

$$6x + 4y + 10z = 108$$

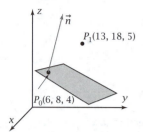

10. Show numerically that point $P_0(6, 8, 4)$ is on the plane and that point $P_1(13, 18, 5)$ is not on the plane.

11. Find $\vec{n}$, a vector normal to the plane.

12. Find vector $\vec{v}$ from P_0 to P_1.

13. Find the angle between $\vec{n}$ and $\vec{v}$.

14. On the figure, show the scalar projection, p, of $\vec{v}$ on $\vec{n}$. By suitable trigonometry, calculate p.

15. On the given figure, draw the perpendicular distance, d, from P_1 to the plane. Explain why d is equal to the scalar projection p in Problem 14.

For Problems 16-23, the figure represents this line (not to scale).

$$\vec{r} = \left(5 + \frac{3}{7}d\right)\vec{i} + \left(3 + \frac{6}{7}d\right)\vec{j} + \left(7 + \frac{2}{7}d\right)\vec{k}$$

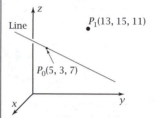

16. Show that $P_0(5, 3, 7)$ is on the line.

17. Find a unit vector, $\vec{u}$, in the direction of the line. Show that $\vec{u}$ really *is* a unit vector.

18. Find vector $\overrightarrow{P_0P_1}$ from P_0 to $P_1(13, 15, 11)$.

19. Find the angle between $\overrightarrow{P_0P_1}$ and $\vec{u}$.

20. On the figure, draw the perpendicular distance, p, from P_1 to the line. By suitable trigonometry, calculate p.

21. Find $\overrightarrow{P_0P_1} \times \vec{u}$.

22. Show that the distance p in Problem 20 is equal to the length of $\overrightarrow{P_0P_1} \times \vec{u}$.

23. Based on the definition of cross product and on your work in the previous problems, explain *why* the distance in Problem 20 is equal to the length of the cross product in Problem 22.

24. What did you learn as a result of taking this test that you did not know before?

Test 29, Sections 11-1 to 11-4

Form A

Objective: Use matrix multiplication to transform plane figures iteratively.

Part 1: No calculators allowed (1–8)

1. Add these matrices.

$$\begin{bmatrix} 5 & 8 \\ 3 & 2 \end{bmatrix} + \begin{bmatrix} 4 & 6 \\ 1 & 9 \end{bmatrix}$$

2. Multiply these matrices.

$$\begin{bmatrix} 2 & 3 & -1 \\ 5 & 4 & 2 \end{bmatrix} \begin{bmatrix} 6 & 2 \\ 3 & 0 \\ 1 & -3 \end{bmatrix}$$

3. In what way is matrix multiplication similar to multiplication of two vectors?

4. Explain why the matrices in Problem 2 are commensurate for multiplication.

5. What transformation is represented by this matrix?

$$\begin{bmatrix} 0.9\cos(-30°) & 0.9\cos 60° & 2 \\ 0.9\sin 30° & 0.9\sin 60° & 4 \\ 0 & 0 & 1 \end{bmatrix}$$

6. A line segment is transformed by iterative matrix multiplication. The matrices for the pre-image and the first and second iterations are

Pre-image: $\begin{bmatrix} 2 & 2 \\ 3 & 7 \\ 1 & 1 \end{bmatrix}$, First iteration: $\begin{bmatrix} 4.9 & 6.8 \\ 5.0 & 8.6 \\ 1 & 1 \end{bmatrix}$

Second iteration: $\begin{bmatrix} 8.3 & 11.1 \\ 6.0 & 7.6 \\ 1 & 1 \end{bmatrix}$

Draw the pre-image and the first and second iterations of the given figure.

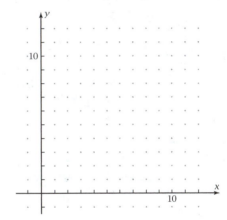

7. Explain what will happen to the line segments as more and more iterations are done.

8. What are the dimensions of this matrix?

$$\begin{bmatrix} 3 & 5 & 1 & 2 & 6 \\ 4 & 9 & 8 & 7 & 4 \\ 0 & 2 & 4 & 2 & 3 \\ 5 & 7 & 1 & 8 & 3 \end{bmatrix}$$

(Hand in this page to get the rest of the test.)

Part 2: Graphing calculators allowed (9–19)

9. Write a 3 × 4 pre-image matrix [D] for this kite.

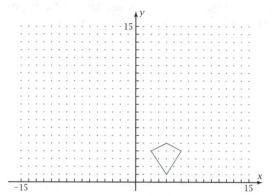

10. Enter this transformation matrix as [A] in your grapher.

$$[A] = \begin{bmatrix} 0.9\cos 15° & 0.9\cos 105° & 3 \\ 0.9\sin 15° & 0.9\sin 105° & 2 \\ 0 & 0 & 1 \end{bmatrix}$$

Multiply [A][D]. Write the resulting image matrix [E] with elements rounded to one decimal place.

11. Plot the image matrix [E] on the graph paper in Problem 9.

12. Set the window as shown in the figure in Problem 9. Then run the program ITRANS to show the pattern followed by the images. Sketch on the figure the path followed by the top point of the pre-image as the images spiral around toward the fixed point.

13. Find the coordinates of the fixed point numerically. Write the answers in ellipsis format with four decimal places. Explain how you did the computation.

14. If the pre-image is changed to the rectangle

$$\begin{bmatrix} -10 & -6 & -6 & -10 \\ 2 & 2 & 4 & 4 \\ 1 & 1 & 1 & 1 \end{bmatrix}$$

what will be the coordinates of the fixed point using the transformation in Problem 10?

15. If the transformation matrix is changed to

$$\begin{bmatrix} 0.9\cos 15° & 0.9\cos 105° & 4 \\ 0.9\sin 15° & 0.9\sin 105° & 1 \\ 0 & 0 & 1 \end{bmatrix}$$

what will be the coordinates of the fixed point?

16. Suppose that the transformation in Problem 15 is applied to an image matrix representing the point (X, Y). Write the results of this multiplication.

$$\begin{bmatrix} 0.9\cos 15° & 0.9\cos 105° & 4 \\ 0.9\sin 15° & 0.9\sin 105° & 1 \\ 0 & 0 & 1 \end{bmatrix}\begin{bmatrix} X \\ Y \\ 1 \end{bmatrix}$$

17. If the point (X, Y) in Problem 16 happens to be the fixed point for the transformation, then what other matrix does the product in Problem 16 equal?

18. Use the result of Problem 17 to find algebraically the coordinates of the fixed point. Do they agree with the numerical answer in Problem 13?

19. What did you learn as a result of taking this test that you did not know before?

Precalculus with Trigonometry: Assessment Resources
© 2007 Key Curriculum Press

Test 29, Sections 11-1 to 11-4   Form B

Objective: Use matrix multiplication to transform plane figures iteratively.

Part 1: No calculators allowed (1–8)

1. Add these matrices.

$$\begin{bmatrix} 3 & 2 \\ 8 & 5 \end{bmatrix} + \begin{bmatrix} 7 & 6 \\ 9 & 1 \end{bmatrix}$$

2. Multiply these matrices.

$$\begin{bmatrix} 5 & 4 & 2 \\ 3 & 2 & -1 \end{bmatrix} \begin{bmatrix} 3 & 1 \\ 6 & 0 \\ 2 & -1 \end{bmatrix}$$

3. In what way is matrix multiplication similar to multiplication of two vectors?

4. Explain why the matrices in Problem 2 are commensurate for multiplication.

5. What transformation is represented by this matrix?

$$\begin{bmatrix} 0.7\cos(-70°) & 0.7\cos 20° & 3 \\ 0.7\sin(-70°) & 0.7\sin 20° & 5 \\ 0 & 0 & 1 \end{bmatrix}$$

6. A line segment is transformed by iterative matrix multiplication. The matrices for the pre-image and the first and second iterations are

Pre-image: $\begin{bmatrix} 2 & 2 \\ 3 & 7 \\ 1 & 1 \end{bmatrix}$, First iteration: $\begin{bmatrix} 4.9 & 6.8 \\ 5.0 & 8.6 \\ 1 & 1 \end{bmatrix}$

Second iteration: $\begin{bmatrix} 8.3 & 11.1 \\ 6.0 & 7.6 \\ 1 & 1 \end{bmatrix}$

Draw the pre-image and the first and second iterations of the given figure.

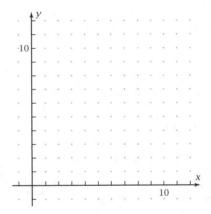

7. Explain what will happen to the line segments as more and more iterations are done.

8. What are the dimensions of this matrix?

$$\begin{bmatrix} 3 & 5 & 1 & 2 \\ 4 & 9 & 8 & 7 \\ 0 & 2 & 4 & 2 \end{bmatrix}$$

(Hand in this page to get the rest of the test.)

Test 29, Sections 11-1 to 11-4 continued   Form B

Part 2: Graphing calculators allowed (9–19)

9. Write a 3 × 4 pre-image matrix [D] for this kite.

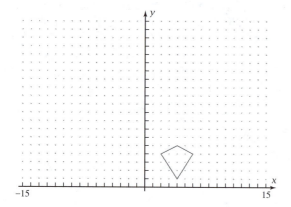

10. Enter this transformation matrix as [A] in your grapher.

$$[A] = \begin{bmatrix} 0.9\cos 15° & 0.9\cos 105° & 3 \\ 0.9\sin 15° & 0.9\sin 105° & 2 \\ 0 & 0 & 1 \end{bmatrix}$$

Multiply [A][D]. Write the resulting image matrix [E] with elements rounded to one decimal place.

11. Plot the image matrix [E] on the graph paper in Problem 9.

12. Set the window as shown in the figure in Problem 9. Then run the program ITRANS to show the pattern followed by the images. Sketch on the figure the path followed by the top point of the pre-image as the images spiral around toward the fixed point.

13. Find the coordinates of the fixed point numerically. Write the answers in ellipsis format with four decimal places. Explain how you did the computation.

14. If the pre-image is changed to the rectangle

$$\begin{bmatrix} -8 & -2 & -2 & -8 \\ 3 & 3 & 5 & 5 \\ 1 & 1 & 1 & 1 \end{bmatrix}$$

what will be the coordinates of the fixed point using the transformation in Problem 10?

15. If the transformation matrix is changed to

$$\begin{bmatrix} 0.9\cos 15° & 0.9\cos 105° & 5 \\ 0.9\sin 15° & 0.9\sin 105° & 6 \\ 0 & 0 & 1 \end{bmatrix}$$

what will be the coordinates of the fixed point?

16. Suppose that the transformation in Problem 15 is applied to an image matrix representing the point (X, Y). Write the results of this multiplication.

$$\begin{bmatrix} 0.9\cos 15° & 0.9\cos 105° & 5 \\ 0.9\sin 15° & 0.9\sin 105° & 6 \\ 0 & 0 & 1 \end{bmatrix}\begin{bmatrix} X \\ Y \\ 1 \end{bmatrix}$$

17. If the point (X, Y) in Problem 16 happens to be the fixed point for the transformation, then what other matrix does the product in Problem 16 equal?

18. Use the result of Problem 17 to find algebraically the coordinates of the fixed point. Do they agree with the numerical answer in Problem 13?

19. What did you learn as a result of taking this test that you did not know before?

Test 30, Chapter 11   Form A

Objective: Use matrix transformations to generate fractal figures.

Part 1: No calculators allowed (1–8)

1. If $[M]$ is an invertible 3×3 matrix, what does the product $[M][M]^{-1}$ equal?

2. Multiply these matrices.

$$\begin{bmatrix} 4 & 2 & 3 \\ -1 & 5 & 2 \end{bmatrix}\begin{bmatrix} 3 & -2 \\ 1 & 5 \\ 4 & 0 \end{bmatrix}$$

3. Explain why these matrices are commensurate for multiplication,

$$\begin{bmatrix} 1 & 2 & 3 \\ 4 & 5 & 6 \end{bmatrix}\begin{bmatrix} 9 & 8 & 7 \\ 6 & 5 & 4 \\ 3 & 2 & 1 \end{bmatrix}$$

but these matrices are not,

$$\begin{bmatrix} 9 & 8 & 7 \\ 6 & 5 & 4 \\ 3 & 2 & 1 \end{bmatrix}\begin{bmatrix} 1 & 2 & 3 \\ 4 & 5 & 6 \end{bmatrix}$$

4. Write a 3×3 transformation matrix to
   - Dilate by a factor of 0.7.
   - Rotate counterclockwise by 50°.
   - Translate right 10 spaces in the x-direction.
   - Translate down 6 spaces in the y-direction.

5. The closed figure represented by $[D]$ is the pre-image for a transformation. Plot $[D]$ on this dot paper.

$$[D] = \begin{bmatrix} 2 & 8 & 4 & 2 \\ 3 & 3 & 5 & 9 \\ 1 & 1 & 1 & 1 \end{bmatrix}$$

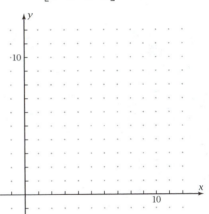

6. If transformation $[A]$ from Problem 4 is done iteratively starting with pre-image $[D]$ in Problem 5, then operating on the answer from the previous iteration, what will happen to the images eventually?

7. The figure shows the pre-image and first iteration for a set of transformations. If the iterations are carried on infinitely, the resulting fractal figure will have dimension given by

$$\text{Dimension} = \frac{\log N}{\log \frac{1}{r}}$$

   What do N and r equal for this fractal?

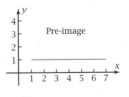
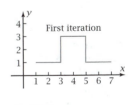

   $N =$ _____ $r =$ _____

8. How many images will there be in the seventh iteration for the transformations in Problem 7?

(Hand in this page to get the rest of the test.)

Test 30, Chapter 11 continued   Form A

Part 2: Graphing calculators allowed (9–20)

Rotated Square Problem (9–12): The figure shows a 10×10 square centered at the origin. The darker-shaded square is the image of this square, dilated by a factor of 0.8 and rotated about the origin by exactly the number of degrees, θ, so that its corners touch the sides of the parent square. The corners of the rotated square divide the sides of the 10×10 square into segments of length a and b.

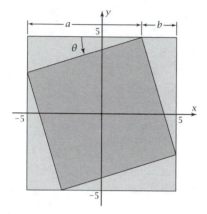

9. Explain why $a = 8 \cos \theta$ and $b = 8 \sin \theta$.

10. Use the fact that a and b add up to 10 to find the value of θ. Store this value in your grapher.

11. Write a 3×3 matrix $[A]$ to do the transformation described in this problem.

12. Write a 3×4 pre-image matrix for the 10×10 square. Run your ITRANS program, iterating enough times to see no more change in the images. Show your grapher to your instructor, or sketch the resulting figures.

Wave Problem (13–19): The figure shows a "wave" generated by performing three transformations iteratively using Barnsley's method.

13. Circle two parts of the wave of different size, each of which is self-similar to the entire wave.

14. One of the transformations used to generate the wave is

$$[A] = \begin{bmatrix} 0.5 \cos 30° & 0.5 \cos 120° & 7 \\ 0.5 \sin 30° & 0.5 \sin 120° & 0 \\ 0 & 0 & 1 \end{bmatrix}$$

Give the dilation, rotation, and translation represented by this matrix.

15. Find the fixed point to which the images will converge if transformation $[A]$ in Problem 14 is applied iteratively. Show how you get your answer.

16. The fixed point in Problem 15 shows up at an interesting place on the wave figure. Show this point on the figure.

17. The other two transformations that generate the wave each have the same dilation as $[A]$. Use this information to calculate the dimension of the wave.

18. What name is given to figures such as this wave to indicate that the dimension is a fraction, not an integer?

19. What name is given to figures such as this wave to indicate that points are attracted to only certain regions in the plane and not to others?

20. What did you learn as a result of taking this test that you did not know before?

Precalculus with Trigonometry: Assessment Resources
© 2007 Key Curriculum Press

Test 30, Chapter 11   Form B

Objective: Use matrix transformations to generate fractal figures.

Part 1: No calculators allowed (1–8)

1. If $[M]$ is an invertible 2×2 matrix, what does the product $[M][M]^{-1}$ equal?

2. Multiply these matrices.

$$\begin{bmatrix} 3 & -2 \\ 1 & 5 \\ 4 & 0 \end{bmatrix} \begin{bmatrix} 4 & 2 \\ -1 & 5 \end{bmatrix}$$

3. Explain why these matrices are commensurate for multiplication,

$$\begin{bmatrix} 3 & -2 \\ 1 & 5 \\ 4 & 0 \end{bmatrix} \begin{bmatrix} 4 & 2 \\ -1 & 5 \end{bmatrix}$$

but these matrices are not,

$$\begin{bmatrix} 4 & 2 \\ -1 & 5 \end{bmatrix} \begin{bmatrix} 3 & -2 \\ 1 & 5 \\ 4 & 0 \end{bmatrix}$$

4. Write a 3×3 transformation matrix to
   - Dilate by a factor of 0.8.
   - Rotate clockwise by 40°.
   - Translate left 10 spaces in the x-direction.
   - Translate up 6 spaces in the y-direction.

5. The closed figure represented by $[D]$ is the pre-image for a transformation. Plot $[D]$ on this dot paper.

$$[D] = \begin{bmatrix} 1 & 7 & 3 & 1 \\ 2 & 2 & 4 & 8 \\ 1 & 1 & 1 & 1 \end{bmatrix}$$

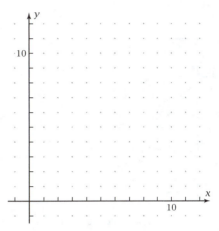

6. If transformation $[A]$ from Problem 4 is done iteratively starting with pre-image $[D]$ in Problem 5, then operating on the answer from the previous iteration, what will happen to the images eventually?

7. The figure shows the pre-image and first iteration for a set of transformations. If the iterations are carried on infinitely, the resulting fractal figure will have dimension given by

$$\text{Dimension} = \frac{\log N}{\log \frac{1}{r}}$$

What do N and r equal for this fractal?

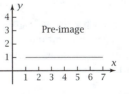 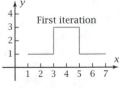

$N = $ _____ $r = $ _____

8. How many images will there be in the seventh iteration for the transformations in Problem 7?

(Hand in this page to get the rest of the test.)

Test 30, Chapter 11 continued   Form B

Part 2: Graphing calculators allowed (9–20)

Rotated Square Problem (9–12): The figure shows a 10×10 square centered at the origin. The darker-shaded square is the image of this square, dilated by a factor of 0.8 and rotated about the origin by exactly the number of degrees, θ, so that its corners touch the sides of the parent square. The corners of the rotated square divide the sides of the 10×10 square into segments of length a and b.

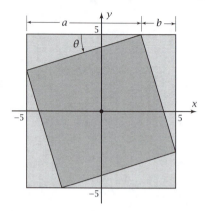

9. Explain why $a = 8 \cos \theta$ and $b = 8 \sin \theta$.

10. Use the fact that a and b add up to 10 to find the value of θ. Store this value in your grapher.

11. Write a 3×3 matrix $[A]$ to do the transformation described in this problem.

12. Write a 3×4 pre-image matrix for the 10×10 square. Run your ITRANS program, iterating enough times to see no more change in the images. Show your grapher to your instructor, or sketch the resulting figures.

Wave Problem (13-19): The figure shows a "wave" generated by performing three transformations iteratively using Barnsley's method.

13. Circle two parts of the wave of different size, each of which is self-similar to the entire wave.

14. One of the transformations used to generate the wave is

$$[A] = \begin{bmatrix} 0.5 \cos 30° & 0.5 \cos 120° & 7 \\ 0.5 \sin 30° & 0.5 \sin 120° & 0 \\ 0 & 0 & 1 \end{bmatrix}$$

Give the dilation, rotation, and translation represented by this matrix.

15. Find the fixed point to which the images will converge if transformation $[A]$ in Problem 14 is applied iteratively. Show how you get your answer.

16. The fixed point in Problem 15 shows up at an interesting place on the wave figure. Show this point on the figure.

17. The other two transformations that generate the wave each have the same dilation as $[A]$. Use this information to calculate the dimension of the wave.

18. What name is given to figures such as this wave to indicate that the dimension is a fraction, not an integer?

19. What name is given to figures such as this wave to indicate that points are attracted to only certain regions in the plane and not to others?

20. What did you learn as a result of taking this test that you did not know before?

Test 31, Sections 12-1 to 12-4   Form A

Objective: Analyze conic sections and quadric surfaces.

Part 1: No calculators allowed (1–8)

For Problems 1–3, the figure shows an ellipse of eccentricity e with certain dimensions marked.

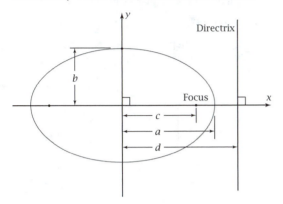

1. Give the special names for

   a _____

   b _____

   c _____

   d _____

2. Pick a point (x, y) on the ellipse in Quadrant I. Draw these distances.
   - d_1 from point (x, y) to the directrix
   - d_2 from point (x, y) to the focus on the right
   - d_3 from point (x, y) to the focus on the left

3. Write equations for these relationships.
   - The relationship among d_1, d_2, and e

   - The relationship among d_2, d_3, and the major axis

   - The Pythagorean property relating a, b, and c

   - The relationship among a, c, and e

   - The relationship among a, d, and e

Hyperbola Problem: For Problems 4 and 5, a hyperbola has this Cartesian equation.

$$-\left(\frac{x-2}{5}\right)^2 + \left(\frac{y+1}{3}\right)^2 = 1$$

4. Find the
   - Direction in which it opens: _____
   - Coordinates of the center: _____
   - Slopes of the asymptotes: _____

5. Sketch the graph, showing the asymptotes.

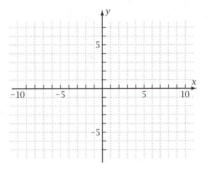

6. Sketch the paraboloid formed by rotating this parabola about its axis of symmetry.

7. Sketch the ellipsoid formed by rotating this ellipse about its major axis.

8. Give the name of this quadric surface.

(Hand in this page to get the rest of the test.)

Part 2: Graphing calculators allowed (9–28)

For Problems 9–13, an ellipse has this Cartesian equation.

$$\left(\frac{x-2}{5}\right)^2 + \left(\frac{y-4}{3}\right)^2 = 1$$

9. Sketch the graph.

10. Find the focal radius and the eccentricity.

11. Write parametric equations for the ellipse.

12. Transform the given equation to the form

$$Ax^2 + Bxy + Cy^2 + Dx + Ey + F = 0$$

13. How can you tell from the answer to Problem 12 that the graph really is an ellipse?

Problems 14–21 refer to the hyperbola graphed here with equation

$$9x^2 - 16y^2 = 144$$

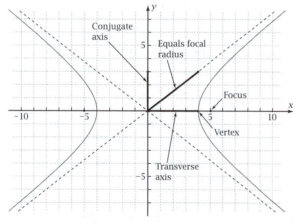

14. Plot the hyperbola on your grapher. Does the result agree with the given figure?

15. Transform the equation to make the right side equal 1. From the result, write the x-radius and the y-radius.

16. What are the slopes of the asymptotes? How can you calculate these slopes using the x- and y-radii?

17. The transverse radius, *a*, of a hyperbola goes from the center to a vertex. The conjugate radius, *b*, is the other radius. Which radius is which for this hyperbola?

18. One focus of this hyperbola is at the point (5, 0), so the focal radius (center to focus) is *c* = 5. By direct measurement, show that the length of the segment from the center along the asymptote to the point (4, 3) also equals the focal radius.

19. The segment you measured in Problem 18 is the hypotenuse of a right triangle. Use the fact that *c* is the length of this hypotenuse and that *a* and *b* are the two legs to write the Pythagorean property for hyperbolas.

20. Calculate the eccentricity of this hyperbola.

21. Calculate the directrix radius of this hyperbola.

For Problems 22–25, the hyperbola graphed here has the y-radius equal to the transverse radius.

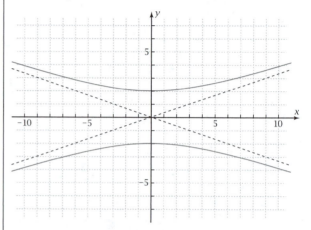

22. Draw the transverse and conjugate radii.

23. Calculate the focal radius. Show both foci.

24. True or false: "The transverse radius of a hyperbola is always longer than the conjugate radius."

25. Write parametric equations for the hyperbola.

Problems 26 and 27 refer to the ellipse with these parametric equations.

$$x = -3 + 4\cos t$$
$$y = 2 + 7\sin t$$

26. Sketch the graph of the ellipse.

27. Transform the equations to a single equation in Cartesian form. Start by isolating cos *t* in the first equation and sin *t* in the second equation. Then square both equations. Add the two equations, left side to left side and right side to right side. The Pythagorean property for cosine and sine will let you eliminate the parameter *t*.

28. What did you learn as a result of taking this test that you did not know before?

Precalculus with Trigonometry: Assessment Resources
© 2007 Key Curriculum Press

Test 31, Sections 12-1 to 12-4 Form B

Objective: Analyze conic sections and quadric surfaces.

Part 1: No calculators allowed (1–8)

For Problems 1–3, the figure shows an ellipse of eccentricity e with certain dimensions marked.

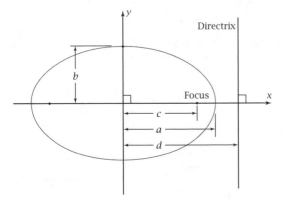

1. Give the special names for

   a _____

   b _____

   c _____

   d _____

2. Pick a point (x, y) on the ellipse in Quadrant I. Draw these distances.
   • d_1 from point (x, y) to the directrix
   • d_2 from point (x, y) to the focus on the right
   • d_3 from point (x, y) to the focus on the left

3. Write equations for these relationships.
   • The relationship among d_1, d_2, and e

   • The relationship among d_2, d_3, and the major axis

   • The Pythagorean property relating a, b, and c

   • The relationship among a, c, and e

   • The relationship among a, d, and e

Hyperbola Problem: For Problems 4 and 5, a hyperbola has this Cartesian equation.

$$\left(\frac{x + 2}{3}\right)^2 - \left(\frac{y - 1}{5}\right)^2 = 1$$

4. Find the
   • Direction in which it opens: _____
   • Coordinates of the center: _____
   • Slopes of the asymptotes: _____

5. Sketch the graph, showing the asymptotes.

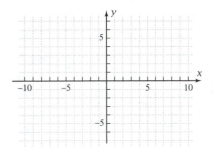

6. Sketch the paraboloid formed by rotating this parabola about its axis of symmetry.

7. Sketch the ellipsoid formed by rotating this ellipse about its major axis.

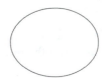

8. Give the name of this quadric surface.

(Hand in this page to get the rest of the test.)

Test 31, Sections 12-1 to 12-4 continued   Form B

Part 2: Graphing calculators allowed (9–28)

For Problems 9–13, an ellipse has this Cartesian equation.

$$\left(\frac{x-4}{3}\right)^2 + \left(\frac{y-2}{5}\right)^2 = 1$$

9. Sketch the graph.

10. Find the focal radius and the eccentricity.

11. Write parametric equations for the ellipse.

12. Transform the given equation to the form

$$Ax^2 + Bxy + Cy^2 + Dx + Ey + F = 0$$

13. How can you tell from the answer to Problem 12 that the graph really is an ellipse?

Problems 14–21 refer to the hyperbola graphed here with equation

$$16x^2 - 9y^2 = 144$$

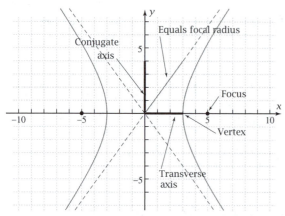

14. Plot the hyperbola on your grapher. Does the result agree with the given figure?

15. Transform the equation to make the right side equal 1. From the result, write the x-radius and the y-radius.

16. What are the slopes of the asymptotes? How can you calculate these slopes using the x- and y-radii?

17. The transverse radius, a, of a hyperbola goes from the center to a vertex. The conjugate radius, b, is the other radius. Which radius is which for this hyperbola?

18. One focus of this hyperbola is at the point (5, 0), so the focal radius (center to focus) is c = 5. By direct measurement, show that the length of the segment from the center along the asymptote to the point (4, 3) also equals the focal radius.

19. The segment you measured in Problem 18 is the hypotenuse of a right triangle. Use the fact that c is the length of this hypotenuse and that a and b are the two legs to write the Pythagorean property for hyperbolas.

20. Calculate the eccentricity of this hyperbola.

21. Calculate the directrix radius of this hyperbola.

For Problems 22–25, the hyperbola graphed here has the y-radius equal to the transverse radius.

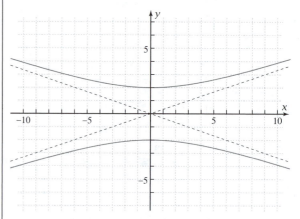

22. Draw the transverse and conjugate radii.

23. Calculate the focal radius. Show both foci.

24. True or false: "The transverse radius of a hyperbola is always longer than the conjugate radius."

25. Write parametric equations for the hyperbola.

Problems 26 and 27 refer to the ellipse with these parametric equations.

$$x = -4 + 6\cos t$$
$$y = 3 + 4\sin t$$

26. Sketch the graph of the ellipse.

27. Transform the equations to a single equation in Cartesian form. Start by isolating cos t in the first equation and sin t in the second equation. Then square both equations. Add the two equations, left side to left side and right side to right side. The Pythagorean property for cosine and sine will let you eliminate the parameter t.

28. What did you learn as a result of taking this test that you did not know before?

Objective: Analyze and apply conic sections and quadric surfaces.

Part 1: No calculators allowed (1–10)

For Problems 1–4, recall that the general equation of a conic section is

$$Ax^2 + Bxy + Cy^2 + Dx + Ey + F = 0$$

1. What is the major effect the xy-term has on the graph?

2. Write the discriminant for this general equation.

3. Recall that if $B = 0$ and A and C have opposite signs, then the graph is a hyperbola. Show how you can use this information to remember which sign the discriminant is if the conic section is a hyperbola.

4. Use the discriminant to show that the graph of this equation will be a parabola, even though it has both x^2- and y^2-terms.

$$x^2 - 6xy + 9y^2 + 11x - 20y - 57 = 0$$

5. Sketch an ellipsoid formed by rotating this ellipse about its minor axis.

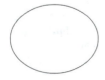

Hyperbola Problem: For Problems 6–10, the figure shows a hyperbola of transverse radius 10 and eccentricity 2 centered at the origin.

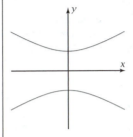

6. In which direction does the hyperbola open?

7. Darken the transverse radius.

8. Recall that the transverse radius and focal radius are related by the equation $\frac{c}{a} = e$. Use this fact and the given information to calculate c. Mark the upper focus on the given figure.

9. Also recall that the directrix radius and transverse radius are related by $\frac{a}{d} = e$. Use this fact and the given information to calculate the directrix radius. Sketch the directrix corresponding to the focus you drew in Problem 8.

10. Draw a point (x, y) on the hyperbola in the first quadrant. Draw the distances d_1 and d_2 from this point to the directrix and to the focus, respectively. How are d_1 and d_2 related to each other?

(Hand in this page to get the rest of the test.)

Part 2: Graphing calculators allowed (11–23)

Inscribed Cylinder Problem (11–13): The figure shows the paraboloid formed by rotating the graph of $y = 4 - x^2$, where x and y are in centimeters, about the y-axis. A cylinder is inscribed in the paraboloid, with its axis along the y-axis. The bottom base of the cylinder is centered at the origin, and the top base touches the inside of the paraboloid. The sample point (x, y) is on the parabola at the point where it touches the top base of the cylinder.

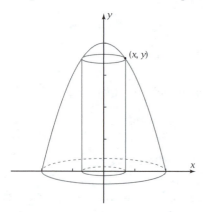

11. At the sample point shown, $x = 0.7$. What does y equal at this point? What is the volume of the cylinder?

12. If the radius of the cylinder is increased to $x = 1$, what is the volume of the cylinder?

13. Write the volume of the cylinder as a function of x. Plot volume as a function of x. Sketch the graph. What is the maximum volume the cylinder can have?

xy-Term Problem (14–16): Two conic sections have equations

$$x^2 + 4y^2 - 16 = 0 \quad \text{and} \quad x^2 + 5xy + 4y^2 - 16 = 0$$

They differ only in the xy-term.

14. Explain why the x- and y-intercepts for the second conic section are the same as for the first.

15. Use the discriminant to show that the second conic is a hyperbola, even though the squared terms have the same sign.

16. Use the program CONIC2 to plot the graphs on the same screen. For x, use a friendly window with a range of about $[-10, 10]$, with integers at the grid points. Use a window for y that gives equal scales on the two axes. Sketch the two graphs.

Mars and Sun Problem (17–22): Mars is in an elliptical orbit with the Sun at one focus, as shown in the figure. At its aphelion, Mars is 156 million miles from the Sun. At its perihelion, Mars is only 128 million miles from the Sun.

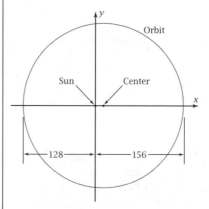

17. How long is the major axis of the ellipse? What is the major radius?

18. Find the focal radius, the minor radius, and the eccentricity of the ellipse.

19. Write a Cartesian equation of the ellipse.

20. A planet's equinox (equal day and night) occurs when the angle at the Sun between the major axis and the planet is 90°. How far from the Sun is Mars on the equinox?

21. How far from the Sun are the directrices of the ellipse?

22. Write parametric equations for the ellipse. Use these to plot the ellipse, using equal scales on the two axes. Does your graph agree with the given figure?

23. What did you learn as a result of taking this test that you did not know before?

Precalculus with Trigonometry: Assessment Resources
© 2007 Key Curriculum Press

Test 32, Chapter 12   Form B

Objective: Analyze and apply conic sections and quadric surfaces.

Part 1: No calculators allowed (1–10)

For Problems 1–4, recall that the general equation of a conic section is

$$Ax^2 + Bxy + Cy^2 + Dx + Ey + F = 0$$

1. What is the major effect the xy-term has on the graph?

2. Write the discriminant for this general equation.

3. Recall that if $B = 0$ and A and C have same signs, then the graph is an ellipse or a circle. Show how you can use this information to remember which sign the discriminant is if the conic section is an ellipse or a circle.

4. Use the discriminant to show that the graph of this equation will be a parabola, even though it has both x^2- and y^2-terms.

$$x^2 + 6xy + 9y^2 - 3x - 4y - 10 = 0$$

5. Sketch an ellipsoid formed by rotating this ellipse about its major axis.

Hyperbola Problem: For Problems 6–10, the figure shows a hyperbola of transverse radius 10 and eccentricity 2 centered at the origin.

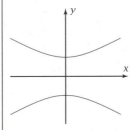

6. In which direction does the hyperbola open?

7. Darken the transverse radius.

8. Recall that the transverse radius and focal radius are related by the equation $\frac{c}{a} = e$. Use this fact and the given information to calculate c. Mark the upper focus on the given figure.

9. Also recall that the directrix radius and transverse radius are related by $\frac{a}{d} = e$. Use this fact and the given information to calculate the directrix radius. Sketch the directrix corresponding to the focus you drew in Problem 8.

10. Draw a point (x, y) on the hyperbola in the first quadrant. Draw the distances d_1 and d_2 from this point to the directrix and to the focus, respectively. How are d_1 and d_2 related to each other?

(Hand in this page to get the rest of the test.)

Test 32, Chapter 12 continued

Form B

Part 2: Graphing calculators allowed (11–23)

Inscribed Cylinder Problem (11–13): The figure shows the paraboloid formed by rotating the graph of $y = 9 - x^2$, where x and y are in centimeters, about the y-axis. A cylinder is inscribed in the paraboloid, with its axis along the y-axis. The bottom base of the cylinder is centered at the origin, and the top base touches the inside of the paraboloid. The sample point (x, y) is on the parabola at the point where it touches the top base of the cylinder.

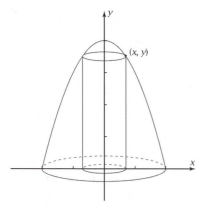

11. At the sample point shown, $x = 0.7$. What does y equal at this point? What is the volume of the cylinder?

12. If the radius of the cylinder is increased to $x = 1$, what is the volume of the cylinder?

13. Write the volume of the cylinder as a function of x. Plot volume as a function of x. Sketch the graph. What is the maximum volume the cylinder can have?

xy-Term Problem (14–16): Two conic sections have equations

$$4x^2 + y^2 - 16 = 0 \quad \text{and} \quad 4x^2 + 5xy + y^2 - 16 = 0$$

They differ only in the xy-term.

14. Explain why the x- and y-intercepts for the second conic section are the same as for the first.

15. Use the discriminant to show that the second conic is a hyperbola, even though the squared terms have the same sign.

16. Use the program CONIC2 to plot the graphs on the same screen. For x, use a friendly window with a range of about $[-10, 10]$, with integers at the grid points. Use a window for y that gives equal scales on the two axes. Sketch the two graphs.

Halley's Comet Problem (17–22): Halley's comet moves in an elliptical orbit around the Sun, with the Sun at one focus. It passes within about 50 million miles of the Sun once every 76 years. The other end of its orbit is about 5000 million miles from the Sun, beyond the orbit of Uranus.

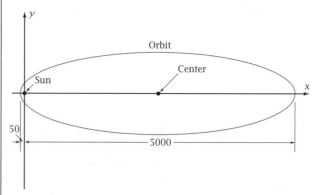

17. Find the eccentricity of the comet's orbit.

18. Find the equation of the orbit. Put the origin at the Sun and the x-axis along the major axis.

19. The orbit's major axis is 5050 million miles long. How wide is it?

20. How far is the comet from the Sun when the line from its position to the Sun is perpendicular to the major axis?

21. Where is the directrix of the ellipse corresponding to the Sun?

22. Write parametric equations for the ellipse.

23. What did you learn as a result of taking this test that you did not know before?

Precalculus with Trigonometry: Assessment Resources
© 2007 Key Curriculum Press

Test 33, Sections 13-1 to 13-4 Form A

Objective: Apply polar coordinates to geometrical figures and complex numbers.

Part 1: No calculators allowed (1–10)

1. Sketch the points in polar coordinates, showing that you understand the meanings of θ and r.

(5, 230°)   (−3, 150°)

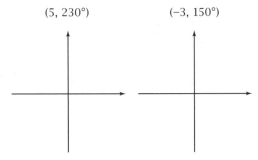

For Problems 2–5, the figure shows the point (5, 70°). Show how the same point can have different polar coordinates by writing another set of polar coordinates for the point, as described.

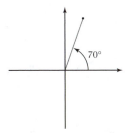

2. Positive r, positive θ

3. Positive r, negative θ

4. Negative r, positive θ

5. Negative r, negative θ

6. Multiply and simplify: $(2 + 7i)(5 + 4i)$

7. Plot these points in polar coordinates. Connect the points with a smooth curve.

θ	r	θ	r
0°	4.1	195°	2.8
15°	4.7	210°	0.6
30°	4.9	225°	−2.3
45°	5.0	240°	−5.5
60°	5.0	255°	−8.0
75°	5.0	270°	−9.0
90°	5.0	285°	−8.0
105°	5.0	300°	−5.5
120°	5.0	315°	−2.3
135°	5.0	330°	0.6
150°	4.9	345°	2.8
165°	4.7	360°	4.1
180°	4.1		

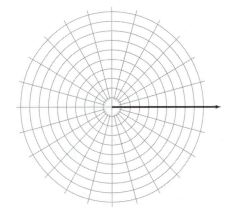

For Problems 8-10, evaluate the expressions.

8. (10 cis 200°)(2 cis 50°)

9. $\dfrac{10 \text{ cis } 200°}{2 \text{ cis } 50°}$

10. $(2 \text{ cis } 40°)^3$

(Hand in this page to get the rest of the test.)

Test 33, Sections 13-1 to 13-4 continued   Form A

Part 2: Graphing calculators allowed (11–25)

Problems 11–13 refer to the limaçon graphed here.

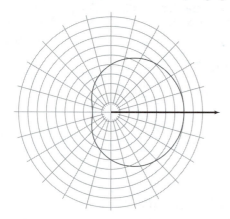

11. Approximately what does r equal when $\theta = 60°$?

12. Find the values of θ for two distinct points at which $r = 5$.

13. The general equation of the limaçon is

    $r = a + b \cos \theta$

    Find the particular equation by finding the values of the constants a and b.

Problems 14–17 refer to the spiral $r_1 = 2 + \theta/90$ and the rose $r_2 = 7 \cos 2\theta$ shown here for $\theta \in [0°, 720°]$.

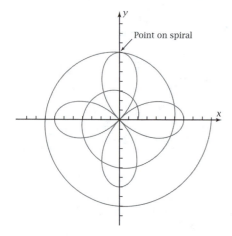

Point on spiral

14. Plot both graphs on your grapher. By appropriate tracing, find the value of θ for the point shown on the spiral, where $r = 7$.

15. The rose has a point at the same place as the point on the spiral with $r = 7$. Is this a solution to the system of equations? How can you tell?

16. Show on the figure the point with the largest value of θ that is a solution to the system of equations. Approximately what is the value of θ for this point?

17. Find the value of θ in Problem 14 precisely using the solver. Write the answer correct to four decimal places.

18. Write $-6 + 2i$ as a complex number in polar form.

19. Write 5 cis 120° as a complex number in $a + bi$ form.

20. Find the three cube roots of 64 cis 150°. Sketch the answers on the complex plane.

For Problems 21–24, let $z_1 = 2 + 7i$ and $z_2 = 5 + 4i$.

21. Find $z_1 z_2$ using your calculator.

22. Find $|z_1|$, $|z_2|$, and $|z_1 z_2|$ exactly, in radical form. Show that $|z_1 z_2| = |z_1||z_2|$.

23. What special name is given to the absolute value of a complex number?

24. Confirm that the graph of this polar function is an ellipse by transforming the equation to Cartesian coordinates. Explain how you know from your answer that the graph is an ellipse.

    $$r = \frac{6}{3 - 2 \cos \theta}$$

    (Note: $r^2 = x^2 + y^2$, $x = r \cos \theta$, $y = r \sin \theta$.)

25. What did you learn as a result of taking this test that you did not know before?

Precalculus with Trigonometry: Assessment Resources
© 2007 Key Curriculum Press

Test 33, Sections 13-1 to 13-4   Form B

Objective: Apply polar coordinates to geometrical figures and complex numbers.

Part 1: No calculators allowed (1–10)

1. Sketch the points in polar coordinates, showing that you understand the meanings of θ and r.

   (4, 240°)   (−2, 120°)

   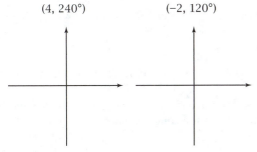

For Problems 2–5, the figure shows the point (4, 60°). Show how the same point can have different polar coordinates by writing another set of polar coordinates for the point, as described.

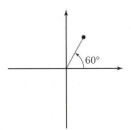

2. Positive r, positive θ

3. Positive r, negative θ

4. Negative r, positive θ

5. Negative r, negative θ

6. Multiply and simplify: $(3 + 5i)(2 + 3i)$

7. Plot these points in polar coordinates. Connect the points with a smooth curve.

θ	r	θ	r
0°	3.3	195°	2.4
15°	3.8	210°	0.9
30°	4.0	225°	−1.2
45°	4.0	240°	−3.5
60°	4.0	255°	−5.3
75°	4.0	270°	−6.0
90°	4.0	285°	−5.3
105°	4.0	300°	−3.5
120°	4.0	315°	−1.2
135°	4.0	330°	0.9
150°	4.0	345°	2.4
165°	3.8	360°	3.3
180°	3.3		

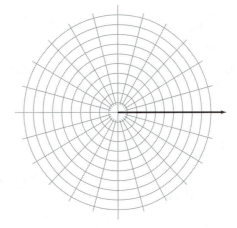

For Problems 8–10, evaluate the expressions.

8. (8 cis 50°)(4 cis 100°)

9. $\dfrac{8 \text{ cis } 150°}{4 \text{ cis } 100°}$

10. $(3 \text{ cis } 40°)^4$

(Hand in this page to get the rest of the test.)

Part 2: Graphing calculators allowed (11–25)

Problems 11–13 refer to the limaçon graphed here.

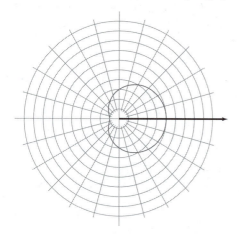

11. Approximately what does r equal when $\theta = 60°$?

12. Find the values of θ for two distinct points at which $r = 3$.

13. The general equation of the limaçon is

    $r = a + b \cos \theta$

    Find the particular equation by finding the values of the constants a and b.

Problems 14–17 refer to the spiral $r_1 = 2 + \theta/90$ and the rose $r_2 = 5 \cos 2\theta$ shown here for $\theta \in [0°, 720°]$.

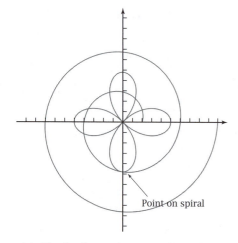

Point on spiral

14. Plot both graphs on your grapher. By appropriate tracing, find the value of θ for the point shown on the spiral, where $r = -5$.

15. The rose has a point at the same place as the point on the spiral with $r = -5$. Is this a solution to the system of equations? How can you tell?

16. Show on the figure the point with the largest value of θ that is a solution to the system of equations. Approximately what is the value of θ for this point?

17. Find the value of θ in Problem 14 precisely using the solver. Write the answer correct to four decimal places.

18. Write $-4 + 2i$ as a complex number in polar form.

19. Write 4 cis 135° as a complex number in $a + bi$ form.

20. Find the three cube roots of 27 cis 120°. Sketch the answers on the complex plane.

For Problems 21–23, let $z_1 = 3 + 5i$ and $z_2 = 2 + 3i$.

21. Find $z_1 z_2$ using your calculator.

22. Find $|z_1|$, $|z_2|$, and $|z_1 z_2|$ exactly, in radical form. Show that $|z_1 z_2| = |z_1||z_2|$.

23. What special name is given to the absolute value of a complex number?

24. Confirm that the graph of this polar function is a parabola by transforming the equation to Cartesian coordinates. Explain how you know from your answer that the graph is an ellipse.

$$r = \frac{6}{1 + \cos \theta}$$

    (Note: $r^2 = x^2 + y^2$, $x = r \cos \theta$, $y = r \sin \theta$.)

25. What did you learn as a result of taking this test that you did not know before?

Test 34, Section 13-5   Form A

Objective: Find parametric equations of geometrical figures.

Part 1: No calculators allowed (1–7)

Running Problem (1–4): Leslie intercepts a pass 8 yards into the end zone, 19 yards from the right side of the field as he faces the opposite end of the field (see figure). He starts running diagonally, moving at a rate of 4 yd/s down the field and 2 yd/s across the field. Let x and y be his coordinates on the field.

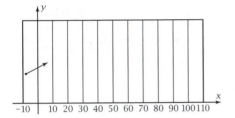

1. Write parametric equations for his x- and y-coordinates as functions of time t, in seconds, since he intercepted the ball.

2. If he keeps going straight at the same velocity, what will be his position when $t = 10$ s?

3. If he keeps going at the same velocity, at what time will he cross the opponent's 40-yard line, $x = 60$?

4. The football field is $53\frac{1}{3}$ yards wide. When he crosses the opponent's 40-yard line, will he still be in bounds?

Ellipse Problem (5–7): The figure shows concentric circles of radii 3 and 5, respectively, centered at the origin of an xy-coordinate system. A ray from the center at an angle of t degrees to the x-axis cuts the two circles at points A and B. From A, a vertical line is drawn; and from B, a horizontal line is drawn. These two lines intersect at point P on an ellipse.

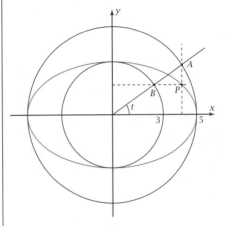

5. Pick a value of t in Quadrant III and construct as described. Show that the point you get is on the ellipse.

6. For the value of t shown, draw a right triangle for which one of the legs equals the x-coordinate of point P. Use the result to write an equation for x as a function of t.

7. For the value of t shown, draw a right triangle for which one of the legs equals the y-coordinate of point P. Use the result to write an equation for y as a function of t.

(Hand in this page to get the rest of the test.)

Test 34, Section 13-5 continued

Form A

Part 2: Graphing calculators allowed (8–16)

8. In Problems 6 and 7, you found the parametric equations

    $x = 5 \cos t$

    $y = 3 \sin t$

    Transform these equations to eliminate the parameter t, thus getting an equation relating x and y. Explain how you know the result is the equation of an ellipse.

Epicycloid Problem (9–15): The figure shows part of a curve traced by a point on the circumference of a circle of radius 4 that rotates, without slipping, around a fixed circle of radius 2. The rotating circle starts with angle $t = 0$ radians and the point $P(x, y)$ at $(10, 0)$. In this problem you will find parametric equations of the resulting epicycloid.

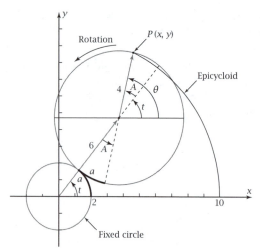

9. In the figure, $t = 0.9$ radian. Find the coordinates of the center of the large moving circle.

10. Because the big circle rotates without slipping, arc a on the big circle equals arc a on the small circle. Find a when $t = 0.9$ radian, as in the figure. Use the answer to find the measure of angle A that subtends arc a on the big circle.

11. Angle θ at the center of the big circle has measure equal to $t + A$. What two theorems from geometry let you conclude that the two angles that compose θ equal t and A? Find θ when $t = 0.9$ radian.

12. Use the answers to Problems 10 and 11 to find the coordinates of point P when $t = 0.9$, as in the figure. Does your answer agree with the figure?

13. In general, what does θ equal as a function of t?

14. By repeating the process you used to arrive at the coordinates of point P when $t = 0.9$, write parametric equations for x and y as functions of t.

15. Plot the epicycloid and the small, fixed circle on your grapher. Explain why it is necessary to use two revolutions of t to generate the entire graph. Sketch the result.

16. What did you learn as a result of taking this test that you did not know before?

Precalculus with Trigonometry: Assessment Resources
© 2007 Key Curriculum Press

Objective: Find parametric equations of geometrical figures.

Part 1: No calculators allowed (1–7)

Walking Problem 2 (1–4): Calvin is walking at a speed of 6 ft/s along a path that makes an angle of 55° with the x-axis. At time $t = 0$ he is at the point (263, 107), where the distances are in feet from a particular traffic light.

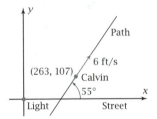

1. What are Calvin's speeds in the x- and y-directions?

2. Write parametric equations for his position as a function of the parameter t seconds.

3. A street goes along the x-axis. Assuming Calvin was walking at his 6 ft/s pace before $t = 0$, at what time t did he cross the street?

4. How far from the light does the path cross the street?

Ellipse Problem (5–7): The figure shows concentric circles of radii 3 and 5, respectively, centered at the origin of an xy-coordinate system. A ray from the center at an angle of t degrees to the x-axis cuts the two circles at points A and B. From A, a vertical line is drawn; and from B, a horizontal line is drawn. These two lines intersect at point P on an ellipse.

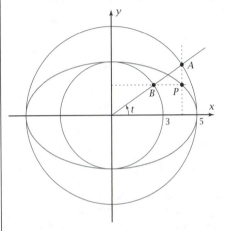

5. Pick a value of t in Quadrant III and construct as described. Show that the point you get is on the ellipse.

6. For the value of t shown, draw a right triangle for which one of the legs equals the x-coordinate of point P. Use the result to write an equation for x as a function of t.

7. For the value of t shown, draw a right triangle for which one of the legs equals the y-coordinate of point P. Use the result to write an equation for y as a function of t.

(Hand in this page to get the rest of the test.)

Part 2: Graphing calculators allowed (8–13)

8. In Problems 6 and 7, you found the parametric equations

   $x = 5 \cos t$

   $y = 3 \sin t$

   Transform these equations to eliminate the parameter t, thus getting an equation relating x and y. Explain how you know the result is the equation of an ellipse.

Serpentine Problem (9–12): The figure shows the serpentine curve, so called for its snakelike shape. A fixed circle of radius 5 has its center on the x-axis and passes through the origin. A variable line from the origin makes an angle of t radians with the x-axis. It intersects the circle at point A, and it intersects the fixed line $y = 5$ at point B. A horizontal line from A and a vertical line from B intersect at point $P(x, y)$ on the serpentine curve.

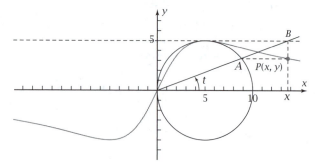

9. Pick a different value of t between 0 and $\frac{\pi}{2}$ and plot the corresponding point P as described. Plot another point for a t-value between $\frac{\pi}{2}$ and π. Show that the resulting points really are on the serpentine curve.

10. Find the parametric equations for x and y in terms of the parameter t. (To find y, first find the distance from the origin to point A. You can do this by recalling the polar equations of a circle or by drawing a right triangle inscribed in the semicircle with right angle at A and hypotenuse 10.)

11. Confirm that your parametric equations are correct by plotting them on your grapher. Use a window with an x-range at least as large as the one shown, and use equal scales on both axes.

12. The point P in the figure corresponds to $t = 0.35$ radian. Confirm that this is correct by showing that the values of x and y you get from the equation agree with the values in the figure.

13. What did you learn as a result of taking this test that you did not know before?

Precalculus with Trigonometry: Assessment Resources
© 2007 Key Curriculum Press

Test 35, Chapter 13   Form A

Objective: Find parametric equations of geometrical figures.

Part 1: No calculators allowed (1–8)

1. The figure shows a point with rectangular coordinates (x, y) and polar coordinates (r, θ). Explain why these relationships between polar and rectangular coordinates are true:

   • $x = r \cos \theta$

   • $y = r \sin \theta$

   • $x^2 + y^2 = r^2$

   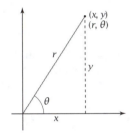

2. Plot the tabulated points on the given polar paper. Connect the points.

θ	r	θ	r
90°	2.0	195°	−7.7
105°	2.1	210°	−4.0
120°	2.3	225°	−2.8
135°	2.8	240°	−2.3
150°	4.0	255°	−2.1
165°	7.7	270°	−2.0
180°	(undefined)		

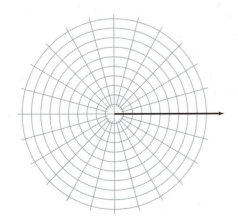

3. The polar equation of the graph in Problem 2 is

$$r = \frac{2}{\sin \theta}$$

Use the relationships in Problem 1 to prove that the graph is a horizontal line.

4. Write a polar equation for the graph in Problem 3 rotated by 40° counterclockwise about the pole.

5. Multiply: $(10 \text{ cis } 60°)(2 \text{ cis } 40°)$

6. Divide: $\dfrac{10 \text{ cis } 60°}{2 \text{ cis } 40°}$

7. Name the theorem that concludes

$$(r \text{ cis } \theta)^n = r^n \text{ cis } n\theta$$

8. Write the three cube roots of $8 \text{ cis } (-30°)$. Sketch the answers on the complex-number plane.

(Hand in this page to get the rest of the test.)

Test 35, Chapter 13 continued

Form A

Part 2: Graphing calculators allowed (9–18)

For Problems 9–12, the figure shows the polar curve

$$r = 10 \cos \theta$$

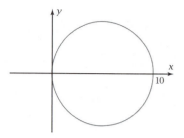

9. Plot the graph on your grapher. Use ZOOM SQUARE to get equal scales on the two axes. Does your graph agree with the given figure?

10. On the given figure, sketch an angle of $\theta = 150°$. Show the point on the graph at this angle, and explain why it is in Quadrant IV, not Quadrant II.

11. Describe what is happening to the graph as θ increases from 180° to 360°.

12. Multiply both sides of $r = 10 \cos \theta$ by r. Transform the resulting equation to Cartesian coordinates. Explain how you know from the result that the graph is really a circle.

For Problems 13–17, the figure in the next column shows a **conchoid of Nicomedes.** The top part is formed by a ray from the origin that rotates through an angle $t°$ with the x-axis. The ray intersects the fixed line $y = 2$ at point A. From A you measure out 7 more units to point P on the graph of the conchoid. The bottom part is formed when the ray is in Quadrants III and IV and you measure 7 units from where the line containing the ray intersects the fixed line.

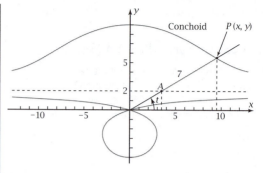

13. Show that you get a point that is *on* the curve when you do the described construction for
   • A value of t between the ray shown and 90°
   • $t = 90°$
   • A value of t between 90° and 180°
   • A value of t between 180° and 270°

14. The parametric equation for x has two parts, one for the segment from the origin to the point on the x-axis below point A, the other from there to the point on the x-axis below point P. Write an equation for x as a function of t.

15. Write the parametric equation for y as a function of t. It, too, will have two parts.

16. Plot your parametric equations from Problems 14 and 15 on the grapher. Does it agree with the given figure?

17. The Cartesian equation of this conchoid is

   $$(x^2 + y^2)(y - 2)^2 = 49y^2$$

   Verify that this equation is correct by calculating the values of x if y is 8 and showing that the points really are on the conchoid.

18. What did you learn as a result of taking this test that you did not know before?

Test 35, Chapter 13   Form B

Objective: Find parametric equations of geometrical figures.

Part 1: No calculators allowed (1–8)

1. The figure shows a point with rectangular coordinates (x, y) and polar coordinates (r, θ). Explain why these relationships between polar and rectangular coordinates are true:

   • $x = r \cos \theta$

   • $y = r \sin \theta$

   • $x^2 + y^2 = r^2$

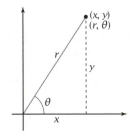

2. Plot the tabulated points on the given polar paper. Connect the points.

θ	r	θ	r
90°	−1.0	195°	3.8
105°	−1.0	210°	2.0
120°	−1.2	225°	1.4
135°	−1.4	240°	1.2
150°	−2.0	255°	1.0
165°	−3.8	270°	1.0
180°	(undefined)		

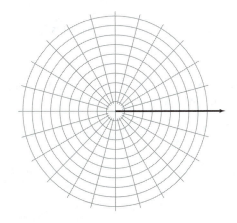

3. The polar equation of the graph in Problem 2 is

   $$r = \frac{-1}{\sin \theta}$$

   Use the relationships in Problem 1 to prove that the graph is a horizontal line.

4. Write a polar equation for the graph in Problem 3 rotated by 50° counterclockwise about the pole.

5. Multiply: $(120 \text{ cis } 60°)(4 \text{ cis } 20°)$

6. Divide: $\dfrac{12 \text{ cis } 60°}{4 \text{ cis } 20°}$

7. Name the theorem that concludes

   $$(r \text{ cis } \theta)^n = r^n \text{ cis } n\theta$$

8. Write the three cube roots of $27 \text{ cis } (-30°)$. Sketch the answers on the complex-number plane.

(Hand in this page to get the rest of the test.)

Part 2: Graphing calculators allowed (9–18)

For Problems 9–12, the figure shows the polar curve

$r = 6 \cos \theta$

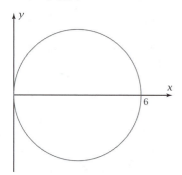

9. Plot the graph on your grapher. Use ZOOM SQUARE to get equal scales on the two axes. Does your graph agree with the given figure?

10. On the given figure, sketch an angle of $\theta = 150°$. Show the point on the graph at this angle, and explain why it is in Quadrant IV, not Quadrant II.

11. Describe what is happening to the graph as θ increases from 180° to 360°.

12. Multiply both sides of $r = 6 \cos \theta$ by r. Transform the resulting equation to Cartesian coordinates. Explain how you know from the result that the graph is really a circle.

For Problems 13–17, the figure in the next column shows a **conchoid of Nicomedes.** The top part is formed by a ray from the origin that rotates through an angle $t°$ with the x-axis. The ray intersects the fixed line $y = 2$ at point A. From A you measure out 7 more units to point P on the graph of the conchoid. The bottom part is formed when the ray is in Quadrants III and IV and you measure 7 units from where the line containing the ray intersects the fixed line.

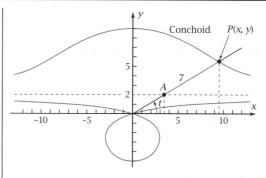

13. Show that you get a point that is *on* the curve when you do the described construction for

   • A value of t between the ray shown and 90°

   • $t = 90°$

   • A value of t between 90° and 180°

   • A value of t between 180° and 270°

14. The parametric equation for x has two parts, one for the segment from the origin to the point on the x-axis below point A, the other from there to the point on the x-axis below point P. Write an equation for x as a function of t.

15. Write the parametric equation for y as a function of t. It, too, will have two parts.

16. Plot your parametric equations from Problems 14 and 15 on the grapher. Does it agree with the given figure?

17. The Cartesian equation of this conchoid is

   $(x^2 + y^2)(y - 2)^2 = 49y^2$

   Verify that this equation is correct by calculating the values of x if y is 8 and showing that the points really are on the conchoid.

18. What did you learn as a result of taking this test that you did not know before?

Precalculus with Trigonometry: Assessment Resources
© 2007 Key Curriculum Press

Name: _____   Date: _____

Test 36, Chapter 14   Form A

Objective: Find terms and partial sums of sequences and series.

Part 1: No calculators allowed (1–12)

1. Show that you know the meaning of arithmetic sequence by writing the next two terms of this arithmetic sequence.

    10, 30, _____ , _____

2. Show that you know the meaning of geometric sequence by writing the next two terms of this geometric sequence.

    10, 30, _____ , _____

3. Show that you know the difference between a sequence and a series by writing the first three terms of a geometric sequence and a geometric series, each of which has first term 5 and common ratio 3.

    Sequence: _____

    Series: _____

4. An arithmetic series has first term 8 and common difference 5. Write the first three terms.

5. Show that this sequence is neither arithmetic nor geometric.

    2, 6, 12, . . .

6. Write the next two terms of this sequence.

    1, 3, 1, 5, 1, 7, _____ , _____

7. Write the next two terms of this series.

    $2 + 6 + 12 + 20 + 30 + 42 +$ _____ $+$ _____

8. Describe the pattern you used in Problem 7.

9. The second and third terms of an arithmetic sequence are, respectively, 19 and 23. Write the first and the fourth terms.

    _____ , 19, 23, _____

10. A geometric series has $t_1 = 3$ and $r = 2$. If $t_n = 96$, write out all the terms from t_1 through t_n.

11. What does n equal in Problem 10?

    $n =$ _____

12. What special name is given to the terms between 3 and 96 for the sequence in Problem 10?

(Hand in this page to get the rest of the test.)

Test 36, Chapter 14 continued

Form A

Part 2: Graphing calculators allowed (13–28)

Wages Problem (13-15): Assume that this year, $n = 1$, the average annual salary for women in the United States is $25,000 and that it is increasing by 5% per year, meaning that each year the salary is 1.05 times what it was the previous year. Assume that the average annual salary for men is $30,000 and that it is increasing by $2,000 per year.

13. Write the first three terms of each sequence of salaries. What kind of sequence is each?

14. In the first three years, whose salaries are increasing faster, women's or men's?

15. Assuming that the same pattern of salaries continues, who will be making more, women or men, in year $n = 25$?

Arithmetic Series Problem (16-20): An arithmetic series has $t_1 = 19$ and $t_2 = 32$.

16. Find the common difference.

17. Find t_{300}, the 300th term.

18. • Find S_{300}, the sum of the first 300 terms, algebraically, using the formula for S_n.

    • Find S_{300} using your SERIES program. Does the answer agree with the one from the formula?

    • Give an advantage of using the formula for S_n.

19. Find n if $t_n = 7377$.

20. Find n if $S_n = 1086$.

Geometric Series Problem (21-26): A geometric series has $t_1 = 100$ and $t_2 = 90$.

21. Find the common ratio.

22. Find t_{30}, the 30th term.

23. Find n if $t_n = 28.2429....$

24. Find S_3, the third partial sum, by writing and adding the first three terms.

25. Find S_3 algebraically, using the formula. Show that the answer is the same as that in Problem 24.

26. Find the number to which S_n converges as n gets very large. Show your method.

27. *Sigma Notation Problem:* This is the fourth partial sum of a series.

$$S_4 = \sum_{k=1}^{4} (k^2 + 1)$$

Show that you understand sigma notation by writing the four terms of the series and adding them.

28. What did you learn as a result of taking this test that you did not know before?

Test 36, Chapter 14

Form B

Objective: Find terms and partial sums of sequences and series.

Part 1: No calculators allowed (1–12)

1. Show that you know the meaning of arithmetic sequence by writing the next two terms of this arithmetic sequence.

    5, 25, _____, _____

2. Show that you know the meaning of geometric sequence by writing the next two terms of this geometric sequence.

    5, 25, _____, _____

3. Show that you know the difference between a sequence and a series by writing the first three terms of a geometric sequence and a geometric series, each of which has first term 10 and common ratio 3.

    Sequence: _____

    Series: _____

4. An arithmetic series has first term 7 and common difference 10. Write the first three terms.

5. Show that this sequence is neither arithmetic nor geometric.

    2, 6, 24, . . .

6. Write the next two terms of this sequence.

    1, 2, 1, 4, 1, 6, _____, _____

7. Write the next two terms of this series.

    $1 + 3 + 6 + 10 + 15 + 21 +$ _____ $+$ _____

8. Describe the pattern you used in Problem 7.

9. The second and third terms of an arithmetic sequence are, respectively, 19 and 23. Write the first and the fourth terms.

    _____, 22, 27, _____

10. A geometric series has $t_1 = 4$ and $r = 3$. If $t_n = 324$, write out all the terms from t_1 through t_n.

11. What does n equal in Problem 10?

    $n =$ _____

12. What special name is given to the terms between 4 and 324 for the sequence in Problem 10?

(Hand in this page to get the rest of the test.)

Part 2: Graphing calculators allowed (13–28)

Wages Problem (13–15): Assume that this year, $n = 1$, the average annual salary for women in the United States is $30,000 and that it is increasing by 4% per year, meaning that each year the salary is 1.04 times what it was the previous year. Assume that the average annual salary for men is $35,000 and that it is increasing by $1,600 per year.

13. Write the first three terms of each sequence of salaries. What kind of sequence is each?

14. In the first three years, whose salaries are increasing faster, women's or men's?

15. Assuming that the same pattern of salaries continues, who will be making more, women or men, in year $n = 25$?

Arithmetic Series Problem (16–20): An arithmetic series has $t_1 = 8$ and $t_2 = 13$.

16. Find the common difference.

17. Find t_{300}, the 300th term.

18. • Find S_{300}, the sum of the first 300 terms, algebraically, using the formula for S_n.

   • Find S_{300} using your SERIES program. Does the answer agree with the one from the formula?

   • Give an advantage of using the formula for S_n.

19. Find n if $t_n = 1637$.

20. Find n if $S_n = 4859$.

Geometric Series Problem (21-26): A geometric series has $t_1 = 100$ and $t_2 = 75$.

21. Find the common ratio.

22. Find t_{30}, the 30th term.

23. Find n if $t_n = 3.1676....$

24. Find S_3, the third partial sum, by writing and adding the first three terms.

25. Find S_3 algebraically, using the formula. Show that the answer is the same as that in Problem 24.

26. Find the number to which S_n converges as n gets very large. Show your method.

27. *Sigma Notation Problem:* This is the fourth partial sum of a series.

$$S_4 = \sum_1^4 3^k$$

   Show that you understand sigma notation by writing the four terms of the series and adding them.

28. What did you learn as a result of taking this test that you did not know before?

Precalculus with Trigonometry: Assessment Resources
© 2007 Key Curriculum Press

Name: _____   Date: _____

Test 37, Section 15-1 to 15-3   Form A

Objective: Find and use equations of polynomial functions.

Part 1: No calculators allowed (1–8)

For Problems 1 and 2, give the degree, the number of real zeros, the number of complex zeros (nonreal), and the sign of the leading coefficient for the polynomial function graphed.

1.

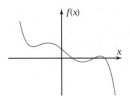

- Degree: _____

- Real zeros: _____

- Complex zeros: _____

- Leading coefficient sign: _____

2.

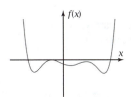

- Degree: _____

- Real zeros: _____

- Complex zeros: _____

- Leading coefficient sign: _____

3. On the graph in Problem 2,
   - Mark one extreme point.
   - Mark one point of inflection.

4. For $f(x) = x^3 - 5x^2 - 7x + 30$, find the

   - Product of the zeros: _____

   - Sum of pairwise products of zeros: _____

   - Sum of the zeros: _____

5. Do synthetic substitution of $x = 2$ into $f(x)$ in Problem 4.

6. From the result of Problem 5, give the

   - Value of $f(2)$: _____

   - Remainder when $f(x)$ is divided by $(x - 2)$: _____

   - Name of the theorem that relates the first two answers to this problem:

     _____

   - Quotient $\frac{f(x)}{x - 2}$ in mixed-number form:

     _____

7. Given $g(x) = (x + 5)(x^2 - 6x + 13)$, find the one real zero of $g(x)$: _____

8. Find the two complex zeros of $g(x)$ in Problem 7.

(Hand in this page to get the rest of the test.)

Part 2: Graphing calculators allowed (9–25)

For Problems 9–13, these are points on the graph of a cubic function.

x	$f(x)$
2	−14.6
3	−10.4
4	−3.8
5	4.0
6	11.8
7	18.4

9. Show that the third differences between the $f(x)$-values are constant.

10. Using only the first four points, find algebraically the particular equation of the function.

11. Perform cubic regression on all six of the points. Does the answer agree with the equation you found algebraically in Problem 10?

12. On this graph of f, $x = -1$ appears to be a zero of $f(x)$. Use the equation from Problem 10 to determine whether $x = -1$ really is a zero.

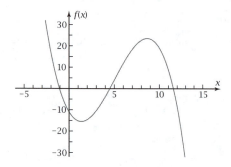

13. Find numerically the largest zero of $f(x)$ in Problem 12. Keep at least three decimal places.

For Problems 14–16, two zeros of a cubic function, $g(x)$, are 3 and $2 + i$.

14. Give the third zero: _____

15. Find the sum, sum of pairwise products, and product of the three zeros of $g(x)$.

16. Write an equation for $g(x)$ that has 1 as the leading coefficient.

Spaceship Problem (17–24): Ella Vader (Darth's daughter) is approaching Alderaan in her spaceship. Her distance from the surface, $d(x)$, in kilometers, at time x, in minutes after she starts a maneuver, is given by

$$d(x) = x^4 - 22x^3 + 158x^2 - 414x + 405$$

17. Plot the graph of function d. Use a window with an x-range of [0, 12] and a window with an appropriate y-range. Sketch the result.

18. How far was Ella from Alderaan when she first started the maneuver? What part of the equation gives you this number?

19. Function d has an extreme point soon after Ella starts the maneuver. What is the closest her spaceship gets to Alderaan at this point before it turns around and starts to pull away? How did you find the answer?

20. Function d has a double zero. What is that zero?

21. Describe what happens to Ella's spaceship at the double zero in Problem 20.

22. Function d has two nonreal complex zeros. One of these zeros is $x = 2 + i$. Show that this number really is a zero of $d(x)$.

23. What is the other nonreal complex zero of $d(x)$?

24. Find the sum of the four zeros of $d(x)$, counting the double zero twice. Where does the answer show up in the equation for $d(x)$?

25. What did you learn as a result of taking this test that you did not know before?

Test 37, Section 15-1 to 15-3   Form B

Objective: Find and use equations of polynomial functions.

Part 1: No calculators allowed (1–8)

For Problems 1 and 2, give the degree, the number of real zeros, the number of complex zeros (nonreal), and the sign of the leading coefficient for the polynomial function graphed.

1.

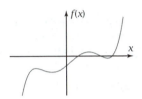

- Degree: _____

- Real zeros: _____

- Complex zeros: _____

- Leading coefficient sign: _____

2.

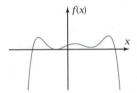

- Degree: _____

- Real zeros: _____

- Complex zeros: _____

- Leading coefficient sign: _____

3. On the graph in Problem 2,
   - Mark one extreme point.
   - Mark one point of inflection.

4. For $f(x) = x^3 - 5x^2 - 2x + 8$, find the

   - Product of the zeros: _____

   - Sum of pairwise products of zeros: _____

   - Sum of the zeros: _____

5. Do synthetic substitution of $x = -2$ into $f(x)$ in Problem 4.

6. From the result of Problem 5, give the

   - Value of $f(-2)$: _____

   - Remainder when $f(x)$ is divided by $(x + 2)$: _____

   - Name of the theorem that relates the first two answers to this problem:

   _____

   - Quotient $\frac{f(x)}{x + 2}$ in mixed-number form:

   _____

7. Given $g(x) = (x + 1)(x^2 - 4x + 13)$, find the one real

   zero of $g(x)$: _____

8. Find the two complex zeros of $g(x)$ in Problem 7.

(Hand in this page to get the rest of the test.)

Part 2: Graphing calculators allowed (9–25)

For Problems 9–13, these are points on the graph of a cubic function.

x	f(x)
2	25.4
3	13.1
4	−3.8
5	−23.5
6	−44.2
7	−64.1

9. Show that the third differences between the $f(x)$-values are constant.

10. Using only the first four points, find algebraically the particular equation of the function.

11. Perform cubic regression on all six of the points. Does the answer agree with the equation you found algebraically in Problem 10?

12. On this graph of f, $x = 4$ appears to be a zero of $f(x)$. Use the equation from Problem 10 to determine whether $x = 4$ really is a zero.

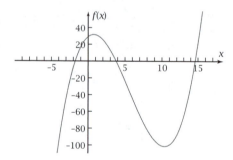

13. Find numerically the largest zero of $f(x)$ in Problem 12. Keep at least three decimal places.

For Problems 14–16, two zeros of a cubic function, $g(x)$, are 2 and $3 + i$.

14. Give the third zero: _____

15. Find the sum, sum of pairwise products, and product of the three zeros of $g(x)$.

16. Write an equation for $g(x)$ that has 1 as the leading coefficient.

Spaceship Problem (17–24): Ella Vader (Darth's daughter) is approaching Alderaan in her spaceship. Her distance from the surface, $d(x)$, in kilometers, at time x, in minutes after she starts a maneuver, is given by

$$d(x) = 2x^4 - 44x^3 + 316x^2 - 828x + 810$$

17. Plot the graph of function d. Use a window with an x-range of [0, 12] and a window with an appropriate y-range. Sketch the result.

18. How far was Ella from Alderaan when she first started the maneuver? What part of the equation gives you this number?

19. Function d has an extreme point soon after Ella starts the maneuver. What is the closest her spaceship gets to Alderaan at this point before it turns around and starts to pull away? How did you find the answer?

20. Function d has a double zero. What is that zero?

21. Describe what happens to Ella's spaceship at the double zero in Problem 20.

22. Function d has two nonreal complex zeros. One of these zeros is $x = 2 + i$. Show that this number really is a zero of $d(x)$.

23. What is the other nonreal complex zero of $d(x)$?

24. Find the sum of the four zeros of $d(x)$, counting the double zero twice. Where does the answer show up in the equation for $d(x)$?

25. What did you learn as a result of taking this test that you did not know before?

Precalculus with Trigonometry: Assessment Resources
© 2007 Key Curriculum Press

Test 38, Chapter 15 | Form A

Objective: Use polynomial and rational functions, and find instantaneous rates of change.

Part 1: No calculators allowed (1–8)

1. Give the degree, the number of real zeros, the number of (nonreal) complex zeros, and the sign of the leading coefficient for this polynomial function.

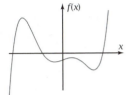

   • Degree: _____

   • Real zeros: _____

   • Complex zeros: _____

   • Sign of leading coefficient: _____

2. Sketch the graph of $y = \frac{1}{x}$.

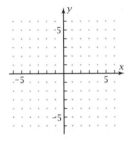

3. The function $y = \frac{1}{x + 2}$ is what transformation of $y = \frac{1}{x}$ in Problem 2?

4. What kind of discontinuity does the graph in Problem 3 have at $x = -2$?

5. Simplify and then sketch the graph of

$$y = \frac{(x - 3)(x - 2)}{(x - 3)}$$

What kind of discontinuity will the graph have at $x = 3$?

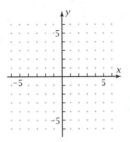

6. This cubic function has *three* zeros, although only two of them seem to show up on the graph. Write the three zeros.

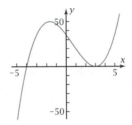

7. For the zeros in Problem 6, write their sum, their product, and the sum of the pairwise products.

8. Find an equation of the form $y = x^3 + bx^2 + cx + d$ for the function in Problem 6 using the sum and product answers from Problem 7.

(Hand in this page to get the rest of the test.)

Test 38, Chapter 15 continued   Form A

Part 2: Graphing calculators allowed (9–21)

Motor Oil Viscosity Problem (9-12): The viscosity (resistance to flow) of normal motor oil decreases as its temperature increases. "All-weather" motor oils retain roughly the same viscosity over a range of temperatures. Suppose that the viscosity of 10W-40 oil is given by

$$\mu = -4T^3 + 15T^2 - 12T + 185 \qquad \text{for } 0 \le T \le 3$$

where μ (Greek letter "mu") is the viscosity, in centipoise (cP), and T is the temperature, in hundreds of degrees.

9. Plot the graph of μ versus T. Sketch the part of the graph that is in the given domain.

10. Find the maximum and minimum viscosities in the domain and the temperatures at which these viscosities occur.

11. Show that the function has one real zero, but not in the given domain.

12. By synthetic substitution, factor the cubic expression into a linear times a quadratic. Show that the quadratic has no real zeros. How does this fact agree with the graph in Problem 9?

Rational Function Problem (13-15): The figure shows the graph of the rational function

$$y = \frac{5x - 13}{(x - 1)(x - 5)}$$

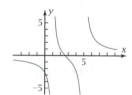

13. Explain why the discontinuities at $x = 1$ and $x = 5$ are vertical asymptotes rather than removable discontinuities.

14. Find algebraically the real zero of the function.

15. Resolve the expression for y into partial fractions.

Graphical Complex Zeros Problem (16-20): The figure shows the graph of the cubic function

$$f(x) = x^3 - 18x^2 + 105x - 146$$

In this problem you will learn a way to find the complex zeros graphically, without using the equation.

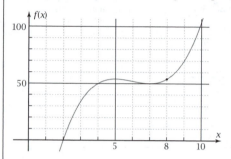

16. Through the point $(2, 0)$, the one real zero of $f(x)$, construct a line that is tangent to the graph at another point. (The point of tangency is $(8, 54)$.) What is the slope of this line?

17. Write a rational function for the slope, $m(x)$, of the secant line connecting the fixed point $(8, 54)$ and the variable point $(x, f(x))$. Simplify the equation for $m(x)$ by removing the removable discontinuity.

18. The value of $m(x)$ is the average rate of change of $f(x)$ over the interval $[8, x]$. The instantaneous rate is the limit of $m(x)$ as x approaches 8. Show that this limit equals 9, the slope of the tangent line in Problem 16.

19. The two complex zeros of $f(x)$ are $8 \pm 3i$. Show that the real part of these complex conjugates is the x-coordinate of the point of tangency and that the imaginary parts are the two square roots of the slope of the tangent line.

20. Show that you understand the properties in Problem 19 by estimating the complex zeros of this cubic function.

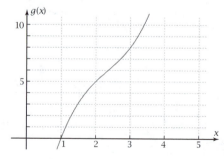

21. What did you learn as a result of taking this test that you did not know before?

Precalculus with Trigonometry: Assessment Resources
© 2007 Key Curriculum Press

Objective: Use polynomial and rational functions, and find instantaneous rates of change.

Part 1: No calculators allowed (1–8)

1. Give the degree, the number of real zeros, the number of (nonreal) complex zeros, and the sign of the leading coefficient for this polynomial function.

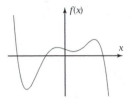

   • Degree: _____

   • Real zeros: _____

   • Complex zeros: _____

   • Sign of leading coefficient: _____

2. Sketch the graph of $y = \frac{1}{x}$.

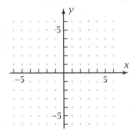

3. The function $y = \frac{1}{x-3}$ is what transformation of $y = \frac{1}{x}$ in Problem 2?

4. What kind of discontinuity does the graph in Problem 3 have at $x = 3$?

5. Simplify and then sketch the graph of

$$y = \frac{(x+2)(x+3)}{(x+3)}$$

   What kind of discontinuity will the graph have at $x = -3$?

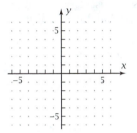

6. This cubic function has *three* zeros, although only two of them seem to show up on the graph. Write the three zeros.

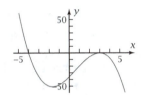

7. For the zeros in Problem 6, write their sum, their product, and the sum of the pairwise products.

8. Find an equation of the form $y = -x^3 + bx^2 + cx + d$ for the function in Problem 6 using the sum and product answers from Problem 7. (Note that $a = -1$.)

(Hand in this page to get the rest of the test.)

Part 2: Graphing calculators allowed (9–21)

Motor Oil Viscosity Problem (9–12): The viscosity (resistance to flow) of normal motor oil decreases as its temperature increases. "All-weather" motor oils retain roughly the same viscosity over a range of temperatures. Suppose that the viscosity of 10W-40 oil is given by

$$\mu = -4T^3 + 15T^2 - 12T + 185 \qquad \text{for } 0 \le T \le 3$$

where μ (Greek letter "mu") is the viscosity, in centipoise (cP), and T is the temperature, in hundreds of degrees.

9. Plot the graph of μ versus T. Sketch the part of the graph that is in the given domain.

10. Find the maximum and minimum viscosities in the domain and the temperatures at which these viscosities occur.

11. Show that the function has one real zero, but not in the given domain.

12. By synthetic substitution, factor the cubic expression into a linear times a quadratic. Show that the quadratic has no real zeros. How does this fact agree with the graph in Problem 9?

Rational Function Problem (13–15): The figure shows the graph of the rational function

$$y = \frac{10x - 26}{(x - 1)(x - 3)}$$

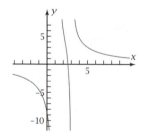

13. Explain why the discontinuities at $x = 1$ and $x = 3$ are vertical asymptotes rather than removable discontinuities.

14. Find algebraically the real zero of the function.

15. Resolve the expression for y into partial fractions.

Graphical Complex Zeros Problem (16–20): The figure shows the graph of the cubic function

$$f(x) = x^3 - 18x^2 + 105x - 146$$

In this problem you will learn a way to find the complex zeros graphically, without using the equation.

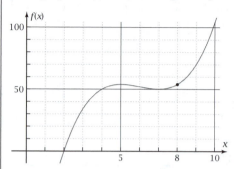

16. Through the point (2, 0), the one real zero of $f(x)$, construct a line that is tangent to the graph at another point. (The point of tangency is (8, 54).) What is the slope of this line?

17. Write a rational function for the slope, $m(x)$, of the secant line connecting the fixed point (8, 54) and the variable point $(x, f(x))$. Simplify the equation for $m(x)$ by removing the removable discontinuity.

18. The value of $m(x)$ is the average rate of change of $f(x)$ over the interval $[8, x]$. The instantaneous rate is the limit of $m(x)$ as x approaches 8. Show that this limit equals 9, the slope of the tangent line in Problem 16.

19. The two complex zeros of $f(x)$ are $8 \pm 3i$. Show that the real part of these complex conjugates is the x-coordinate of the point of tangency and that the imaginary parts are the two square roots of the slope of the tangent line.

20. Show that you understand the properties in Problem 19 by estimating the complex zeros of this cubic function.

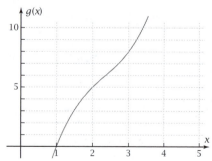

21. What did you learn as a result of taking this test that you did not know before?

Precalculus with Trigonometry: Assessment Resources
© 2007 Key Curriculum Press

Name: _____ Date: _____

Test 39, Cumulative Test, Chapters 10–15 (Two hours)   Form A

Objective: Apply knowledge of vectors, matrix transformations, conic sections, polar coordinates, series, and polynomials.

Graphing calculators allowed on entire test.

Answer the following questions on separate paper. You may draw on the graphs and figures on these sheets where specified.

Vector Problems (1–10)

For Problems 1–6,

$$\vec{a} = 7\vec{i} - 2\vec{j} + 3\vec{k}$$
$$\vec{b} = \vec{i} + 4\vec{j} - 6\vec{k}$$

1. If the vectors are translated so that they are tail-to-tail, find the vector from the head of $\vec{a}$ to the head of $\vec{b}$.

2. Find the angle between $\vec{a}$ and $\vec{b}$ when they are placed tail-to-tail.

3. Find $\vec{a} \times \vec{b}$. Show algebraically that $(\vec{a} \times \vec{b})$ is normal to $\vec{a}$.

4. Find a Cartesian equation of the plane containing $\vec{a}$ and $\vec{b}$ if the point $(3, 4, 5)$ is on the plane.

5. Find the area of the triangle for which $\vec{a}$ and $\vec{b}$ form two sides.

6. Find the scalar projection of $\vec{b}$ on $\vec{a}$.

7. Sketch the vector projection of $\vec{c}$ on $\vec{d}$.

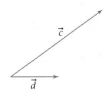

8. A line in space has vector equation

$$\vec{r} = \left(4 + \frac{6}{7}d\right)\vec{i} + \left(1 + \frac{2}{7}d\right)\vec{j} + \left(10 - \frac{3}{7}d\right)\vec{k}$$

   Write the coordinates of the fixed point and the coordinates of the point at $d = 21$ units from the fixed point.

9. Write the unit vector that appears in the equation of Problem 8. Show that it really is a unit vector.

10. Write the direction cosines and the direction angles for the unit vector in Problem 9.

Matrix Transformation Problems (11–16)

Doug's Iterative Transformation Problem (11–13): Doug Upp unearths the fossil of a snail. He figures that it could have come to its current state and position by transformation [A] performed iteratively:

- Dilation to 90% of the original size
- Rotation of 30° counterclockwise
- *x*-translation of 6 units
- *y*-translation of 2 units

11. Write the 3 × 3 transformation matrix, [A].

12. The pre-image matrix is

$$[D] = \begin{bmatrix} 2 & -2 & -5 & 5 \\ 5 & 5 & -5 & -5 \\ 1 & 1 & 1 & 1 \end{bmatrix}$$

   Set your grapher's window to [−20, 20] for *x* and [−5, 22] for *y*, and then ZOOM SQUARE to get equal scales on the two axes. Then do at least 40 iterations of your ITRANS program. Sketch the resulting figure.

13. To what fixed point are the images in Problem 12 attracted?

Fractional Dimension Problem (14–16): Five transformations are done on a line segment 12 cm long. Each part of the image is a self-similar segment 4 cm long (one-third the length of the pre-image), as shown in the figure.

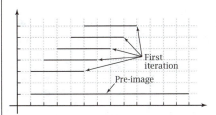

14. How many images, *N*, will there be in the second iteration and in the third iteration? What is the total length of the images in the first iteration, in the second iteration, and in the third iteration?

Iteration	N	Length of Each	Total Length
0	1	12	12
1	5	4	
2			
3			

15. By following the pattern in Problem 14, find the total length of the 50th iteration.

16. If the transformations in Problem 14 are performed using Barnsley's method, what will be the dimension of the resulting fractal image?

(Next page.)

Test 39, Cumulative Test, Chapters 10–15 (Two hours) continued   Form A

Conic Sections Problems (17–24)

Ellipse Problem: Problems 17-21 concern the ellipse shown here.

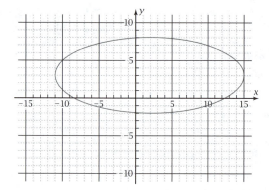

17. Draw the major and minor radii. How long are they?

    $a =$ _____ $b =$ _____

18. The focal radius of the ellipse is $c = 12$.
    • Mark the two foci on the figure.
    • Draw the triangle used to find c.
    • Show the calculations used to find c.

19. Calculate the eccentricity of the ellipse.

20. Write the Cartesian equation for the ellipse. (It is not necessary to simplify the equation.)

21. Write parametric equations for the ellipse. Plot these on your grapher. Does the graph agree with the given figure?

22. *Quadric Surface Problem:* Sketch the hyperboloid of two sheets formed by rotating this hyperbola around the y-axis.

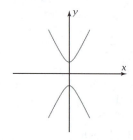

Inscribed Figure Problem (23-24): The figure shows a cylinder inscribed in a paraboloid. The paraboloid was formed by rotating about the y-axis the graph of $y = 16 - x^2$.

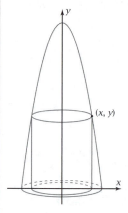

23. Find the volume of the cylinder as a function of x and y at the sample point on the parabola. Then substitute for y to get the volume as a function of x alone. (The volume of a cylinder is the area of the base multiplied by the altitude.)

24. Find the value of x, correct to three decimal places, that gives the cylinder with the maximum volume.

Sequence and Series Problems (25–29)

25. What is the main difference in the meaning of *sequence* and *series*?

26. An arithmetic series has $t_1 = 19$ and $t_2 = 32$.
    • Find the common difference.
    • Write the next three terms.
    • Find S_{300}, the sum of the first 300 terms.

27. A geometric series has $t_1 = 100$ and common ratio $r = 0.8$.
    • Write the next three terms.
    • Find S_{20}, the sum of the first 20 terms.
    • Find the limit S_n approaches as $n \to \infty$.

28. This is the fourth partial sum of a particular series.

$$S_4 = \sum_{k=1}^{4} (k^2 + 1)$$

    Show that you know what sigma notation means by writing out and adding the terms of the partial sum.

29. Use sigma notation to write S_{20} for the geometric series in Problem 27.

(Next page.)

Precalculus with Trigonometry: Assessment Resources
© 2007 Key Curriculum Press

Test 39, Cumulative Test, Chapters 10–15 (Two hours) continued Form A

Polar Coordinates Problems (30–34)

30. *Polar Graph Problem:* Plot the tabulated points on the given polar paper. Connect the points.

θ	r	θ	r
150°	–8.4	195°	–5.6
165°	–5.6	210°	–8.4
180°	–5.0		

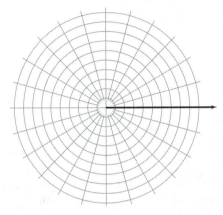

31. *Intersection Problem:* The figure shows the graphs of

$$r_1 = \frac{5}{2 + 3\cos\theta} \qquad \text{and} \qquad r_2 = 6$$

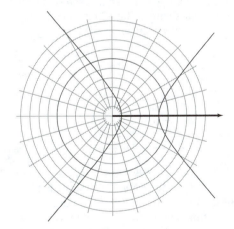

Is the point in Quadrant I where the graphs cross a solution to the system of equations? How can you tell?

32. Write in $a + bi$ form: 5 cis 330°

33. Multiply: (6 cis 100°)(2 cis 70°)

34. Write the two square roots of 25 cis 70° as complex numbers in polar form. Plot the answers on the complex-number plane.

Polynomials Problems (35–40)

Bungee Jumping Problem (35–40): Lucy Lastic bungee jumps from a high tower. On the way down she passes an elevated walkway on which her friends are standing. Starting at time $x = 2$ seconds after she jumped, her distance, $f(x)$, in feet, above the walkway is approximately this cubic function of x, graphed here.

$$f(x) = -x^3 + 13x^2 - 50x + 56, \; x \geq 2$$

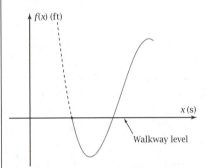

35. Explain how the negative leading coefficient agrees with the graph.

36. By synthetic substitution, show that 2 is a zero of $f(x)$ and therefore that Lucy was passing the walkway at $x = 2$ seconds.

37. Lucy travels $f(x) - f(2)$ in time $x - 2$. So her average velocity is

$$v_{av} = \frac{f(x) - f(2)}{x - 2}$$

or simply

$$v_{av} = \frac{f(x)}{x - 2}$$

because $f(2) = 0$. The average velocity has a removable discontinuity at $x = 2$. Show how to use values you have already calculated to remove the discontinuity. Use the result to calculate $\lim_{x \to 2} v_{av}$.

38. How fast and in which direction was Lucy going at $t = 2$?

39. Explain why the cubic function has the wrong endpoint behavior for large values of x.

40. You can make the leading coefficient in $f(x)$ equal to 1 by factoring out –1:

$$f(x) = -(x^3 - 13x^2 + 50x - 56)$$

What is the sum of the zeros of $f(x)$? Given that two of the zeros are 2 and 4, quickly find the third zero.

41. What did you learn as a result of taking this test that you did not know before?

Test 39, Cumulative Test, Chapters 10–15 (Two hours)   Form B

Objective: Apply knowledge of vectors, matrix transformations, conic sections, polar coordinates, series, and polynomials.

Graphing calculators allowed on entire test.

Answer the following questions on separate paper. You may draw on the graphs and figures on these sheets where specified.

Vector Problems (1–10)

For Problems 1–6,

$$\vec{a} = 8\vec{i} - 2\vec{j} + 13\vec{k}$$
$$\vec{b} = 3\vec{i} + 10\vec{j} - 4\vec{k}$$

1. If the vectors are translated so that they are tail-to-tail, find the vector from the head of $\vec{a}$ to the head of $\vec{b}$.

2. Find the angle between $\vec{a}$ and $\vec{b}$ when they are placed tail-to-tail.

3. Find $\vec{a} \times \vec{b}$. Show algebraically that $(\vec{a} \times \vec{b})$ is normal to $\vec{a}$.

4. Find a Cartesian equation of the plane containing $\vec{a}$ and $\vec{b}$ if the point (3, 4, 5) is on the plane.

5. Find the area of the triangle for which $\vec{a}$ and $\vec{b}$ form two sides.

6. Find the scalar projection of $\vec{b}$ on $\vec{a}$.

7. Sketch the vector projection of $\vec{c}$ on $\vec{d}$.

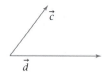

8. A line in space has vector equation

$$\vec{r} = \left(5 + \frac{6}{11}d\right)\vec{i} + \left(3 + \frac{9}{11}d\right)\vec{j} + \left(7 + \frac{2}{11}d\right)\vec{k}$$

Write the coordinates of the fixed point and the coordinates of the point at $d = 22$ units from the fixed point.

9. Write the unit vector that appears in the equation of Problem 8. Show that it really is a unit vector.

10. Write the direction cosines and the direction angles for the unit vector in Problem 9.

Matrix Transformation Problems (11–16)

Doug's Iterative Transformation Problem (11–13): Doug Upp unearths the fossil of a snail. He figures that it could have come to its current state and position by transformation [A] performed iteratively:

- Dilation to 90% of the original size
- Rotation of 30° counterclockwise
- *x*-translation of 6 units
- *y*-translation of 2 units

11. Write the 3×3 transformation matrix, [A].

12. The pre-image matrix is

$$[D] = \begin{bmatrix} 2 & -2 & -5 & 5 \\ 5 & 5 & -5 & -5 \\ 1 & 1 & 1 & 1 \end{bmatrix}$$

Set your grapher's window to [−20, 20] for *x* and [−5, 22] for *y*, and then ZOOM SQUARE to get equal scales on the two axes. Then do at least 40 iterations of your ITRANS program. Sketch the resulting figure.

13. To what fixed point are the images in Problem 12 attracted?

Fractional Dimension Problem (14–16): Five transformations are done on a line segment 12 cm long. Each part of the image is a self-similar segment 3 cm long (one-fourth the length of the pre-image), as shown in the figure.

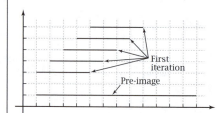

14. How many images, *N*, will there be in the second iteration and in the third iteration? What is the total length of the images in the first iteration, in the second iteration, and in the third iteration?

Iteration	N	Length of Each	Total Length
0	1	12	12
1	5	3	
2			
3			

15. By following the pattern in Problem 14, find the total length of the 50th iteration.

16. If the transformations in Problem 14 are performed using Barnsley's method, what will be the dimension of the resulting fractal image?

(Next page.)

Conic Sections Problems (17–24)

Ellipse Problem: Problems 17–21 concern the ellipse shown here.

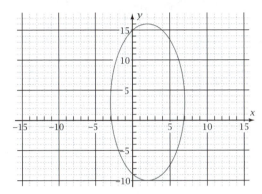

17. Draw the major and minor radii. How long are they?

    $a =$ _____ $b =$ _____

18. The focal radius of the ellipse is $c = 12$.
    • Mark the two foci on the figure.
    • Draw the triangle used to find c.
    • Show the calculations used to find c.

19. Calculate the eccentricity of the ellipse.

20. Write the Cartesian equation for the ellipse. (It is not necessary to simplify the equation.)

21. Write parametric equations for the ellipse. Plot these on your grapher. Does the graph agree with the given figure?

22. *Quadric Surface Problem:* Sketch the hyperboloid of two sheets formed by rotating this hyperbola around the y-axis.

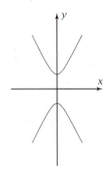

Inscribed Figure Problem (23–24): The figure shows a cylinder inscribed in a paraboloid. The paraboloid was formed by rotating about the y-axis the graph of $y = 9 - x^2$.

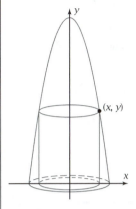

23. Find the volume of the cylinder as a function of x and y at the sample point on the parabola. Then substitute for y to get the volume as a function of x alone. (The volume of a cylinder is the area of the base multiplied by the altitude.)

24. Find the value of x, correct to three decimal places, that gives the cylinder with the maximum volume.

Sequence and Series Problems (25–29)

25. What is the main difference in the meaning of *sequence* and *series*?

26. An arithmetic series has $t_1 = 17$ and $t_2 = 36$.
    • Find the common difference.
    • Write the next three terms.
    • Find S_{300}, the sum of the first 300 terms.

27. A geometric series has $t_1 = 100$ and common ratio $r = 0.9$.
    • Write the next three terms.
    • Find S_{20}, the sum of the first 20 terms.
    • Find the limit S_n approaches as $n \rightarrow \infty$.

28. This is the fifth partial sum of a particular series.

    $$\sum_{k=1}^{5} (k^3 - 1)$$

    Show that you know what sigma notation means by writing out and adding the terms of the partial sum.

29. Use sigma notation to write S_{20} for the geometric series in Problem 27.

(Next page.)

Test 39, Cumulative Test, Chapters 10–15 (Two hours) continued   Form B

Polar Coordinates Problems (30–34)

30. *Polar Graph Problem:* Plot the tabulated points on the given polar paper. Connect the points.

θ	r	θ	r
150°	−8.4	195°	−5.6
165°	−5.6	210°	−8.4
180°	−5.0		

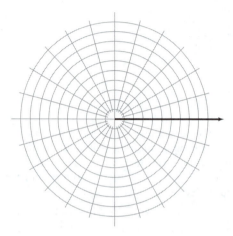

31. *Intersection Problem:* The figure shows the graphs of

$$r_1 = \frac{5}{2 + 3\cos\theta} \quad \text{and} \quad r_2 = 6$$

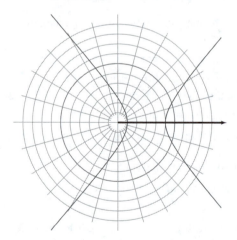

Is the point in Quadrant I where the graphs cross a solution to the system of equations? How can you tell?

32. Write in $a + bi$ form: 7 cis 240°

33. Multiply: (5 cis 130°)(4 cis 60°)

34. Write the two square roots of 64 cis 80° as complex numbers in polar form. Plot the answers on the complex-number plane.

Polynomials Problems (35–40)

Bungee Jumping Problem (35–40): Lucy Lastic bungee jumps from a high tower. On the way down she passes an elevated walkway on which her friends are standing. Starting at time $x = 2$ seconds after she jumped, her distance, $f(x)$, in feet, above the walkway is approximately this cubic function of x, graphed here.

$$f(x) = -2x^3 + 26x^2 - 100x + 112, \ x \geq 2$$

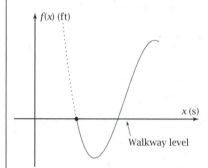

Walkway level

35. Explain how the negative leading coefficient agrees with the graph.

36. By synthetic substitution, show that 2 is a zero of $f(x)$ and therefore that Lucy was passing the walkway at $x = 2$ seconds.

37. Lucy travels $f(x) - f(2)$ in time $x - 2$. So her average velocity is

$$v_{\text{av}} = \frac{f(x) - f(2)}{x - 2}$$

or simply

$$v_{\text{av}} = \frac{f(x)}{x - 2}$$

because $f(2) = 0$. The average velocity has a removable discontinuity at $x = 2$. Show how to use values you have already calculated to remove the discontinuity. Use the result to calculate $\lim_{x \to 2} v_{\text{av}}$.

38. How fast and in which direction was Lucy going at $t = 2$?

39. Explain why the cubic function has the wrong endpoint behavior for large values of x.

40. You can make the leading coefficient in $f(x)$ equal to 1 by factoring out −2:

$$f(x) = -2(x^3 - 13x^2 + 50x - 56)$$

What is the sum of the zeros of $f(x)$? Given that two of the zeros are 2 and 4, quickly find the third zero.

41. What did you learn as a result of taking this test that you did not know before?

Solutions to Tests

Test 1 Form A

1.

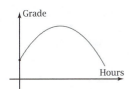

2. Quadratic function

3. Power function (Accept cubic or polynomial.)

4. Exponential function

5. Range: $-4.9 \le y \le 4.1$

6. Rational algebraic function

7. Equation: $g(x) = f(4x)$

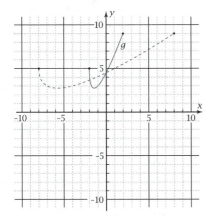

8. Vertical translation by -7

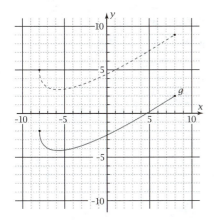

9. Enter $y_1 = x^2 - 2x - 3/(x \ge -1$ and $x \le 4)$.
   The graph checks.

10. Horizontal translation by -8
    Equation: $g(x) = f(x + 8)$
    Check? Yes

11. Vertical dilation by a factor of $\frac{1}{4}$
    Equation: $g(x) = \frac{1}{4}f(x)$ (Accept $g(x) = \frac{1}{5}f(x)$.)
    Check? Yes

12. Horizontal dilation by a factor of 2
    Equation: $g(x) = f\left(\frac{1}{2}x\right)$
    Check? Yes

13. Vertical translation by -2
    Equation: $g(x) = f(x) - 2$
    Check? Yes

14. Horizontal translation by 5
    Vertical translation by 1
    Equation: $g(x) = f(x - 5) + 1$
    Check? Yes

15.

16. Adding five carts $(6 - 1)$ increases the length by 57 inches
    $(109 - 52)$. So each cart adds $\frac{57}{5} = 11.4$ inches.

17. $f(n) = 52 + 11.4(n - 1)$ or $f(n) = 40.6 + 11.4n$

18. Linear function

19. $f(15) = 211.6$ in.

20. $f(n) = 240$
    $40.6 + 11.4n = 240$
    $11.4n = 199.4$
    $n = 17.4912\ldots$
    17 carts (round downward)

21. Answers will vary.

Test 1 Form B

1.

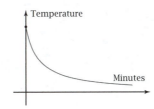

2. Exponential function

3. Inverse variation function (Accept direct variation.)

4. Polynomial function (Accept quadratic or direct variation.)

5. Range: $-4 \le y \le 4$

6. Rational algebraic function

7. Equation: $g(x) = f(2x)$

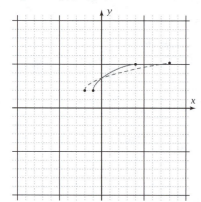

8. Vertical translation by -7

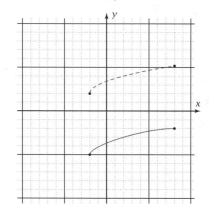

9. Enter $y = -x^2 + 2x + 3/(x \ge -1$ and $x \le 4)$.
   The graph checks.

10. Vertical translation by 3
    Equation: $g(x) = f(x) + 3$
    Check? Yes

11. Horizontal dilation by a factor of 2
    Equation: $g(x) = f\left(\left(\frac{1}{2}\right)x\right)$
    Check? Yes

12. Vertical dilation by a factor of $\frac{1}{2}$
    Equation: $g(x) = \left(\frac{1}{2}\right)f(x)$
    Check? Yes

13. Horizontal translation by -3
    Equation: $g(x) = f(x + 3)$
    Check? Yes

14. Horizontal translation by -2
    Vertical translation by 1
    Equation: $g(x) = f(x + 2) + 1$
    Check? Yes

15.

16. Adding four cups $(5 - 1)$ increases the length by 2 cm $(9.5 - 7.5)$. So each cup adds $\frac{2}{4} = 0.5$ cm.

17. $f(n) = 7.5 + 0.5(n - 1)$ or $f(n) = 7 + 0.5n$

18. Linear function

19. $f(15) = 14.5$ cm

20. $f(n) = 32.2$
    $7 + 0.5n = 32.2$
    $0.5n = 25.2$
    $n = 50.4$
    50 cups (round downward)

21. Answers will vary.

Test 2 Form A

1. f: Domain: $1 \le x \le 7$; range: $5 \le y \le 8$
   g: Domain: $2 \le x \le 6$; range: $0 \le y \le 4$

2.

x	$g(x)$	$f(g(x))$
0	None	None
1	None	None
2	4	6.5
3	3	6
4	2	5.5
5	1	5
⑥	0	None
7	None	None
8	None	None
9	None	None

3. $f(g(4)) = f(2) = 5.5$

4. See table in Problem 2.

5. Circle $x = 6$ in the table.

6.

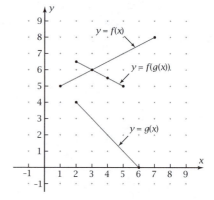

7. Domain: $2 \leq x \leq 5$
   Range: $5 \leq y \leq 6.5$

8. $f^{-1}(7) = 5$

9.
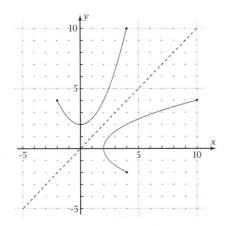

10. $f^{-1}(4)$ could be 2 or -2. So f^{-1} is not a function.

11. $1 \leq g(x) < 7$
    $1 \leq 6 - x \leq 7$
    $-5 \leq -x \leq 1$
    $5 \geq x \geq -1$ or $-1 \leq x \leq 5$

12. The domain is $2 \leq x \leq 5$. Find the intersection of the intervals $2 \leq x \leq 6$ and $-1 \leq x \leq 5$.

13. The graph is the same as in Problem 6.

14. $f(g(x)) = f(6 - x) = 0.5(6 - x) + 4.5$
    $f(g(x)) = -0.5x + 7.5$

15. The graph agrees with y_3, provided the domain is restricted to $2 \leq x \leq 5$.

16. $f(x) = 0.5x + 4$

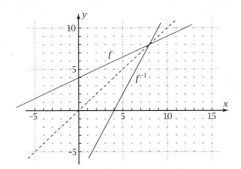

17. Inverse: $x = 0.5y + 4$
    $2x = y + 8$
    $y = 2x - 8$
    Graph is in Problem 16.

18. Graph of $y = x$ is in Problem 16. The graphs of f and f^{-1} are reflections of each other across this line.

19. The graph agrees with the given figure.

20. $x = 0.5t^2 + 2$, $y = t$

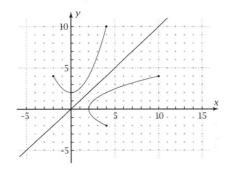

21. The domain of f is the range of f^{-1}, and vice versa.

22. Enter $x_3 = t$ and $y_3 = t$. Graph is in Problem 20.

23. The graphs of f and f^{-1} are reflections of each other across the line $y = x$.

24. Answers will vary.

Test 2 Form B

1. f: Domain: $1 \leq x \leq 7$; range: $5 \leq y \leq 8$
   g: Domain: $2 \leq x \leq 6$; range: $0 \leq y \leq 4$

2.

x	g(x)	f(g(x))
0	None	None
1	None	None
②	0	None
3	1	8
4	2	7.5
5	3	7
6	4	6.5
7	None	None
8	None	None
9	None	None

3. $f(g(4)) = f(2) = 7.5$

4. See table in Problem 2.

5. Circle $x = 2$ in the table.

6.

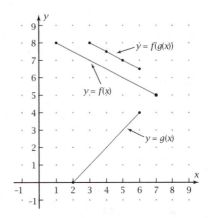

7. Domain: $3 \leq x \leq 6$
   Range: $6.5 \leq y \leq 8$

8. $f^{-1}\left(\frac{1}{5}\right) = 3$

9.

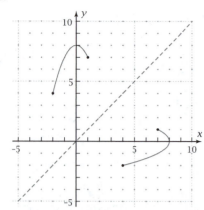

10. $f^{-1}(7)$ could be 1 or -1. So f^{-1} is not a function.

11. $1 \le g(x) < 7$
$1 \le x - 2 \le 7$
$3 \le x \le 9$

12. The domain is $3 \le x \le 6$.
Find the intersection of the intervals
$2 \le x \le 6$ and $3 \le x \le 9$.

13. The graph is the same as in Problem 6.

14. $f(g(x)) = f(x - 2) = -0.5(x - 2) + 8.5$
$f(g(x)) = -0.5x + 9.5$

15. The graph agrees with y_3, provided the domain is restricted to $3 \le x \le 6$.

16. $f(x) = -2x + 3$

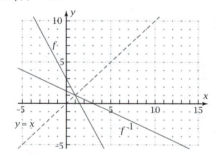

17. Inverse: $x = -2y + 3$
$y = -0.5(x - 3)$
Graph is in Problem 16.

18. Graph of $y = x$ is in Problem 16.
The graphs of f and f^{-1} are reflections of each other across this line.

19. The graph agrees with the given figure.

20. $x = -t^2 + 8,\ y = t$

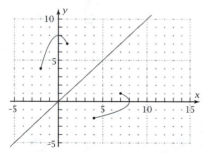

21. The domain of f is the range of f^{-1}, and vice versa.

22. Enter $x_3 = t$ and $y_3 = t$.
Graph is in Problem 20.

23. The graphs of f and f^{-1} are reflections of each other across the line $y = x$.

24. Answers will vary.

Test 3 Form A

1. Quadratic. $y = ax^2 + bx + c$

2. Power. $y = ax^b$

3. Linear. $y = mx + b$

4. Exponential. $y = ab^x$

5. Odd

6. Even

7. Vertical dilation by a factor of 2. $g(x) = 2f(x)$

8. Horizontal translation by -5. $g(x) = f(x + 5)$

9. Inverse relation

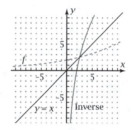

10. See $y = x$ in Problem 9. They are reflections of each other across this line.

11. The inverse relation is a function because there is no place where there is more than one y-value for the same x-value.

12. Domain: $-5 \le x \le 4$; range: $-4 \le y \le 6$

13. Vertical dilation by a factor of 1.5

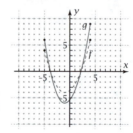

14. Horizontal dilation by a factor of 2

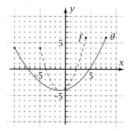

15. There would be more than one value of y for the same value of x.

16. Domain: $2 \le x \le 5$; range: $1.5 \le y \le 3$

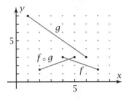

17. $f(g(3)) = f(6) = 2$

18. $f(g(6)) = f(3)$, and 3 is not in the domain of f.

19. $4 \le g(x) \le 7$
    $4 \le -x + 9 \le 7$
    $-5 \le -x \le -2$
    $5 \ge x \ge 2$ or $2 \le x \le 5$
    Domain of g is $1 \le x \le 6$.
    The intersection of these is $2 \le x \le 5$.

20. $x_1 = t \qquad x_2 = 2 \cdot 1.1^t$
    $y_1 = 2 \cdot 1.1^t \qquad y_2 = t$
    The graph is the same as in Problem 9.

21. Linear function

22. $f(1) = 2.7(1) + 6.3 = 9.0$ cm

23. $f(2) = 2.7(2) + 6.3 = 11.7$ cm
    This is not twice as high because the second pot fits down inside the first pot.

24. $y = 2.7n + 6.3$
    $y - 6.3 = 2.7n$
    $n = \dfrac{y - 6.3}{2.7}$

25. $n = \dfrac{35 - 6.3}{2.7} = 10.6296\ldots$
    Maximum is 10 pots (round downward).

26. Answers will vary.

Test 3 Form B

1. Linear. $y = mx + b$

2. Quadratic. $y = ax^2 + bx + c$

3. Exponential. $y = ab^x$

4. Inverse variation $y = k/x$ or power. $y = ax^b$

5. $f(-x) = f(x)$ for all x in the domain

6. $f(-x) = -f(x)$ for all x in the domain

7. Reflection over the y-axis. $g(x) = f(-x)$

8. Vertical translation by 3. $g(x) = f(x) + 3$

9. Inverse relation

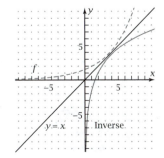

10. See $y = x$ in Problem 9. They are reflections of each other across this line.

11. The inverse relation is a function because there is no place where there is more than one y-value for the same x-value.

12. Domain: $-1 \le x \le 4$; range: $-8 \le y \le 2$

13. Vertical dilation by a factor of 0.5

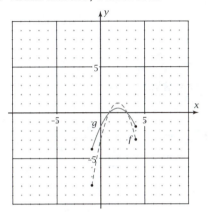

14. Horizontal dilation by a factor of 2

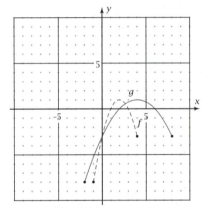

15. There would be more than one value of y for the same value of x.

16. Domain: $2 \le x \le 3$; range: $-3 \le y \le -1$

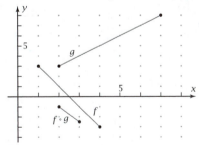

17. $f(g(2)) = f(3) = -1$

18. $f(g(4)) = f(5)$, and 5 is not in the domain of f.

19. $1 \le g(x) \le 4$
    $1 \le x + 1 \le 4$
    $0 \le x \le 3$
    Domain of g is $2 \le x \le 7$.
    The intersection of these is $2 \le x \le 3$.

20. $x_1 = t \qquad x_2 = 1.5 \cdot 1.3^t$
    $y_1 = 1.5 \cdot 1.3^t \qquad y_2 = t$
    The graph is the same as in Problem 9.

21. Linear function

22. $f(1) = 1.5(1) + 3.5 = 5.0$ in.

23. $f(2) = 1.5(2) + 3.5 = 6.5$ in.
    This is not twice as high because the second basket fits down inside the first basket.

24. $y = 1.5n + 3.5$
    $y - 3.5 = 1.5n$
    $n = \dfrac{y - 3.5}{1.5}$

25. $n = \dfrac{36 - 3.5}{1.5} = 21.666...$
    Maximum is 21 baskets (round downward).

26. Answers will vary.

Test 4 Form A

1.

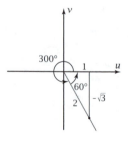

$\sin \theta = \dfrac{-2}{\sqrt{29}}$ $\cos \theta = \dfrac{-5}{\sqrt{29}}$

$\tan \theta = \dfrac{2}{5}$ $\cot \theta = \dfrac{5}{2}$

$\sec \theta = \dfrac{-\sqrt{29}}{5}$ $\csc \theta = \dfrac{-\sqrt{29}}{2}$

2. $\theta = 300°$ and $\theta_{ref} = 60°$

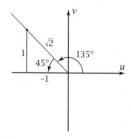

$\sin 300° = -\dfrac{\sqrt{3}}{2}$ $\cos 300° = \dfrac{1}{2}$

$\tan 300° = -\sqrt{3}$ $\cot 300° = -\dfrac{1}{\sqrt{3}}$

$\sec 300° = 2$ $\csc 300° = -\dfrac{2}{\sqrt{3}}$

3. $\theta = 135°$ and $\theta_{ref} = 45°$

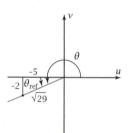

$\sin 135° = \dfrac{1}{\sqrt{2}}$ $\cos 135° = -\dfrac{1}{\sqrt{2}}$

$\tan 135° = -1$ $\cot 135° = -1$

$\sec 135° = -\sqrt{2}$ $\csc 135° = \sqrt{2}$

4. Horizontal dilation by a factor of $\frac{1}{2}$
   Vertical translation by 4
   $g(\theta) = 4 + \cos 2\theta$

5. $\cot 179° = -57.2899...$ 6. $\sec(-58°) = 1.8870...$

7. $\csc 290° = -1.0641...$

8. $\theta_{ref} = 80°$ 9. $\theta_c = 112°$, $\theta_{ref} = 68°$

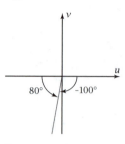
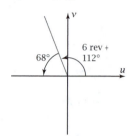

10. $\theta = \theta_{ref} = 85°$

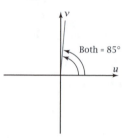

11. $\sin 153° = 0.4539...$, $\sin 207° = -0.4539$
    The reference triangles are congruent because both reference angles are 27°. For 153° the opposite side is positive, and for 207° the opposite side is negative.

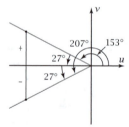

12. $\cos 180° = -1$
    $\cos 180° = \dfrac{u}{r} = \dfrac{-1}{1} = -1$

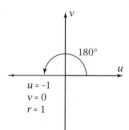

$u = -1$
$v = 0$
$r = 1$

13. $\sin 20° = 0.3420...$, $\cos 70° = 0.3420...$ (the same!)
    $\sin 20° = \dfrac{\text{opposite}}{\text{hypotenuse}}$ and $\cos 70° = \dfrac{\text{adjacent}}{\text{hypotenuse}}$

Precalculus with Trigonometry: Assessment Resources
© 2007 Key Curriculum Press

The opposite side for the 20° angle is the same as the adjacent side for the 70° angle.

∴ $\sin 20° = \cos 70°$

14. • $\sin 30° = 0.5$

    • $\sin^{-1} 0.5 = 30°$

    • $\sin^{-1} 0.5$ means the angle whose sine is 0.5.

    • $\dfrac{1}{\sin 0.5°} = 114.593... \neq 30° = \sin^{-1} 0.5$

15. • $\theta = \sin^{-1} 0.9 = 64.1580...°$

    • $\sin (\text{Ans}) = 0.9$

    • $\sin (\sin^{-1} 0.9) = 0.9$

16. $\tan \theta = \dfrac{7}{5}$

    $\theta = \tan^{-1} \dfrac{7}{5} = 54.4623...°$

17. Points come from table on grapher.

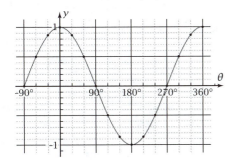

18. The graph on the grapher agrees with the graph in Problem 17.

19. Answers will vary.

Test 4 Form B

1.

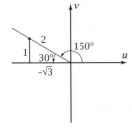

$\sin \theta = \dfrac{-2}{\sqrt{20}} = \dfrac{-1}{\sqrt{5}}$ $\cos \theta = \dfrac{4}{\sqrt{20}} = \dfrac{2}{\sqrt{5}}$

$\tan \theta = -\dfrac{1}{2}$ $\cot \theta = -2$

$\sec \theta = \dfrac{\sqrt{20}}{4} = \dfrac{\sqrt{5}}{2}$ $\csc \theta = \dfrac{-\sqrt{20}}{2} = -\sqrt{5}$

2. $\theta = 150°$ and $\theta_{\text{ref}} = 30°$

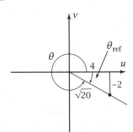

$\sin 150° = \dfrac{1}{2}$ $\cos 150° = -\dfrac{\sqrt{3}}{2}$

$\tan 150° = -\dfrac{1}{\sqrt{3}}$ $\cot 150° = -\sqrt{3}$

$\sec 150° = -\dfrac{2}{\sqrt{3}}$ $\csc 150° = 2$

3. $\theta = 225°$ and $\theta_{\text{ref}} = 45°$

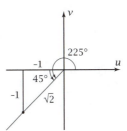

$\sin 225° = -\dfrac{1}{\sqrt{2}}$ $\cos 225° = -\dfrac{1}{\sqrt{2}}$

$\tan 225° = 1$ $\cot 225° = 1$

$\csc 225° = -\sqrt{2}$ $\sec 225° = -\sqrt{2}$

4. Horizontal dilation by a factor of 2
Vertical translation by −2
$g(\theta) = -2 + \sin \left(\tfrac{1}{2} \theta \right)$

5. $\cot 129° = -0.8097...$

6. $\sec (-98°) = -7.1852...$

7. $\csc 171° = 6.3924...$

8. $\theta_{\text{ref}} = 40°$ 9. $\theta_C = 261°$, $\theta_{\text{ref}} = 99°$

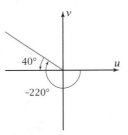
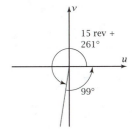

10. $\theta = \theta_{\text{ref}} = 54°$

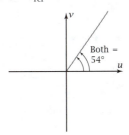

11. $\sin 147° = 0.5446...$, $\sin 213° = -0.5446...$
The reference triangles are congruent because both reference angles are 33°. For 147° the opposite side is positive, and for 213° the opposite side is negative.

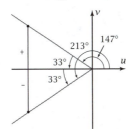

12. $\sin 270° = -1$

$\sin 270° = \dfrac{v}{r} = \dfrac{-1}{1} = -1$

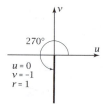

13. $\sin 35° = 0.57357...$, $\cos 55° = 0.57357...$ (the same!)

$\sin 35° = \dfrac{\text{opposite}}{\text{hypotenuse}}$ and $\cos 55° = \dfrac{\text{adjacent}}{\text{hypotenuse}}$

The opposite side for the 35° angle is the same as the adjacent side for the 55° angle.

$\therefore \sin 20° = \cos 70°$

14. • $\cos 60° = 0.5$

• $\cos^{-1} 0.5 = 60°$

• $\cos^{-1} 0.5$ means the angle whose cosine is 0.5.

• $\dfrac{1}{\cos 0.5°} = 1.000038... \neq 60° = \cos^{-1} 0.5$

15. • $\theta = \cos^{-1} 0.9 = 25.8419...°$

• $\cos \text{(Ans)} = 0.9$

• $\cos (\cos^{-1} 0.9) = 0.9$

16. $\tan \theta = \dfrac{3}{2}$

$\theta = \tan^{-1} \dfrac{3}{2} = 56.3099...°$

17. Points come from the table on the grapher.

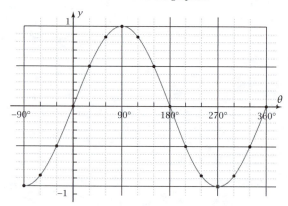

18. The graph on the grapher agrees with the graph in Problem 17.

19. Answers will vary.

Test 5 Form A

1. $\sin M = \dfrac{m}{f}$, $\cos M = \dfrac{p}{f}$, $\tan M = \dfrac{m}{p}$

2. $5^2 + 12^2 = 169 = 13^2$

$\therefore$ hypotenuse is 13.

3. $C = \sin^{-1} \dfrac{5}{13}$

4. $C = \cos^{-1} \dfrac{12}{13}$

5. $C = \tan^{-1} \dfrac{5}{12}$

6.

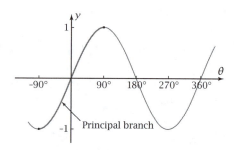

7. The principal branch is one-to-one because each y-value is generated by exactly one x-value.

8. The inverse of the principal branch is a function because there is only one y-value for each x-value in the domain. The inverse of the entire function is not a function because there are many y-values for the same x-value.

9. Graph showing an angle of elevation and an angle of depression.

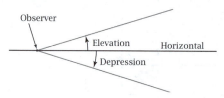

10. $A = \tan^{-1} \dfrac{20}{90} = 12.5288...° \approx 12.5°$

11.

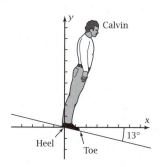

12. Calvin will fall over because the vertical line from his center of gravity will make a 13° angle with his body, and the angle from his center of gravity to his toe is only 12.5°.

13. Let x = no. of cm horizontally.
Let y = no. of cm down.

$\dfrac{x}{65} = \cos 13° \Rightarrow x = 65 \cos 13° = 63.3340...$

$\dfrac{y}{65} = \sin 13° \Rightarrow y = 65 \sin 13° = 14.6218...$

About 14.6 cm down and 63.3 cm horizontally

14. Let y = no. of m down.
Let z = no. of m slant distance.

$\dfrac{y}{330} = \tan 13° \Rightarrow y = 330 \tan 13° = 76.1865...$

$\dfrac{330}{z} = \cos 13° \Rightarrow z = \dfrac{330}{\cos 13°} = 338.6803...$

About 76.2 m down and 338.7 m slant

Precalculus with Trigonometry: Assessment Resources
© 2007 Key Curriculum Press

15. On actual diagram, tick marks should be 1 cm apart.

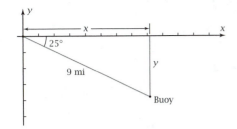

16. Let x = no. of mi to closest point of approach.
Let y = no. of mi from closest point of approach to buoy.

$\dfrac{y}{9} = \sin 25° \Rightarrow y = 9 \sin 25° = 3.8035...$

$\dfrac{x}{9} = \cos 25° \Rightarrow x = 9 \cos 25° = 8.1567...$

3.8 mi from closest point of approach to buoy
8.2 mi from initial point to closest point of approach

17. Distances measure 3.8 cm and 8.2 cm, which agrees with the calculated distances.

18.

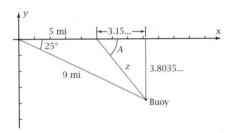

Let z = no. of mi to buoy (see figure).
Let A = no. of degrees to right of path.
Adjacent side = $8.1567... - 5 = 3.1567...$

$\tan A = \dfrac{3.8035...}{3.1567...} = 1.2048...$

$A = \tan^{-1} 1.2048... = 50.3090...°$
About 50.3°

19.

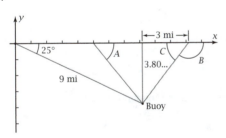

Let B = no. of degrees to right of path.
Let C = supplement of B.

$\tan C = \dfrac{3.8035...}{3} = 1.2678...$

$C = \tan^{-1} 1.2678... = 51.7359...°$
$B = 180° - 51.7359...° = 128.2640...°$
About 128.3°

20. Answers will vary.

Test 5 Form B

1. $\sin P = \dfrac{p}{f}$, $\cos P = \dfrac{m}{f}$, $\tan P = \dfrac{p}{m}$

2. $3^2 + 4^2 = 25 = 5^2$

∴ hypotenuse is 5.

3. $C = \sin^{-1}\left(\dfrac{3}{5}\right)$

4. $C = \cos^{-1}\left(\dfrac{4}{5}\right)$

5. $C = \tan^{-1}\left(\dfrac{3}{4}\right)$

6.

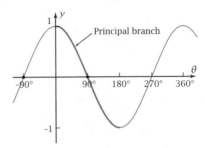

7. The principal branch is one-to-one because each y-value is generated by exactly one x-value.

8. The inverse of the principal branch is a function because there is only one y-value for each x-value in the domain. The inverse of the entire function is not a function because there are many y-values for the same x-value.

9. Graph showing an angle of elevation and an angle of depression.

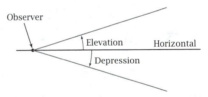

10. $A = \tan^{-1} \dfrac{25}{80} = 17.3540...° \approx 17.4°$

11.

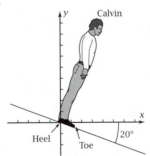

12. Calvin will fall over because the vertical line from his center of gravity will make a 20° angle with his body, and the angle from his center of gravity to his toe is only 17.4°.

13. Let x = no. of cm horizontally.
Let y = no. of cm down.

$\dfrac{x}{55} = \cos 20° \Rightarrow x = 55 \cos 20° = 51.6830...$

$\dfrac{y}{55} = \sin 20° \Rightarrow y = 55 \sin 20° = 18.8111...$

About 18.8 cm down and 15.6 cm horizontally

14. Let y = no. of m down.
Let z = no. of m slant distance.

$\dfrac{y}{350} = \tan 20° \Rightarrow y = 350 \tan 20° = 127.3895...$

$\dfrac{350}{z} = \cos 20° \Rightarrow z = \dfrac{350}{\cos 20°} = 372.4622...$

About 127.4 m down and 372.5 m slant

15. On the actual diagram, tick marks should be 1 cm apart.

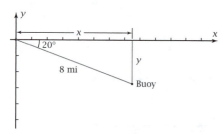

16. Let x = no. of mi to closest point of approach.
Let y = no. of mi from closest point of approach to buoy.

$\dfrac{y}{8} = \sin 20° \Rightarrow y = 8 \sin 20° = 2.7361...$

$\dfrac{x}{8} = \cos 20° \Rightarrow x = 8 \cos 20° = 7.5175...$

2.7 mi from closest point of approach to buoy
7.5 mi from initial point to closest point of approach

17. Distances measure 2.7 cm and 7.5 cm, which agrees with the calculated distances.

18.

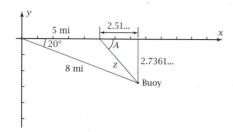

Let z = no. of mi to buoy (see figure).
Let A = no. of degrees to right of path.
Adjacent side = $7.5175... - 5 = 2.5175...$

$\tan A = \dfrac{2.7361...}{2.5175...} = 1.0868...$

$A = \tan^{-1} 1.0868... = 47.3828...°$
About 47.4°

19.

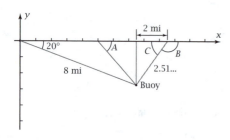

Let B = no. of degrees to right of path.
Let C = supplement of B.

$\tan C = \dfrac{2.5175...}{2} = 1.3680...$

$C = \tan^{-1} 1.3680... = 53.8350...°$
$B = 180° - 53.8350...° = 126.1649...°$
About 126.2°

20. Answers will vary.

Test 6 Form A

1.

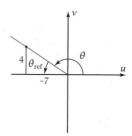

$\sin \theta = \dfrac{4}{\sqrt{65}}$ $\cos \theta = \dfrac{-7}{\sqrt{65}}$

$\tan \theta = \dfrac{-4}{7}$ $\cot \theta = \dfrac{-7}{4}$

$\sec \theta = -\dfrac{\sqrt{65}}{7}$ $\csc \theta = \dfrac{\sqrt{65}}{4}$

2. Reference angle = 60°

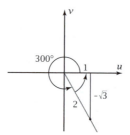

$\sin 300° = -\dfrac{\sqrt{3}}{2}$ $\cos 300° = \dfrac{1}{2}$

$\tan 300° = -\sqrt{3}$ $\cot 300° = -\dfrac{1}{\sqrt{3}}$

$\sec 300° = 2$ $\csc 300° = -\dfrac{2}{\sqrt{3}}$

3. $u = 0$, $v = -1$, and $r = 1$

$\sin 270° = \dfrac{v}{r} = -\dfrac{1}{1} = -1$, Q.E.D.

4. $\sec 270° = \dfrac{r}{u} = \dfrac{1}{0}$, which is undefined, Q.E.D.

5. 45° reference angle

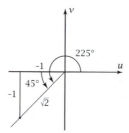

$\sin 225° = -\dfrac{1}{\sqrt{2}}$

6.

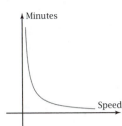

7.

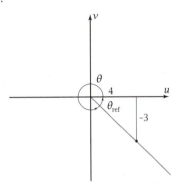

8. The function in Problem 7 is periodic.

9. $\sec 77° = \dfrac{1}{\cos 77°} = 4.4454...$

10. $\cot 158° = \dfrac{1}{\tan 158°} = -2.4750...$

11. $\csc(-190°) = \dfrac{1}{\sin(-190°)} = 5.7587...$

12. $\cos^{-1} 0.3 = 72.5423...°$
This means that $\cos 72.5423...° = 0.3$.

13. $\dfrac{2812}{360} = 7.8111...$

$360(0.8111...) = 292$
Coterminal angle is 292°.
$\theta_{cot} = 292°$ and $\theta_{ref} = 68°$

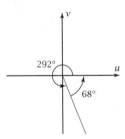

14. $\dfrac{x}{7} = \cos 33° \Rightarrow x = 7\cos 33° = 5.8706... \approx 5.9$ m

15. $\dfrac{5}{y} = \sin 64° \Rightarrow y = \dfrac{5}{\sin 64°} = 5.5630... \approx 5.6$ in.

16. $\tan A = \dfrac{100}{230} = 0.4347...$
$A = \tan^{-1} 0.4347... = 23.4985...° \approx 23.5°$

17. $\tan A = \dfrac{5}{33} = 0.1515...$
$A = \tan^{-1} 0.1515... = 8.6156... \approx 8.6°$

18. $g(\theta) = f(\theta - 90°) + 3 = \cos(\theta - 90°) + 3$

19. Graph below is not to scale.

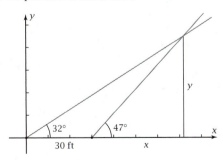

20. About 4.5 cm, so height $\approx$ 45 ft.

21. Let x = no. of feet from 47° angle to perpendicular.
Let y = no. of feet high.
$\dfrac{y}{x} = \tan 47°$ and $\dfrac{y}{x+30} = \tan 32°$
$y = x \tan 47°$ and $y = (x + 30)\tan 32°$
$x \tan 47° = (x + 30)\tan 32°$
$x(\tan 47° - 30\tan 32°) = 30$
$x = \dfrac{30}{\tan 47° - 30\tan 32°} = 41.8907...$
$y = 41.8907... \tan 47° = 44.9223...$
Height is about 44.9 ft, which agrees with the measurement.

22. Answers will vary.

Test 6 Form B

1.

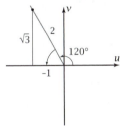

$\sin \theta = -\dfrac{3}{5}$ $\cos \theta = \dfrac{4}{5}$

$\tan \theta = -\dfrac{3}{4}$ $\cot \theta = -\dfrac{4}{3}$

$\sec \theta = \dfrac{5}{4}$ $\csc \theta = -\dfrac{5}{3}$

2. Reference angle = 60°

$\sin 120° = \dfrac{\sqrt{3}}{2}$ $\csc 120° = \dfrac{2}{\sqrt{3}}$

$\cos 120° = -\dfrac{1}{2}$ $\sec 120° = -2$

$\tan 120° = -\sqrt{3}$ $\cot 120° = -\dfrac{1}{\sqrt{3}}$

3. $u = -1$, $v = 0$, and $r = 1$
$\cos 180° = \dfrac{u}{r} = -\dfrac{1}{1} = -1$, Q.E.D.

4. $\csc 180° = \dfrac{r}{v} = \dfrac{1}{0}$, which is undefined, Q.E.D.

5. 45° reference angle

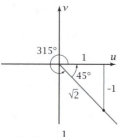

$$\sin 315° = -\frac{1}{\sqrt{2}}$$

6.

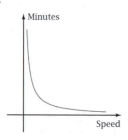

7.

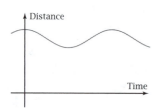

8. The function in Problem 7 is periodic.

9. $\csc 33° = \dfrac{1}{\sin 33°} = 1.8360\ldots$

10. $\cot 122° = \dfrac{1}{\tan 122°} = -0.6248\ldots$

11. $\sec(-130°) = \dfrac{1}{\cos(-130°)} = -1.5557\ldots$

12. $\tan^{-1}(0.7) = 34.9920\ldots°$
This means that $\tan 34.9920\ldots° = 0.7$.

13. $\frac{3025}{360} = 8.4027,$
$360(0.4027\ldots) = 145$
Coterminal angle is 145°.
$\theta_{\cot} = 145°$ and $\theta_{\text{ref}} = 35°$

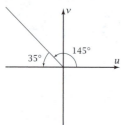

14. $\dfrac{x}{9}\cos 37° \Rightarrow x = 9\cos 37° = 7.1877\ldots \text{ m} \approx 7.2 \text{ m}$

15. $\dfrac{7}{y}\sin 56° \Rightarrow y = \dfrac{7}{\sin 56°} = 8.4435\ldots \text{ in.} \approx 8.4 \text{ in.}$

16. $\tan A = \dfrac{200}{460} = 0.4347\ldots°$
$A = \tan^{-1} 0.4347\ldots = 23.4985\ldots°$

17. $\tan A = \dfrac{10}{66} = 0.1515\ldots$
$A = \tan^{-1} 0.1515\ldots = 8.6156\ldots°$

18. $g(\theta) = f(\theta - 60°) + 4\sin(\theta - 60°) + 4$

19. Graph below is not to scale.

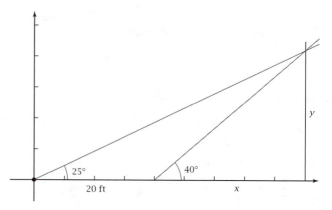

20. About 2 cm, so height $\approx$ 20 ft.

21. Let x = no. of feet from 40° angle to perpendicular.
Let y = no. of feet high.
$$\frac{y}{x} = \tan 40°$$
$$y = x\tan 40°$$
$$\frac{y}{x+20} = \tan 25°$$
$$y = \tan 25°(x+20)$$
$$x\tan 40° = \tan 25°(x+20)$$
$$x = \frac{20\tan 25°}{\tan 40 - \tan 25°} = 25.0170\ldots \text{ ft}$$
$$y = 25.0710\ldots \tan 40° = 20.9917\ldots \text{ ft}$$
which agrees with the measurement.

22. Answers will vary.

Test 7 Form A

1.

2.

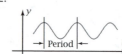

3. Possible answer:

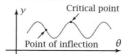

4.

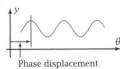

Phase displacement

5. Concave up

6. Period = (dilation)(360°) = $\frac{1}{6} \cdot 360° = 60°$

7.

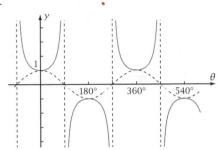

8.

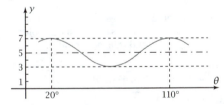

9. $y = 5 + 2 \cos 4(\theta - 20°)$

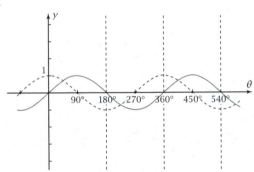

10. • Vertical dilation: 3
    • Vertical translation: −7
    • Horizontal dilation: $\frac{1}{5}$
    • Horizontal translation: 13°

11. • Amplitude: 3
    • Period: $(\frac{1}{5})(360°) = 72°$
    • Phase displacement: 13°
    • Sinusoidal axis location: $y = -7$

12.

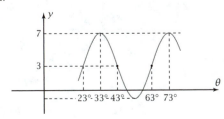

13. $y = 3 + 4 \cos 9(\theta - 33°)$ or
    $y = 3 + 4 \cos 9(\theta - 73°)$ or
    $y = 3 - 4 \cos 9(\theta - 53°)$ (Others possible.)

14. $y = 3 + 4 \sin 9(\theta - 63°)$ or
    $y = 3 + 4 \sin 9(\theta - 23°)$ (Others possible.)

15. $y = 1.7639...$

16.

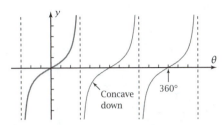

17.

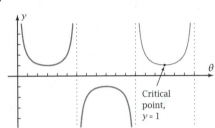

18. The amplitude goes from the axis to a high or low point. Because the tangent function has vertical asymptotes, it has no high and low points and thus no amplitude.

19. $\theta = 18(0 + 3) = 54°$
    $y = 25 + 20 \sin 54° = 41.1803... \approx 41.2$ ft

20. $\theta = 18(1 + 3) = 72°$
    Wheel rotated $72 - 54 = 18°$/s.
    18 is the coefficient of t in the equation.

21. $y = 25 + 20 \sin 18(1 + 3)° = 44.0211... \approx 44.0$ ft

22. Period = $\left(\frac{1}{18}\right)(360) = 20$ s

23.

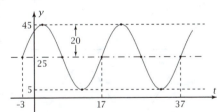

24. Answers will vary.

Test 7 Form B

1. One cycle of the sinusoid is darkened on the graph.

2. The vertical lines show the period of the sinusoid.

3. Point A is an inflection point. Point B is a critical point.

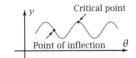

4. The phase displacement for the cosine graph is shown.

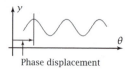

Phase displacement

5. Concave down

6. Period = (dilation)(360°) = $\frac{1}{4} \cdot 360° = 90°$

7.

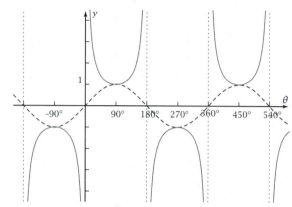

8.

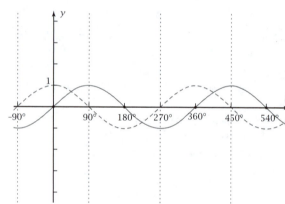

9. $y = -5 + 3 \cos 6(\theta - 30°)$

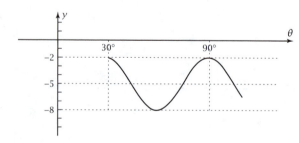

10. • Vertical dilation: 7
   • Vertical translation: 3
   • Horizontal dilation: $\frac{1}{4}$
   • Horizontal translation: 20°

11. • Amplitude: 7
   • Period: $\left(\frac{1}{4}\right)(360°) = 90°$
   • Phase displacement: 20°
   • Sinusoidal axis location: $y = 3$

12.

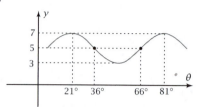

13. $y = 5 + 2 \cos 6(\theta - 21°)$ (Others possible.)

14. $y = 5 + 2 \sin 9(\theta - 6°)$ (Others possible.)

15. $y = 6.4862...$

16.

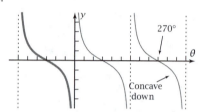

17.

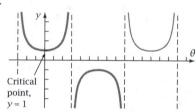

18. The amplitude goes from the axis to a high or low point. Because the cotangent function has vertical asymptotes, it has no high and low points and thus no amplitude.

19. $\theta = 15(0 + 3) = 45°$
   $y = 30 + 25 \sin 45° = 47.6776... \approx 47.7$ ft

20. $\theta = 15(1 + 3) = 60°$
   Wheel rotated $60 - 45 = 15°$/s.
   15 is the coefficient of t in the equation.

21. $y = 30 + 25 \sin 15(1 + 3)° = 51.6506... \approx 51.7$ ft

22. Period $= \left(\frac{1}{15}\right)(360) = 24$ s

23.

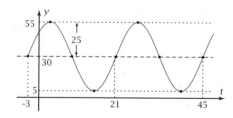

24. Answers will vary.

Test 8 Form A

1. $y = \sin x$

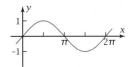

2. $y = \cos x$

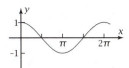

3. $\dfrac{\pi}{3} \cdot \dfrac{180°}{\pi} = 60°$

4. $120° \cdot \dfrac{\pi}{180°} = \dfrac{2\pi}{3}$

5. $\arccos 0.3 = \pm \cos^{-1} 0.3 + 2\pi n$

6. Arc of 13 ft. Angle is $\frac{13}{10} = 1.3$ radians.

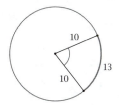

7. Period = 12

   Horizontal dilation $= \dfrac{12}{2\pi} = \dfrac{6}{\pi}$

   Amplitude = 3
   Vertical translation = 6
   Phase displacement = 2

8. $y = 6 + 3 \cos \dfrac{\pi}{6}(x - 2)$

9. At $y = 6$, $x \approx 5, 13, 19$.

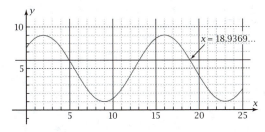

10. $x = 4.9369\ldots \approx 4.937$ or $x = 13.0630\ldots \approx 13.063$

11. Period $= \dfrac{7}{\pi}(2\pi) = 14$

    $n = 1$: $x = 4.9369\ldots + 14 = 18.9369\ldots$
    $n = 2$: $x = 4.9369\ldots + 28 = 32.9369\ldots$
    $n = 3$: $x = 4.9369\ldots + 42 = 46.9369\ldots$
    See graph in Problem 9, showing $x = 18.9369\ldots$ agrees.

12. $n = 1$: $x = 13.0630\ldots + 14 = 27.0630\ldots$
    $n = 2$: $x = 13.0630\ldots + 28 = 41.0630\ldots$
    $n = 3$: $x = 13.0630\ldots + 42 = 55.0630\ldots$

13. $n = -1$: $x = 13.0630\ldots + (-1)(14) = -0.9369\ldots$

14. $5 + 4 \cos \dfrac{\pi}{7}(x - 2) = 6$

    $4 \cos \dfrac{\pi}{7}(x - 2) = 1$

    $\cos \dfrac{\pi}{7}(x - 2) = \dfrac{1}{4}$

    $\dfrac{\pi}{7}(x - 2) = \arccos \dfrac{1}{4}$

    $\dfrac{\pi}{7}(x - 2) = \pm \cos^{-1} \dfrac{1}{4} + 2\pi n$

    $x - 2 = \dfrac{7}{\pi}(\pm 1.3181\ldots + 2\pi n)$

    $x - 2 = \pm 2.9369\ldots + 14n$
    $x = 4.9369\ldots + 14n$ or $-0.9369\ldots + 14n$
    $x = 4.9369\ldots, 13.0630\ldots, 18.9369\ldots$
    These agree with Problems 10, 11, and 12.

15. High point is at $(-140, 80)$.

16. Period $= \dfrac{110}{\pi}(2\pi) = 220$ ft

17. $y = 60 + 20 \cos \dfrac{\pi}{110}(637 + 140) = 40.3983\ldots \approx 40.4$ ft

18. Answers will vary.

Test 8 Form B

1. $y = \sin x$

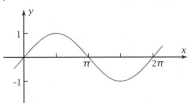

2. $y = \cos x$

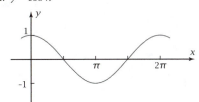

3. $\dfrac{\pi}{6} \cdot \dfrac{180°}{\pi} = 30°$

4. $420° \cdot \dfrac{\pi}{180°} = \dfrac{7\pi}{3}$

5. $\arccos 0.7 = \pm \cos^{-1} 0.7 + 2\pi n$

6. Arc of 30 ft. Angle is $\frac{30}{20} = 1.5$ radians.

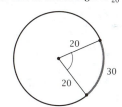

7. Period = 6

Horizontal dilation = $\dfrac{6}{2\pi} = \dfrac{3}{\pi}$

Amplitude = 2

Vertical translation = 3

Phase displacement = 4 or −2

8. $y = 3 + 2\cos\dfrac{\pi}{3}(x-4)$ or $y = 3 + 2\cos\dfrac{\pi}{3}(x+2)$

9. At $y = 6$, $x \approx 1.1,\ 8.9,\ 14.1$

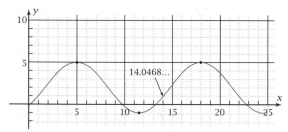

10. $x = 1.0468... \approx 1.047$ or $x = 8.9531... \approx 8.953$

11. Period = $2\pi \cdot \dfrac{13}{2\pi} = 13$

$n = 1$: $x = 1.0468... + 13 = 14.0468...$

$n = 2$: $x = 1.0468... + 26 = 27.0468...$

$n = 3$: $x = 1.0468... + 39 = 40.0468...$

See graph in Problem 9, showing $x = 14.0468...$ agrees.

12. $n = 1$: $x = 8.9531... + 13 = 21.9531...$

$n = 2$: $x = 8.9531... + 26 = 34.9531...$

$n = 3$: $x = 8.9531... + 39 = 47.9531...$

13. $n = -1$: $x = 8.9531... + (-1)(13) = -4.0468...$

14. $y = 2 + 3\cos\dfrac{2\pi}{13}(x-5)$

$3\cos\dfrac{2\pi}{13}(x-5) = -1$

$\cos\dfrac{2\pi}{13}(x-5) = -\dfrac{1}{3}$

$\dfrac{2\pi}{13}(x-5) = \arccos\left(-\dfrac{1}{3}\right)$

$\dfrac{2\pi}{13}(x-5) = \pm\cos^{-1}\left(-\dfrac{1}{3}\right) + 2\pi n$

$x - 5 = \pm\dfrac{13}{2\pi}\cos^{-1}\left(-\dfrac{1}{3}\right) + 2\pi n$

$x = 5 \pm \dfrac{13}{2\pi}(1.9106... + 2\pi n)$

$x = 5 \pm 3.9531... + 13n$

$x = 1.0468... + 13n$ or $8.9531... + 13n$

These agree with Problems 10, 11, and 12.

15. Frequency = 60 cycles/s, period = $\dfrac{1}{60}$ s

16. Wavelength = $\dfrac{1100}{60} = 18.3333...$ ft = 220 in.

17. $\dfrac{1}{2} \cdot \dfrac{1100}{16} = 34.375...$ ft = 34 ft 4.5 in.

18. Answers will vary.

Test 9 Form A

1. $x = 2.7$ mapped onto unit circle

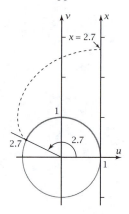

2. See graph in Problem 1, showing angle of 2.7 radians

3. $\theta = 2.7 \cdot \dfrac{180}{\pi}$ degrees

Angle terminates in the second quadrant.

4. $30° \cdot \dfrac{\pi}{180} = \dfrac{\pi}{6}$ radians

5. $\dfrac{-2\pi}{3} \cdot \dfrac{180}{\pi} = -120°$

6. $\cos^{-1}\left(-\dfrac{3}{5}\right)$

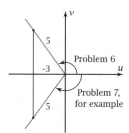

Problem 6

Problem 7, for example

7. See graph in Problem 6, showing another arccos (−3.5).

8. $\arccos\left(-\dfrac{3}{5}\right) = \pm\cos^{-1}\left(-\dfrac{3}{5}\right) + 360°n$ (or $+2\pi n$)

9. $y = \sin\theta$

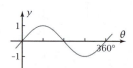

10. $y = \cos x$

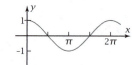

11. $y = 4 + 3\cos\frac{\pi}{8}(x - 5)$

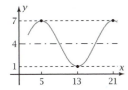

12. Angle $= \frac{7}{5} = 1.4$ radians

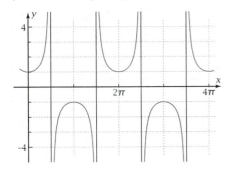

13. $3.5 \cdot \frac{180}{\pi} = 200.5352...°$

14. $y = \sec x$, showing asymptotes

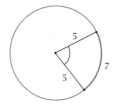

15. $y = \cot x = \frac{1}{\tan x}$

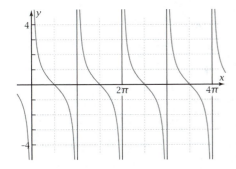

16. Because $\cot x = \frac{1}{\tan x}$, $y = \cot x$ will have asymptotes wherever $\tan x = 0$.

17. Period $= 29 - 3 = 26$

Horizontal dilation $= \frac{26}{2\pi} = \frac{13}{\pi}$

$y = 6 + 4\cos\frac{\pi}{13}(x - 3)$

18. $y = 6 + 4\sin\frac{\pi}{13}(x - 22.5)$

19. Given: $y = 141 + 93\cos\frac{\pi}{390}(x - 140)$

Horizontal dilation $= \frac{390}{\pi}$

Period $= \frac{390}{\pi}(2\pi) = 780$ days

Amplitude = 93 million mi
Phase displacement = 140 days
Vertical translation = 141 million mi

20. Closest at $x = 140 + 0.5(780) = 530$ days

21. About $390 \le x \le 670$

22. $391.67... \le x \le 668.32...$

23. $141 + 93\cos\frac{\pi}{390}(x - 140) = 100$

$93\cos\frac{\pi}{390}(x - 140) = -41$

$\cos\frac{\pi}{390}(x - 140) = -\frac{41}{93}$

$\frac{\pi}{390}(x - 140) = \arccos\left(-\frac{41}{93}\right)$

$\frac{\pi}{390}(x - 140) = \pm 2.0273... + 2\pi n$

$x - 140 = \pm 251.6773... + 780n$
$x = 391.6773... + 780n$ or $-111.6773... + 780n$
$x = 391.6773...$ or $-111.6773... + 780 = 668.3226...$
Interval is $391.6773... \le x \le 668.3226...$

24. Answers will vary.

Test 9 Form B

1. $x = 1.8$ mapped onto unit circle

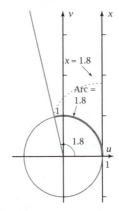

2. See graph in Problem 1, showing angle of 1.8 radians

3. $\theta = 1.8 \cdot \frac{180°}{\pi}$

Angle terminates in the second quadrant.

4. $240° \cdot \frac{\pi}{180°} = \frac{4\pi}{3}$

5. $-\frac{5\pi}{6} \cdot \frac{180°}{\pi} = -150°$

6. $\cos^{-1}\left(-\dfrac{2}{3}\right)$

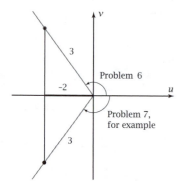

Problem 6

Problem 7,
for example

7. See graph in Problem 6, showing another $\arccos\left(-\dfrac{2}{3}\right)$.

8. $\arccos\left(-\dfrac{2}{3}\right) = \pm\cos^{-1}\left(-\dfrac{2}{3}\right) + 360n°$ (or $+2\pi n$)

9. $y = \sin\theta$

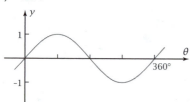

10. $y = \cos x$

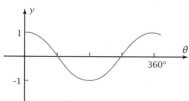

11. $y = -2 + 4\cos\dfrac{\pi}{12}(x + 3)$

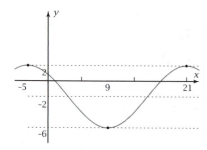

12. Angle $= \dfrac{8}{6} = \dfrac{4}{3}$ radians

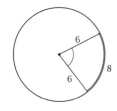

13. $4.8 \cdot \dfrac{180°}{\pi} = 275.0197...°$

14. $y = \csc x$, showing asymptotes

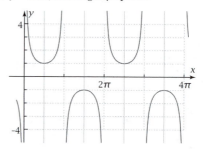

15. $y = \cot x = \dfrac{1}{\tan x}$

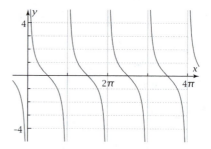

16. Because $\csc x = \dfrac{1}{\sin x}$, cosecant will have vertical tangents whenever $\sin x = 0$.

17. $y = 2 + 3\cos\dfrac{\pi}{8}(x - 12)$

18. $y = 2 + 3\sin\dfrac{\pi}{8}(x - 8)$

19. Given: $y = 3 + 4\cos\dfrac{\pi}{5.8}(x - 1)$

Horizontal dilation $= \dfrac{5.8}{\pi}$

Period $= 2\pi \cdot \dfrac{5.8}{\pi} = 11.6$ hours

Amplitude $= 4$ ft
Phase displacement $= 1$ hour
Vertical translation $= 3$ feet

20. 4:00 p.m. is $x = 16$; $y(16) = 1.9298...$ ft ≈ 1.9 ft

21. Because this happens at the end of the second complete cycle, it is where

$\dfrac{\pi}{5.8}(x - 1) = 4\pi \Rightarrow x = 24.2$ h which is 12:12 a.m.

on January 2

22. $5.465...$ h $\le x \le 8.1343...$ h or approximately 5:28 a.m.
$\le x \le$ 8:08 a.m.

23. $3 + 4\cos\dfrac{\pi}{5.8}(x - 1) = 0$

$4\cos\dfrac{\pi}{5.8}(x - 1) = -3$

$\cos\dfrac{\pi}{5.8}(x - 1) = -\dfrac{3}{4}$

$\dfrac{\pi}{5.8}(x - 1) = \arccos\left(-\dfrac{3}{4}\right)$

$\dfrac{\pi}{5.8}(x - 1) = \pm 2.4188\ldots + 2\pi n$

$x - 1 = \pm 4.4656\ldots + 11.6n$

$x = 5.4656\ldots + 11.6n$ or $-3.4656\ldots + 11.6n$

First value of x greater than 48 (January 3),

$n = 4$: $x = 5.4656 + 11.6(4) = 51.8656\ldots \approx 3{:}52$ a.m.

24. Answers will vary.

Test 10 Form A

1. $\cot x = \dfrac{1}{\tan x}$, $\sec x = \dfrac{1}{\cos x}$, $\csc x = \dfrac{1}{\sin x}$

2. $\tan x = \dfrac{\sin x}{\cos x}$ or $\tan x = \dfrac{\sec x}{\csc x}$

   $\cot x = \dfrac{\cos x}{\sin x}$ or $\cot x = \dfrac{\csc x}{\sec x}$

3. $\cos^2 x + \sin^2 x = 1$
   $1 + \tan^2 x = \sec^2 x$
   $\cot^2 x + 1 = \csc^2 x$

4. Calvin, you should start with the more complicated side.

5. "I have two terms and want only one term. Find a common denominator, then add the fractions."

6. Proof:
   $\dfrac{\sec\theta}{\sin\theta} - \dfrac{\sin\theta}{\cos\theta} = \dfrac{\cos\theta}{\cos\theta}\cdot\dfrac{\sec\theta}{\sin\theta} - \dfrac{\sin\theta}{\sin\theta}\cdot\dfrac{\sin\theta}{\cos\theta}$

   $= \dfrac{1 - \sin^2\theta}{\sin\theta\cos\theta}$

   $= \dfrac{\cos^2\theta}{\sin\theta\cos\theta}$

   $= \dfrac{\cos\theta}{\sin\theta} = \cot\theta$

   $\therefore \dfrac{\sec\theta}{\sin\theta} - \dfrac{\sin\theta}{\cos\theta} = \cot\theta$, Q.E.D.

7. $\cot x + \tan x = \dfrac{\cos x}{\sin x} + \dfrac{\sin x}{\cos x}$

   $= \dfrac{\cos^2 x + \sin^2 x}{\sin x\cos x}$

   $= \dfrac{1}{\sin x\cos x} = \csc x\sec x$, Q.E.D.

8. $y_1 = (1 + 2\cos x)(1 - 2\cos x)$ and $y_2 = 4\sin^2 x - 3$, which coincide with each other.

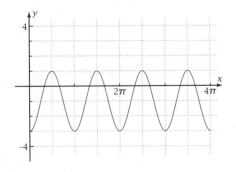

9. Proof:
   $(1 + 2\cos x)(1 - 2\cos x) = 1 - 4\cos^2 x$
   $= 1 - 4(1 - \sin^2 x)$
   $= 1 - 4 + 4\sin^2 x$
   $= 4\sin^2 x - 3$
   $\therefore (1 + 2\cos x)(1 - 2\cos x) = 4\sin^2 x - 3$, Q.E.D.

10. $y = \cot x = \dfrac{1}{\tan x}$

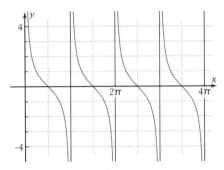

11. $\cot x = \dfrac{\cos x}{\sin x}$, so the cotangent graph has asymptotes at $x = 0$, π, 2π, 3π, 4π, . . . , where $\sin x = 0$.

12. Proof:
   $\cos^3 A\sin^2 A = \cos^3 A(1 - \cos^2 A)$
   $= \cos^3 A - \cos^5 A$
   $\therefore \cos^3 A\sin^2 A = \cos^3 A - \cos^5 A$, Q.E.D.

13. Proof:
   $\dfrac{1}{1 - \cos B} + \dfrac{1}{1 + \cos B}$

   $= \dfrac{1 + \cos B}{1 + \cos B}\cdot\dfrac{1}{1 - \cos B} + \dfrac{1}{1 + \cos B}\cdot\dfrac{1 - \cos B}{1 - \cos B}$

   $= \dfrac{(1 + \cos B) + (1 - \cos B)}{1 - \cos^2 B}$

   $= \dfrac{2}{\sin^2 B}$

   $= 2\csc^2 B$

   $\therefore \dfrac{1}{1 - \cos B} + \dfrac{1}{1 + \cos B} = 2\csc^2 B$, Q.E.D.

14. Proof:
   $(5\cos C - 2\sin C)^2 + (2\cos C + 5\sin C)^2$
   $= 25\cos^2 C - 20\cos C\sin C + 4\sin^2 C$
   $\quad + 4\cos^2 C + 20\cos C\sin C + 25\sin^2 C$
   $= 29(\cos^2 C + \sin^2 C) + 0$
   $= 29$
   $\therefore (5\cos C - 2\sin C)^2 + (2\cos C + 5\sin C)^2 = 29$, Q.E.D.

15. Answers will vary.

Test 10 Form B

1. $\sec x = \dfrac{1}{\cos x}$, $\csc x = \dfrac{1}{\sin x}$, $\cot x = \dfrac{1}{\tan x}$

2. $\tan x = \dfrac{\sin x}{\cos x}$ or $\tan x = \dfrac{\sec x}{\csc x}$

   $\cot x = \dfrac{\cos x}{\sin x}$ or $\cot x = \dfrac{\csc x}{\sec x}$

3. $\cos^2 x + \sin^2 x = 1$
   $1 + \tan^2 x = \sec^2 x$
   $\cot^2 x + 1 = \csc^2 x$

4. Calvin, you should start with the more complicated side.

5. "I have two terms and want only one term. Find a common denominator, then add the fractions."

6. Proof:

$$\frac{1}{\sin\theta\cos\theta} - \frac{\cos\theta}{\sin\theta} = \frac{1}{\sin\theta\cos\theta} - \frac{\cos\theta}{\sin\theta}\cdot\frac{\cos\theta}{\cos\theta}$$
$$= \frac{1-\cos^2\theta}{\sin\theta\cos\theta}$$
$$= \frac{\sin^2\theta}{\sin\theta\cos\theta}$$
$$= \frac{\sin\theta}{\cos\theta} = \tan\theta$$
$$\therefore \frac{1}{\sin\theta\cos\theta} - \frac{\cos\theta}{\sin\theta} = \tan\theta, \text{ q.e.d.}$$

7. $\csc x - \sin x$
$$= \frac{1}{\sin x} - \frac{\sin x}{\sin x}\cdot\sin x$$
$$= \frac{1}{\sin x} - \frac{\sin^2 x}{\sin x}$$
$$= \frac{1-\sin^2 x}{\sin x}$$
$$= \frac{\cos^2 x}{\sin x}$$
$$= \frac{\cos x}{\sin x}\cdot\cos x$$
$$= \cot x\cos x, \text{ q.e.d.}$$

8. $y_1 = (3-4\sin x)(3+4\sin x)$ and $y_2 = 9 - 16\sin^2 x$, which coincide with each other.

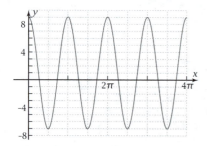

9. Proof:
$$(3-4\sin x)(3+4\sin x) = 9 - 16\sin^2 x$$
$$= 9 - 16(1-\cos^2 x)$$
$$= 9 - 16 + 16\cos^2 x$$
$$= 16\cos^2 x - 7$$
$$\therefore (3-4\sin x)(3+4\sin x) = 16\cos^2 x - 7, \text{ q.e.d.}$$

10. $y = \tan x = \dfrac{\sin x}{\cos x}$

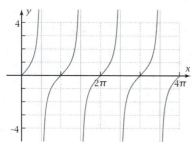

11. $\tan x = \dfrac{\sin x}{\cos x}$ so the tangent graph has asymptotes at $x = \frac{\pi}{2}, \frac{3\pi}{2}, \frac{5\pi}{2}, \ldots,$ where $\cos x = 0$.

12. Proof:
$$\csc^2 A + \cot^2 A\csc^2 A$$
$$= \frac{1}{\sin^2 A} + \frac{\cos^2 A}{\sin^2 A}\cdot\frac{1}{\sin^2 A}$$
$$= \frac{\sin^2 A + \cos^2 A}{\sin^4 A}$$
$$= \frac{1}{\sin^4 A}$$
$$= \csc^4 A$$
$$\therefore \csc^2 A + \cot^2 A\csc^2 A = \csc^4 A, \text{ q.e.d.}$$

13. Proof:
$$\frac{1}{1+\sin B} + \frac{1}{1-\sin B}$$
$$= \frac{1-\sin B + 1 + \sin B}{1-\sin^2 B}$$
$$= \frac{2}{\cos^2 B} = 2\sec^2 B$$
$$\therefore \frac{1}{1+\sin B} + \frac{1}{1-\sin B} = 2\sec^2 B, \text{ q.e.d.}$$

14. Proof:
$$(3\cos x + 4\sin x)^2 + (3\cos x - 4\sin x)^2$$
$$= 9\cos^2 x + 24\cos x\sin x + 16\sin^2 x$$
$$\quad + 9\cos^2 x - 24\cos x\sin x + 16\sin^2 x$$
$$= 9(\cos^2 x + \sin^2 x) + 16(\cos^2 x + \sin^2 x)$$
$$= 9 + 16$$
$$= 25$$
$$\therefore (3\cos x + 4\sin x)^2 + (3\cos x - 4\sin x)^2 = 25, \text{ q.e.d.}$$

15. Answers will vary.

Test 11 Form A

1. $\arcsin A = 180° - (-50°) = 230°$, or $\arcsin A = -130°$
$\arcsin A = -50° + 360°n$ or $230° + 360°n$

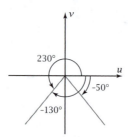

2. $\arctan A = 180° + 20° = 200°$
$\arctan A = 20° + 180°n$

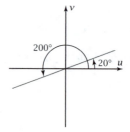

3. arccos $A = -2$ radians

   arccos $A = \pm 2 + 2\pi n$

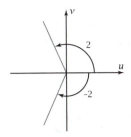

4. arcsin $A = 1 + 2\pi n$ or $(\pi - 1) + 2\pi n$

5. $\theta = 70° + 360°n$ or $-10° + 360°n$

6. $x = 0.9 + \pi n$

7. $2\cos(\theta - 13°) = \sqrt{3}$

   $\cos(\theta - 13°) = \dfrac{\sqrt{3}}{2}$

   $\theta - 13° = \arccos\left(\dfrac{\sqrt{3}}{2}\right)$

   $\theta - 13° = \pm 30° + 360°n$

   $\theta = 43° + 360n°$ or $-17° + 360°n$

   $S = \{43°, 403°; 343°, 703°\}$

8. $\tan^2 x - 3\tan x - 4 = 0$

   $(\tan x - 4)(\tan x + 1) = 0$

   $\tan x = 4$ or $\tan x = -1$

   $x = \arctan 4$ or $x = \arctan(-1)$

   $x = 1.3258... + \pi n$ or $-0.7853... + \pi n$

   $S = \{1.3258..., 4.4674..., 7.6090...; 2.3561..., 5.4977..., 9.6393...\}$

9. $5 - 7\sin\theta = 2\cos^2\theta$

   $5 - 7\sin\theta = 2(1 - \sin^2\theta)$

   $2\sin^2\theta - 7\sin\theta + 3 = 0$

   $(2\sin\theta - 1)(\sin\theta - 3) = 0$

   $\sin\theta = 0.5$ or $\sin\theta = 3$ (no solution)

   $\theta = \arcsin 0.5 = 30° + 360n°$ or $150° + 360n°$

   $S = \{-330°, 30°, 390°; 150°, -210°\}$

10.

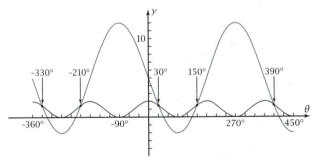

11. Answers will vary.

Test 11 Form B

1. arcsin $A = 180° - (-20°) = 200°$, or arcsin $A = -20°$

   arcsin $A = -20° + 360°n$ or $200° + 360°n$

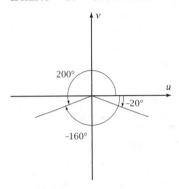

2. arctan $A = 180° + 35° = 215°$

   arctan $A = 35° + 180°n$

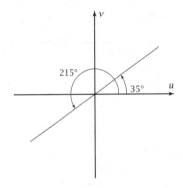

3. arccos $A = -1$ radians

   arccos $A = \pm 1 + 2\pi n$

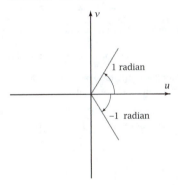

4. arcsin $A = 2 + 2\pi n$ or $(\pi - 2) + 2\pi n$

5. $\theta = 90° + 360°n$ or $50° + 360°n$

6. $x = 0.6 + 0.5\pi n$

7. $2\sin(\theta + 21°) = \sqrt{3}$

   $\sin(\theta + 21°) = \sqrt{3}/2$

   $\theta + 21° = \arcsin(\sqrt{3}/2)$

   $\theta + 21° = 60° + 360°n$ or $120° + 360\pi n$

   $\theta = 39° + 360n°$ or $99° + 360°n$

   $S = \{39°, 99°; 399°, 459°\}$

8. $\tan^2 x - 2\tan x - 3 = 0$
$(\tan x - 3)(\tan x + 1) = 0$
$\tan x = 3$ or $\tan x = -1$
$x = \arctan 3$ or $x = \arctan(-1)$
$x = 1.2490... + \pi n$ or $x = -0.7853... + \pi n$
$S = \{1.2490..., 2.3561..., 4.3906..., 5.4977..., 7.5322..., 8.6393...\}$

9. $1 + 3\cos\theta = \sin^2\theta$
$1 + 3\cos\theta = (1 - \cos^2\theta)$
$\cos^2\theta + 3\cos\theta = 0$
$\cos\theta(\cos\theta + 3) = 0$
$\cos\theta = 0$ or $\cos\theta = -3$ (no solution)
$\theta = \arccos 0 = \pm 90° + 360n°$ or $270° + 360n°$
$S = \{-270°, -90°, 90°, 270°, 450°\}$

10.

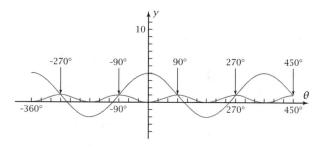

11. Answers will vary.

Test 12 Form A

1. $\csc x = \dfrac{1}{\sin x}$

2. $\tan x = \dfrac{\sin x}{\cos x}$ or $\tan x = \dfrac{\sec x}{\csc x}$

3. $\cos^2 x + \sin^2 x = 1$

4. $1 - \tan^2 x = \sec^2 x$ is true only for certain values of x in the domain.
$1 + \tan^2 x = \sec^2 x$ is true for all values of x in the domain.

5. Find a common denominator and add fractions so that you will have only one term instead of two terms.

6. $\sin^{-1} y = 50°$ and another $\arcsin y = 130°$.
General solution: $\arcsin y = 50° + 360°n$ or $130° + 360°n$

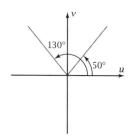

7. $x = -2 + 9\cos t$
$y = 4 + 5\sin t$

8. Range: $0 \le y \le \pi$
Criteria (any three):
- Must be a function.
- Must use all of domain.
- Should be continuous if possible.
- Should be centrally located.
- If there is a choice of two branches, use positive one.

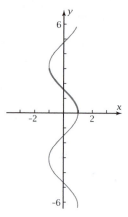

9. $\cos A(\sec A - \cos A) = 1 - \cos^2 A$
$\qquad\qquad\qquad\qquad\quad = \sin^2 A$, Q.E.D.

10. Proof:
$$\dfrac{\cos^2\theta}{1 + \sin\theta} = \dfrac{1 - \sin^2\theta}{1 + \sin\theta}$$
$$= \dfrac{(1 - \sin\theta)(1 + \sin\theta)}{1 + \sin\theta}$$
$$= 1 - \sin\theta$$
$$\therefore \dfrac{\cos^2\theta}{1 + \sin\theta} = 1 - \sin\theta, \text{ Q.E.D.}$$

11. $\theta \approx 0°, 180°, 210°, 330°, 360°, 540°, 570°, 690°, 720°$

12. $2 + \sin\theta = 2\cos^2\theta$
$2 + \sin\theta = 2(1 - \sin^2\theta)$
$2 + \sin\theta = 2 - 2\sin^2\theta$
$2\sin^2\theta + \sin\theta = 0$
$\sin\theta(2\sin\theta + 1) = 0$
$\sin\theta = 0$ or $2\sin\theta + 1 = 0$
$\sin\theta = 0$ or $\sin\theta = -0.5$
$\theta = \arcsin 0$ or $\theta = \arcsin(-0.5)$
$\theta = 0 + 360n°$ or $180° + 360n°$
or $\theta = -30° + 360n°$ or $210° + 360n°$
$S = \{0°, 180°, 210°, 330°, 360°, 540°, 570°, 690°, 720°\}$

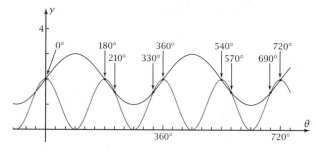

13. The expression $\sin^{-1} 1.2$ means "the angle whose sine is 1.2." Because no angles have sines greater than 1, there is no value for $\sin^{-1} 1.2$, which is why the calculator gives an error message.

Precalculus with Trigonometry: Assessment Resources
© 2007 Key Curriculum Press

14. The graph agrees with the given figure.

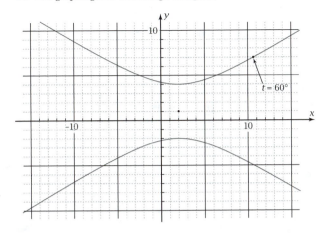

15. $t = 420°$: $x = 10.6602...$, $y = 7$
    The values of x and y are the same because $420°$ is one cycle further around from $60°$.

16. $x = 2 + 5 \tan t$
    $y = 1 + 3 \sec t$
    $\dfrac{x - 2}{5} = \tan t$
    $\dfrac{y - 1}{3} = \sec t$
    $-\left(\dfrac{x-2}{5}\right)^2 + \left(\dfrac{y-1}{3}\right)^2 = \sec^2 t - \tan^2 t$
    $-\left(\dfrac{x-2}{5}\right)^2 + \left(\dfrac{y-1}{3}\right)^2 = 1$

17. This is the equation of a hyperbola centered at the point (2, 1), opening in the y-direction, with horizontal dilation 5 and vertical dilation 3.

18. In parametric mode, enter
    $x = \tan t$
    $y = t$
    Set the window as shown and plot the graph.

19. Answers will vary.

Test 12 Form B

1. $\sec x = \dfrac{1}{\cos x}$

2. $\cot x = \dfrac{\cos x}{\sin x} = \dfrac{\csc x}{\sec x}$

3. $\cos^2 x + \sin^2 x = 1$

4. $\sec^2 x + \tan^2 x = 1$ is true only for certain values of x in the domain.
   $\sec^2 x - \tan^2 x = 1$ is true for all values of x in the domain.

5. Find a common denominator and add fractions so that you will have only one term instead of two terms.

6. $\sin^{-1} y = 70°$ and another arcsin $y = 110°$.
   General solution: arcsin $y = 70° + 360°n$ or $110° + 360°n$

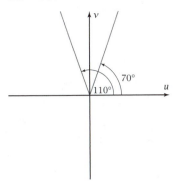

7. $x = 5 \cos t$
   $y = 7 \sin t$

8. Range: $-\dfrac{\pi}{2} \le y \le \dfrac{\pi}{2}$
   Criteria (any three):
   • Must be a function.
   • Must use all of domain.
   • Should be continuous if possible.
   • Should be centrally located.
   • If there is a choice of two branches, use positive one.

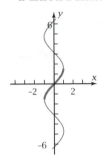

9. $\tan A\,(\cot A \cos A + \sin A) = \cos A + \dfrac{\sin A}{\cos A} \cdot \sin A$
   $= \dfrac{\cos^2 A + \sin^2 A}{\cos A}$
   $= \dfrac{1}{\cos A}$
   $= \sec A$, Q.E.D.

10. Proof:
    $\dfrac{\sin \theta}{\csc \theta - 1} - \dfrac{\sin \theta}{\cot^2 \theta}$
    $= \dfrac{\sin \theta}{\csc \theta - 1} - \dfrac{\sin \theta}{\csc^2 \theta - 1}$
    $= \dfrac{\sin \theta\,(\csc \theta + 1) - \sin \theta}{\csc^2 \theta - 1}$
    $= \dfrac{\sin \theta \cdot \csc \theta + \sin \theta - \sin \theta}{\csc^2 \theta - 1}$
    $= \dfrac{1}{\cot^2 \theta}$
    $= \tan^2 \theta$
    $\therefore \dfrac{\sin \theta}{\csc \theta - 1} - \dfrac{\sin \theta}{\cot^2 \theta} = \tan^2 \theta$, Q.E.D.

11. $\theta \approx 90°, 120°, 240°, 270°, 450°, 480°, 600°, 630°$

12. $2 + \cos\theta = 2\sin^2\theta$
$2 + \cos\theta = 2(1 - \cos^2\theta)$
$2 + \cos\theta = 2 - 2\cos^2\theta$
$2\cos^2\theta + \cos\theta = 0$
$\cos\theta\,(2\cos\theta + 1) = 0$
$\cos\theta = 0$ or $2\cos\theta + 1 = 0$
$\cos\theta = 0$ or $\cos\theta = -0.5$
$\theta = \arccos 0$ or $\theta = \arccos(-0.5)$
$\theta = \pm 90° + 360n°$ or $\pm 120° + 360n°$
$S = \{90°, 120°, 240°, 270°, 450°, 480°, 600°, 630°\}$

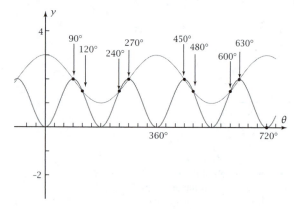

13. The expression $\cos^{-1} -1.3$ means "the angle whose cosine is -1.3." Because no angles have cosines less than -1, there is no value for $\cos^{-1} -1.3$, which is why the calculator gives an error message.

14. The graph agrees with the given figure.

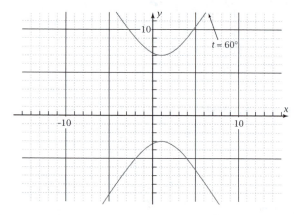

15. $t = 420°$: $x = 6.1961..., y = 12$
The values of x and y are the same because $420°$ is one cycle further around from $60°$.

16. $x = 1 + 3\tan t$
$y = 2 + 5\sec t$
$\dfrac{x - 1}{3} = \tan t$
$\dfrac{y - 2}{5} = \sec t$
$-\left(\dfrac{x-1}{3}\right)^2 + \left(\dfrac{y-2}{5}\right)^2 = \sec^2 t - \tan^2 t$
$-\left(\dfrac{x-1}{3}\right)^2 + \left(\dfrac{y-2}{5}\right)^2 = 1$

17. This is the equation of a hyperbola centered at the point $(1, 2)$, opening in the y-direction, with horizontal dilation 3 and vertical dilation 5.

18. In parametric mode, enter
$x = 1/\tan t$
$y = t$
Set the window as shown and plot the graph.

19. Answers will vary.

Test 13 Form A

1. $\cos(A - B) = \cos A \cos B + \sin A \sin B$
$\cos(A + B) = \cos A \cos B - \sin A \sin B$
$\sin(A - B) = \sin A \cos B - \cos A \sin B$
$\sin(A + B) = \sin A \cos B + \cos A \sin B$

2. "cos (first − second)
   = cos (first) cos (second) + sin (first) sin (second)"

3. $\cos 90° = 0$
$\sin 90° = 1$
$\cos 0° = 1$
$\sin 0° = 0$

4. $\cos(90° - B) = \sin B$
$\sin(90° - B) = \cos B$

5. Proof:
$\sin(90° - B) = \sin 90° \cos B - \cos 90° \sin B$
$\qquad = 1 \cdot \cos B - 0 \cdot \sin B = \cos B$
$\therefore \sin(90° - B) = \cos B$, Q.E.D.

6. Proof:
$\sin(-B) = \sin(0° - B)$
$\qquad = \sin 0° \cos B - \cos 0° \sin B$
$\qquad = 0 \cdot \cos B - 1 \cdot \sin B = -\sin B$
$\therefore \sin(-B) = -\sin B$, Q.E.D.

7. $\cos(-B) = \cos B$

8. $y = \cos(x - 1.3)$
$y = \cos x \cos 1.3 + \sin x \sin 1.3$
$y \approx 0.27\cos x + 0.96\sin x$

9. $\cos(37° - 21°) = \cos 16° = 0.9612...$
$\cos 37° \cos 21° + \sin 37° \sin 21° = 0.9612...$,
check.

10. $\cos(A + B) = \cos A \cos B - \sin A \sin B$
$\qquad = (0.6)(0.96) - (0.8)(0.28) = 0.352$

11. $\cos^{-1} 0.6 = 53.1301...°$ and $\sin^{-1} 0.8 = 53.1301...°$

12. $\cos^{-1} 0.96 = 16.2602...°$ and $\sin^{-1} 0.28 = 16.2602...°$

13. $A + B = 53.1301...° + 16.2602...° = 69.3903...°$
$\cos 69.3903...° = 0.352$ (exactly), which checks.

14. $y = 4\cos\theta + 3\sin\theta$
$A = \sqrt{4^2 + 3^2} = 5$

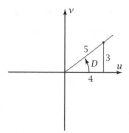

$D = \arctan\dfrac{3}{4} = 36.8698...° + 180°n = 36.8698...°$
$y = 5\cos(\theta - 36.8698...°)$

15. $y = -2 \cos \theta + 5 \sin \theta$

$A = \sqrt{2^2 + 5^2} = \sqrt{29}$

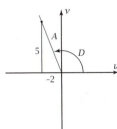

$D = \arctan -\dfrac{5}{2} = -68.1985...° + 180°n = 111.8014...°$

$y = \sqrt{29} \cos(\theta - 111.8014...°)$

16. $y = -3 \cos \theta - 1 \sin \theta$

$A = \sqrt{3^2 + 1^2} = \sqrt{10}$

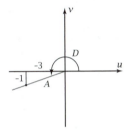

$D = \arctan \dfrac{1}{3} = 18.4349...° + 180°n = 198.4349...°$

$y = \sqrt{10} \cos(\theta - 198.4349...°)$

17. $y = 8 \cos \theta - 15 \sin \theta$

$A = \sqrt{8^2 + 15^2} = 17$

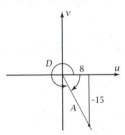

$D = \arctan -\dfrac{15}{8} = -61.9275...° + 180°n$

$\quad = -61.9275...°$ or $298.0724...°$

$y = 17 \cos(\theta + 61.9275...°)$ or

$y = 17 \cos(\theta - 298.0724...°)$

18. $y = 7 \cos(\theta - 20°)$

$y = 7(\cos \theta \cos 20° + \sin \theta \sin 20°)$

$y = (7 \cos 20°) \cos \theta + (7 \sin 20°) \sin \theta$

$y = 6.5778... \cos \theta + 2.3941... \sin \theta$

19. $8 \cos \theta - 15 \sin \theta = 10$

From Problem 17,

$17 \cos(\theta + 61.9275...°) = 10$

$\cos(\theta + 61.9275...°) = \dfrac{10}{17}$

$\theta + 61.9275...° = \arccos \dfrac{10}{17}$

$\theta + 61.9275...° = \pm 53.9681...° + 360°n$

$\theta = -7.9593...° + 360°n$ or $-115.8956...° + 360°n$

$S = \{352.0406...°, -115.8956...°\}$

20. Answers will vary.

Test 13 Form B

1. $\cos A \cos B + \sin A \sin B = \cos(A - B)$

$\cos A \cos B - \sin A \sin B = \cos(A + B)$

$\sin A \cos B - \cos A \sin B = \sin(A - B)$

$\sin A \cos B + \cos A \sin B = \sin(A + B)$

2. "cos (first − second)

$= \cos$ (first) cos (second) + sin (first) sin (second)"

3. $\cos 90° = 0$

$\sin 90° = 1$

$\cos 0° = 1$

$\sin 0° = 0$

4. $\cos(90° - B) = \sin B$

$\sin(90° - B) = \cos B$

5. Proof:

$\cos(90° - B)$

$= \cos 90° \cos B + \sin 90° \sin B$

$= 0 \cdot \cos B + 1 \cdot \sin B$

$= \sin B$

$\therefore \cos(90° - B) = \sin B$, Q.E.D.

6. Proof:

$\cos(-B)$

$= \cos(0° - B)$

$= \cos 0° \cos B + \sin 0° \sin B$

$= 1 \cdot \cos B + 0 \cdot \sin B$

$= \cos B$

$\therefore \cos(-B) = \cos B$, Q.E.D.

7. $\sin(-B) = -\sin B$

8. $y = \sin(x - 1.3)$

$y = \sin x \cos 1.3 - \cos x \sin 1.3$

$y \approx 0.27 \sin x - 0.96 \cos x$

9. $\cos(37° + 21°) = \cos 58° = 0.5299...$

$\cos 37° \cos 21° - \sin 37° \sin 21° = 0.5299...$, which checks.

10. $\cos(A - B) = \cos A \cos B + \sin A \sin B$

$= (0.6)(0.96) + (0.8)(0.28) = 0.8$

11. $\cos^{-1} 0.6 = 53.1301...°$ and $\sin^{-1} 0.8 = 53.1301...°$

12. $\cos^{-1} 0.96 = 16.2602...°$ and $\sin^{-1} 0.28 = 16.2602...°$

13. $A - B = 53.1301...° - 16.2602...° = 36.8698...°$

$\cos 36.8698...° = 0.8$ (exactly), which checks.

14. $y = -4 \cos \theta + 3 \sin \theta$

$A = \sqrt{(-4)^2 + 3^2} = 5;$

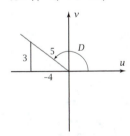

$D = \arctan\left(-\dfrac{3}{4}\right) = -36.8698...° + 180°n = 143.1301...°$

$y = 5 \cos(\theta - 143.1301...°)$

15. $y = 2 \cos \theta - 5 \sin \theta$
$\sqrt{2^2 + (-5^2)} = \sqrt{29}$

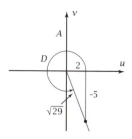

$D = \arctan -\dfrac{5}{2} = -68.1985...° + 180°n = 291.8014...°$

$y = \sqrt{29} \cos(\theta - 291.8014...°)$

16. $y = 3 \cos \theta + 1 \sin \theta$
$A = \sqrt{3^2 + 1^2} = \sqrt{10}$

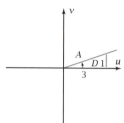

$D = \arctan \dfrac{1}{3} = 18.4349...° + 180°n = 18.4349...°$

$3 \cos \theta + 1 \sin \theta = \sqrt{10} \cos(\theta - 18.4349...°)$

17. $y = -8 \cos \theta - 15 \sin \theta$
$A = \sqrt{8^2 + 15^2} = 17$

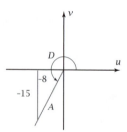

$D = \arctan (-15/-8) = 61.9275...° + 180°n$
$\quad = 241.9275...°$
$y = 17 \cos (\theta - 241.9275...°)$

18. $y = 9 \cos (\theta - 40°)$
$y = 9(\cos \theta \cos 40° + \sin \theta \sin 40°)$
$y = 6.8943... \cos \theta + 5.7850... \sin \theta$

19. From Problem 17,
$17 \cos (\theta - 241.9275...°) = 4$
$\cos (\theta - 241.9275...°) = 4/17$
$\theta - 241.9275...° = \arccos (4/17)$
$\theta - 241.9275...° = \pm 76.3910...° + 360°n$
$\theta = 165.5364...° + 360°n$ or $318.3185...° + 360°n$
$S = \{165.5364...°, 318.3185...°\}$

20. Answers will vary.

Test 14 Form A

1.

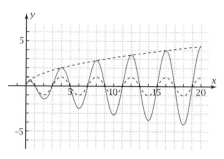

2.

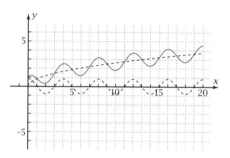

3. Composition of ordinates

4. Harmonic analysis

5. Addition

6. Multiplication

7. Cosine (The composed graph changes sign at $x = 0$ as $\sin x$ changes sign, showing that the other graph does not change sign at $x = 0$.)

8. Sine (The composed graph does not change sign at $x = 0$ even though $\sin x$ does change sign, showing that the second graph must also have changed sign at $x = 0$.)

9. Equation: $y = 3 \sin \theta + 2 \sin 9\theta$ (Grapher checks.)

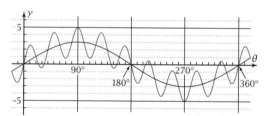

10. Equation: $y = 4 \sin 6\theta \cos 48\theta$ (Grapher checks.)

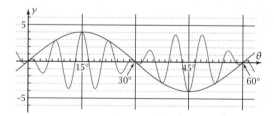

11. Amplitude = 4, period = 60°, horizontal dilation = $\dfrac{1}{6}$

12. Equation: $y = 6 \cos x \sin 10x$ (Grapher checks.)

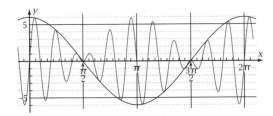

13. Equation: $y = 2 \cos \dfrac{\pi}{3} x + 3 \cos 4\pi x$ (Grapher checks.)

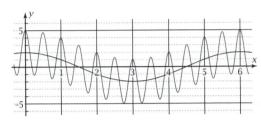

14. Amplitude = 2, period = 6, horizontal dilation = $\dfrac{3}{\pi}$

15. Equation: $y = 3 \cos 120\pi x + \cos 800\pi x$ (Grapher checks.)

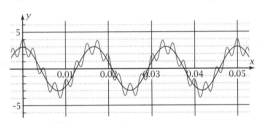

16. Longer: period = $\dfrac{2\pi}{120\pi} = 0.0166\ldots$ s

    Shorter: period = $\dfrac{2\pi}{800\pi} = 0.0025$ s

17. Shorter period: frequency = $\dfrac{1}{0.0166\ldots} = 60$ cycles/s

    Longer period: frequency = $\dfrac{1}{0.0025} = 400$ cycles/s

18. Yes, the sound could be coming from a U.S. submarine.

19. Graph, showing $y_1 = \cos 6\theta + \cos 4\theta$ and $y_2 = 2 \cos 5\theta \cos \theta$. The graphs coincide.

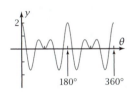

20. Proof:
    $\cos 6\theta + \cos 4\theta = \cos(5\theta + \theta) + \cos(5\theta - \theta)$
    $\qquad = \cos 5\theta \cos \theta - \sin 5\theta \sin \theta + \cos 5\theta \cos \theta$
    $\qquad\quad + \sin 5\theta \sin \theta$
    $\qquad = 2 \cos 5\theta \cos \theta$
    $\therefore \cos 6\theta + \cos 4\theta = 2 \cos 5\theta \cos \theta$, Q.E.D.

21. Answers will vary.

Test 14 Form B

1.

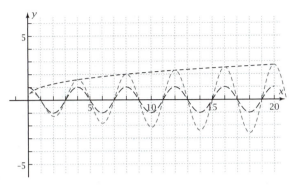

2.

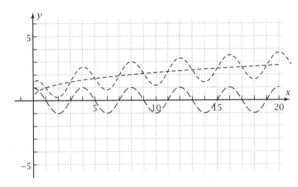

3. Composition of ordinates

4. Harmonic analysis

5. Addition

6. Multiplication

7. Sine (The composed graph changes sign at $x = 0$ even though $\cos x$ does not change sign, showing that the other graph must have changed sign at $x = 0$.)

8. Sine (The composed graph does not change sign at $x = 0$ even though $\sin x$ does change sign, showing that the second graph must also have changed sign at $x = 0$.)

9. Equation: $y = 3 \sin \theta + \cos 4\theta$ (Grapher checks.)

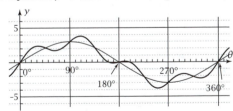

10. Equation: $y = 3 \sin 12\theta \cos 36\theta$ (Grapher checks.)

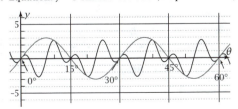

11. Amplitude = 3, period = 30°, horizontal dilation = $\frac{1}{12}$

12. Equation: $y = 3 \cos x \cos 5x$ (Grapher checks.)

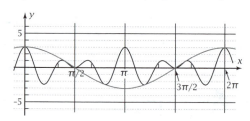

13. Equation: $y = 3 \cos\left(\frac{\pi}{2}x\right) + 2 \cos(2\pi x)$ (Grapher checks.)

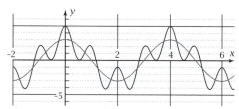

14. Amplitude = 3, period = 4, horizontal dilation = $\frac{2}{\pi}$

15. Equation: $y = 2 \cos(120\pi x) + 3 \cos(800\pi x)$ (Grapher checks.)

16. Longer: period = $\frac{2\pi}{120\pi} = 0.0166...$ s

   Shorter: period = $\frac{2\pi}{800\pi} = 0.0025$ s

17. Shorter period: frequency = $\frac{1}{0.0166...} = 60$ cycles/s

   Longer period: frequency = $\frac{1}{0.0025} = 400$ cycles/s

18. Yes, the sound could be coming from a U.S. submarine.

19. Graph, showing $y_1 = \cos 5\theta + \cos 3\theta$ and $y_2 = 2 \cos 4\theta \cos \theta$. The graphs coincide.

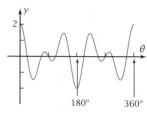

20. Proof:
   $\cos 5\theta + \cos 3\theta$
   $= \cos(4\theta + \theta) + \cos(4\theta - \theta)$
   $= \cos 4\theta \cos \theta - \sin 4\theta \sin \theta + \cos 4\theta \cos \theta + \sin 4\theta \sin \theta$
   $= 2 \cos 4\theta \cos \theta$
   $\therefore \cos 5\theta + \cos 3\theta = 2 \cos 4\theta \cos \theta$, Q.E.D.

21. Answers will vary.

Test 15 Form A

1. $\cos(x - y) = \cos x \cos y + \sin x \sin y$

2. $\sin 2A = 2 \sin A \cos A$

3. $\cos 2A = \cos^2 A - \sin^2 A$
   $\cos 2A = 2 \cos^2 A - 1$
   $\cos 2A = 1 - 2 \sin^2 A$

4. Although 400° terminates in Quadrant I, half of 400° terminates in Quadrant III, where sine is negative. So the negative sign must be used.

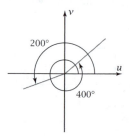

5.

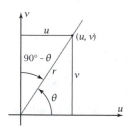

6. Draw two right triangles as shown. For the triangle containing θ, $\cos \theta = \frac{u}{r}$. For the triangle containing $(90° - \theta)$, $\sin(90° - \theta) = \frac{u}{r}$ also. Therefore, $\cos \theta = \sin(90° - \theta)$.

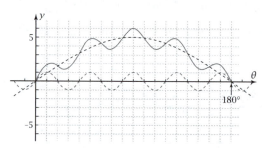

7. Draw right triangles. For the triangle containing A, $\sin A = \frac{v}{r}$. For the one containing $-A$, $\sin(-A) = -\frac{v}{r}$. So $\sin(-A) = -\sin A$.

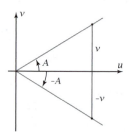

8. $\cos(70° - 23°) = \cos 47° = 0.6819...$
   $\cos 70° - \cos 23° = -0.5784... \neq 0.6819...$

9. $\cos(70° - 23°) = \cos 47° = 0.6819...$
   $\cos 70° \cos 23° + \sin 70° \sin 23° = 0.6819...$, which checks.

Precalculus with Trigonometry: Assessment Resources
© 2007 Key Curriculum Press

10. $y = 7 \cos(\theta - 30°)$
$y = 7(\cos\theta \cos 30° + \sin\theta \sin 30°)$
$y = 6.0621... \cos\theta + 3.5 \sin\theta$

11. $y = -15\cos\theta + 8\sin\theta$
$D = \arctan\left(-\dfrac{8}{15}\right) = -28.0724...° + 180° = 151.9275...°$
$y = 17\cos(\theta - 151.9275...)$

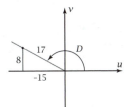

12. Proof:
$\sin(90° - \theta) = \sin 90° \cos\theta - \cos 90° \sin\theta$
$= 1 \cdot \cos\theta - 0 \cdot \sin\theta = \cos\theta$
$\therefore \cos\theta = \sin(90° - \theta)$, Q.E.D.

13. $\sin(A + B) = \sin A \cos B + \cos A \sin B = \dfrac{3}{5} \cdot \dfrac{8}{17} + \dfrac{4}{5} \cdot \dfrac{15}{17} = \dfrac{84}{85}$

14. $A + B = \sin^{-1}\dfrac{3}{5} + \sin^{-1}\dfrac{15}{17} = 98.7974...°$
$\sin 98.7974...° = 0.9882... = \dfrac{84}{85}$ (Checks.)

15. Equation: $y = 4\cos\theta \sin 11\theta$ (Grapher checks.)
The graph shows the envelope curve.

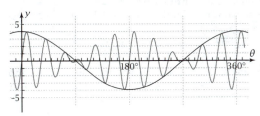

16. Harmonic analysis

17. $\cos(A + B) = \cos A \cos B - \sin A \sin B$
$\underline{\cos(A - B) = \cos A \cos B + \sin A \sin B}$
$\cos(A + B) + \cos(A - B) = 2\cos A \cos B$, Q.E.D.

18. $y = 2\cos 32x \cos x$
$= \cos(32x + x) + \cos(32x - x)$
$= \cos 33x + \cos 31x,$
which have almost equal periods.

19. $\cos 75° - \cos 71° = \cos(73° + 2°) - \cos(73° - 2°)$
$= -2 \sin 73° \sin 2°$
Check: $\cos 75° - \cos 71° = -0.0667...$
$-2 \sin 73° \sin 2° = -0.0667...$, which checks.

20. $\cos 60° = \cos 2(30°)$
$= 1 - 2\sin^2 30°$
Check: $\cos 60° = 0.5$
$1 - 2\sin^2 30° = 1 - 2(0.5)^2 = 0.5$, which checks.

21. $\cos 400° = 1 - 2\sin^2 200°$
$2\sin^2 200° = 1 - \cos 400°$
$\sin 200° = \pm\sqrt{0.5(1 - \cos 400°)}$
Use the negative square root because 200° terminates in Quadrant III.
Check: $\sin 200° = -0.3420...$
$-\sqrt{0.5(1 - \cos 400°)} = -0.3420...$, which checks.

22. Answers will vary.

Test 15 Form B

1. $\cos(x + y) = \cos x \cos y - \sin x \sin y$

2. $\sin 2A = 2 \sin A \cos A$

3. $\cos 2A = \cos^2 A - \sin^2 A$
$\cos 2A = 2\cos^2 A - 1$
$\cos 2A = 1 - 2\sin^2 A$

4. Although 200° terminates in Quadrant III, half of 200° terminates in Quadrant II, where sine is positive. So the positive sign must be used.

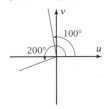

5.

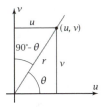

6. Draw two right triangles as shown. For the triangle containing θ, $\sin\theta = \frac{v}{r}$. For the triangle containing $(90° - \theta)$, $\cos(90° - \theta) = \frac{v}{r}$ also. Therefore, $\sin\theta = \cos(90° - \theta)$.

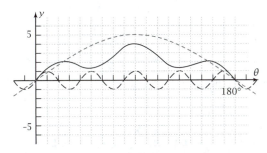

7. Draw right triangles. For the triangle containing A, $\cos A = \frac{u}{1}$. For the one containing $-A$, $\cos(-A) = \frac{u}{1}$. So $\cos(-A) = \cos A$.

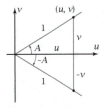

8. $\cos(50° - 17°) = \cos 33° = 0.8386...$
$\cos 50° - \cos 17° = 0.6427... -0.9563... = -0.3135... \neq 0.8386...$

9. $\cos(50° - 17°) = \cos 33° = 0.8386...$
$\cos 50° \cos 17° + \sin 50° \sin 17° = 0.8386...$, which checks.

10. $y = 4\cos(\theta - 60°)$
$y = 4(\cos\theta \cos 60° + \sin\theta \sin 60°)$
$y = 2\cos\theta + 3.4641... \sin\theta$

11. $y = -7 \cos \theta + 2 \sin \theta$

$D = \arctan\left(\dfrac{2}{-7}\right) = -15.9453...° + 180° = 164.0546...°$

$y = \sqrt{53} \cos(\theta - 164.0546...)$

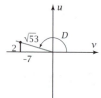

12. Proof:

$\cos(90° - \theta) = \cos 90° \cos \theta + \sin 90° \sin \theta$
$\qquad\qquad = 0 \cdot \cos \theta + 1 \cdot \sin \theta$
$\qquad\qquad = \sin \theta$
$\therefore \sin \theta = \cos(90° - \theta)$, Q.E.D.

13. $\cos(A + B) = \cos A \cos B - \sin A \sin B$

$= \dfrac{4}{5} \cdot \dfrac{8}{17} - \dfrac{3}{5} \cdot \dfrac{15}{17} = -\dfrac{13}{85}$

14. $A + B = \cos^{-1} \dfrac{4}{5} + \cos^{-1} \dfrac{8}{17} = 98.7974...°$

$\cos 98.7974...° = -0.1529... = -\dfrac{13}{85}$ (Checks.)

15. Equation: $y = 3 \cos \theta \sin 9\theta$ (Grapher checks.)

The graph shows the envelope curve.

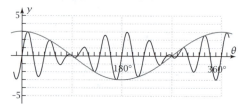

16. Harmonic analysis

17. $\cos(A + B) = \cos A \cos B - \sin A \sin B$
$\dfrac{\cos(A - B) = \cos A \cos B + \sin A \sin B}{\cos(A + B) + \cos(A - B) = 2 \cos A \cos B}$, Q.E.D.

18. $y = 2 \cos 19x \cos x$
$\quad = \cos(19x + x) + \cos(19x - x)$
$\quad = \cos 20x + \cos 18x$,
which have almost equal periods.

19. $\cos 65° - \cos 61°$
$\quad = \cos(63° + 2°) - \cos(63° - 2°)$
$\quad = -2 \sin 63° \sin 2°$
Check:
$\cos 65° - \cos 61° = -0.0621...$
$-2 \sin 63° \sin 2° = -0.0621...$, which checks.

20. $\cos 120° = \cos 2(60°)$
$\qquad\qquad = 1 - 2 \sin^2 60°$
Check: $\cos 120° = -0.5$
$1 - 2 \sin^2 60° = 1 - 2(0.75) = -0.5$, which checks.

21. $\cos 200° = 1 - 2 \sin^2 100°$
$2 \sin^2 100° = 1 - \cos 200°$
$\sin 100° = \pm\sqrt{\dfrac{1 - \cos 200°}{2}}$

Use the positive square root because 100° terminates in Quadrant II.
Check: $\sin 100° = 0.9848...$
$\sqrt{\dfrac{1 - \cos 200°}{2}} = 0.9848$, which checks.

22. Answers will vary.

Test 16 Form A

1.

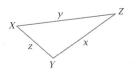

2. $x^2 = y^2 + z^2 - 2yz \cos X$

3. $\dfrac{x}{\sin X} = \dfrac{y}{\sin Y} = \dfrac{z}{\sin Z}$ (or the reciprocal)

4. Area $= \dfrac{1}{2} yz \sin X$

5. $s = \dfrac{1}{2}(x + y + z)$

6. Area $= \sqrt{s(s - x)(s - y)(s - z)}$

7.

8. C is the largest angle because it is opposite the longest side.

9. $7^2 = 3^2 + 5^2 - 2(3)(5) \cos C$

$\cos C = \dfrac{9 + 25 - 49}{30} = \dfrac{-15}{30}$

C is obtuse because its cosine is negative.
(Allow extra credit for the answer $C = 120°$.)

10. Area $= \dfrac{1}{2}(4)(6)(0.2) = 2.4$ square units

11. You can't tell if F is obtuse or acute because there are two values of $\arcsin 0.2$, one acute and one obtuse, that could be angles of the triangle.

12.

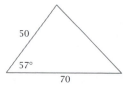

13. $x^2 = 50^2 + 70^2 - 2(50)(70) \cos 57° = 3587.5267...$
$x = 59.8959... \approx 59.9$ ft

14. Area $= \dfrac{1}{2}(50)(70) \sin 57° = 1467.6734... \approx 1467.7$ ft^2

15. Maximum length is the length, x, of the side of the given triangle opposite the 41° angle. Angle opposite the 20-ft side is $180 - (41 + 23) = 116°$.

$\dfrac{x}{\sin 41°} = \dfrac{20}{\sin 116°}$

$x = \dfrac{20 \sin 41°}{\sin 116°} = 14.5986... \approx 14.59$ ft (round down)

16. Let A = measure of angle opposite the 500-ft side.
$500^2 = 250^2 + 300^2 - 2(250)(300) \cos A$

$\cos A = \dfrac{250^2 + 300^2 - 500^2}{2(250)(300)} = -0.65$

$A = \cos^{-1}(-0.65) = 130.5416...°$ (Store this answer.)

17. Area $= \dfrac{1}{2}(250)(300)\sin 130.5416...°$

$= 28{,}497.5327...\ \text{ft}^2$

18. $s = \dfrac{1}{2}(250 + 300 + 500) = 525$

Area $= \sqrt{525(275)(225)(25)} = \sqrt{812{,}109{,}375}$

$= 28{,}497.5327...\ \text{ft}^2$, the same as in Problem 17.

19. Let A be the measure of the largest angle.

$\cos A = \dfrac{3^2 + 4^2 - 8^2}{2(3)(4)} = \dfrac{-39}{24} = -1.625,$

which is out of the range of cosine. Therefore, there is no such triangle.

20. For $A = 1°$, Area $= \dfrac{1}{2}(50)(60)\sin 1° = 26.1786....$

For $A = 2°$, Area $= \dfrac{1}{2}(50)(60)\sin 2° = 52.3492....$

$2(26.1786...) = 52.3572...$, so the area of the $2°$ triangle is almost twice the area of the $1°$ triangle.

21. For $A = 80°$, Area $= \dfrac{1}{2}(50)(60)\sin 80° = 1477.2116....$

For $A = 160°$, Area $= \dfrac{1}{2}(50)(60)\sin 160° = 513.0302...$, which is definitely not twice $1477.2116....$

22. The area varies sinusoidally with the angle.

23. Area $= \dfrac{1}{2}(50)(60)\sin A = 150$

$\sin A = 0.1$

$A = \arcsin 0.1 = 5.7391...° + 360°n$ or $174.2608...° + 360°n$

So A could be $5.7391...°$ or $174.2608...°.$

24. Answers will vary.

Test 16 Form B

1.

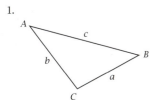

2. $b^2 = a^2 + c^2 - 2bc \cos A$

3. $\dfrac{\sin A}{a} = \dfrac{\sin B}{b} = \dfrac{\sin C}{c}$ (or the reciprocal)

4. Area $= \dfrac{1}{2}bc \sin A$

5. $s = \dfrac{1}{2}(a + b + c)$

6. Area $= \sqrt{s(s - a)(s - b)(s - c)}$

7.

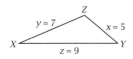

8. Z is the largest angle because it is opposite the longest side.

9. $9^2 = 5^2 + 7^2 - 2(5)(7)\cos Z$

$\cos Z = \dfrac{81 - 25 - 49}{-70} = -\dfrac{1}{10}$

Z is obtuse because its cosine is negative.

10. Area $= \dfrac{1}{2}(3)(4)(0.4) = 3$ square units

11. You can't tell if F is obtuse or acute because there are two values of arcsin 0.4, one acute and one obtuse, that could be angles of the triangle.

12.

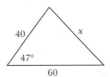

13. $x^2 = 40^2 + 60^2 - 2(40)(60)\cos 47° = 1926.4078...$

$x = 43.8908... \approx 43.9$ ft

14. Area $= \dfrac{1}{2}(40)(60)\sin 47° = 847.6422... \approx 847.6\ \text{ft}^2$

15. Maximum length is the length, x, of the side of the given triangle opposite the 42° angle.

Angle opposite the 23-ft side is $180 - (42 + 23) = 115°.$

$\dfrac{x}{\sin 42°} = \dfrac{23}{\sin 115°}$

$x = \dfrac{23 \sin 42°}{\sin 115°} = 16.9089... \approx 16.90$ ft (round down)

16. Let $A =$ measure of angle opposite the 1000-ft side.

$1000^2 = 500^2 + 600^2 - 2(500)(600)\cos A$

$\cos A = \dfrac{1000^2 - 500^2 - 600^2}{-600{,}000}$

$\cos A = -0.65$

$A = \cos^{-1}(-0.65) = 130.5416...°$ (Store this answer.)

17. Area $= \dfrac{1}{2}(500)(600)\sin 130.5416...°$

$= 113{,}990.1312...\ \text{ft}^2$

18. $s = \dfrac{1}{2}(500 + 600 + 1000) = 1050$

Area $= \sqrt{1050(550)(450)(50)}$

$= 113{,}990.1312...\ \text{ft}^2$, the same as in Problem 17.

19. Let A be the measure of the largest angle.

$\cos A = \dfrac{11^2 - 7^2 - 3^2}{-2(7)(3)} = -1.5$

which is out of the range of cosine. Therefore, there is no such triangle.

20. For $A = 1°$, Area $= \dfrac{1}{2}(45)(55)\sin 1° = 21.5973....$

For $A = 2°$, Area $= \dfrac{1}{2}(45)(55)\sin 2° = 43.1881....$

$2(21.5973...) = 43.1947...$, so the area of the $2°$ triangle is almost twice the area of the $1°$ triangle.

21. For $A = 80°$, Area $= \dfrac{1}{2}(45)(55)\sin 80° = 1218.6995....$

For $A = 160°$, Area $= \dfrac{1}{2}(45)(55)\sin 160° = 423.2499...,$

which is definitely not twice $1218.6995....$

22. The area varies sinusoidally with the angle.

23. Area $= \dfrac{1}{2}(45)(55)\sin A = 160$

$\sin A = 0.1292$

$A = \arcsin 0.1292 = 7.4287... + 360°n$ or

$172.5712... + 360°n$

So A could be $7.4287...$ or $172.5712....$

24. Answers will vary.

Test 17 Form A

1. $\dfrac{f}{\sin F} = \dfrac{g}{\sin G}$ or $\dfrac{\sin F}{f} = \dfrac{\sin G}{g}$

2. $g^2 = f^2 + h^2 - 2fh \cos G$

3. Area $= \dfrac{1}{2} fh \sin G$

4. The law of cosines involves all three sides. Only one side is given in this triangle, leaving two unknowns in the equation.

5. The law of sines requires an angle and an opposite side. The side opposite the 115° angle is not given.

6. The 11-cm side is longer than the sum of the other two sides.

7. The second triangle is shaded.

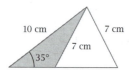

8. The two given vectors are head-to-tail and the sum goes from the beginning of one to the end of the other.

9. $-7\vec{i} + 4\vec{j}$

10. Third side ≈ 2.3 cm

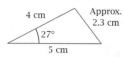

11. Let x = no. of cm for third side.
$x^2 = 5^2 + 4^2 - 2(5)(4) \cos 27° = 5.3597...$
$x = 2.3151... \approx 2.3$ cm, which checks.

12. $A = 180° - (20° + 130°) = 30°$

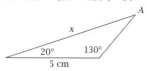

13. Let x = no. of cm longest side.
$\dfrac{x}{\sin 130°} = \dfrac{5}{\sin 30°}$
$x = \dfrac{5 \sin 130°}{\sin 30°} = 7.6604... \approx 7.66$ cm

14.

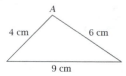

$9^2 = 4^2 + 6^2 - 2(4)(6) \cos A$
$\cos A = \dfrac{4^2 + 6^2 - 9^2}{2(4)(6)} = \dfrac{-29}{48}$
$A = 127.1688...°$ (Store as A.)

15. Area $= \dfrac{1}{2}(4)(6) \sin 127.1688...° = 9.5622... \approx 9.56$ cm^2

16. $S = \dfrac{1}{2}(4 + 6 + 9) = 9.5$
Area $= \sqrt{9.5(5.5)(3.5)(0.5)} = \sqrt{91.4375}$
$= 9.5622...$, which agrees with Problem 15.

17. The two vectors are head-to-tail, with the resultant from the beginning of the plane's velocity to the end of the wind velocity.

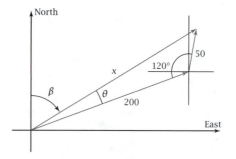

$x^2 = 200^2 + 50^2 - 2(200)(50) \cos 120° = 52,500$
$x = 229.1287...$ (Store as X.)
$50^2 = 200^2 + X^2 - 2(200)X \cos \theta$
$\cos \theta = \dfrac{200^2 + X^2 - 50^2}{2(200)X} = 0.9819...$
$\theta = 10.8933...°$
Bearing, $\beta = 70° - 10.8933...° = 59.1066...°$
Velocity ≈ 229 mi/hr on a bearing of 59°.

18.

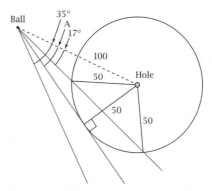

$50^2 = x^2 + 100^2 - 2(x)(100) \cos 17°$
$x^2 - (200 \cos 17°)x + 7500 = 0$
$x = 136.1913...$ or $55.0695...$
About 136.2 yd or 55.1 yd

19. See the graph in Problem 18, showing 35° angle.
$50^2 = x^2 + 100^2 - 2(x)(100) \cos 35°$
$x^2 - (200 \cos 35°)x + 7500 = 0$
$b^2 - 4ac = -3159.5971...$
No real solutions, which agrees with the graph.

20. $\sin A = \dfrac{50}{100} = 0.5$
$A = 30°$

21. Answers will vary.

Test 17 Form B

1. $\dfrac{a}{\sin A} = \dfrac{b}{\sin B}$ or $\dfrac{\sin A}{a} = \dfrac{\sin B}{b}$

2. $b^2 = a^2 + c^2 - 2ac \cos B$

3. Area $= \dfrac{1}{2}\,ac \sin B$

4. The law of cosines involves all three sides. Only one side is given in this triangle, leaving two unknowns in the equation.

5. The law of sines requires an angle and an opposite side. The side opposite the 120° angle is not given.

6. The 13-cm side is longer than the sum of the other two sides.

7. The second triangle is shaded.

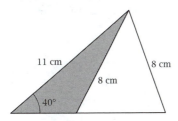

8. The two given vectors are head-to-tail and the sum goes from the beginning of one to the end of the other.

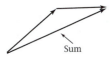

9. $-4\vec{i} + 5\vec{j}$

10. Third side ≈ 8 cm

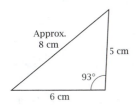

11. Let $x =$ no. of cm for third side.
$x^2 = 5^2 + 6^2 - 2(5)(6) \cos 93° = 64.1401\ldots$
$x = 8.0087\ldots \approx 8.0$ cm, which checks.

12. $A = 180° - (40° + 120°) = 20°$

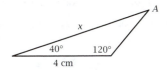

13. Let $x =$ no. of cm longest side.
$$\dfrac{x}{\sin 120°} = \dfrac{4}{\sin 20°}$$
$$x = \dfrac{4 \sin 120°}{\sin 20°} = 10.1283\ldots \text{ cm}$$

14.

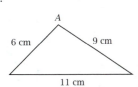

$11^2 = 6^2 + 9^2 - 2(6)(9) \cos A$
$\cos A = \dfrac{11^2 - 6^2 - 9^2}{-2(6)(9)} = -\dfrac{1}{27}$
$A = 92.1225\ldots°$ (Store as A.)

15. Area $= \dfrac{1}{2}\,(6)(9) \sin 91.114\ldots° = 26.9814\ldots \approx 26.98$ cm^2

16. $s = \dfrac{1}{2}\,(6 + 9 + 11) = 13$
Area $= \sqrt{13(7)(4)(2)}$
$\qquad = 26.9814\ldots$, which agrees with Problem 15.

17. The two vectors are head-to-tail, with the resultant from the beginning of the plane's velocity to the end of the wind velocity.

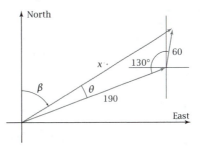

$x^2 = 190^2 + 60^2 - 2(190)(60) \cos 130° = 54355.5575$
$x = 233.1427\ldots$ (Store as X.)
$60^2 = 190^2 + X^2 - 2(190)X \cos \theta$
$\cos \theta = \dfrac{60^2 - 190^2 - X^2}{-2(190)X} = 0.9802\ldots$
$\theta = 11.3699\ldots°$
Bearing, $\beta = 65° - 11.3699\ldots° = 53.6300\ldots°$
Velocity ≈ 233 mi/h on a bearing of 54°.

18.

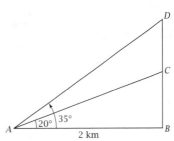

$CD = BD - BC = 2 \tan 33° - 2 \tan 20° = 0.5708\ldots$ km

19. $\dfrac{0.5708\ldots \text{ km}}{4 \text{ s}} = 0.1427\ldots$ km/s

20. $BD = 2 \tan 35°$

15 s $\cdot$ 0.1427... km/s $+ BD = 3.5411\ldots$ km

$\tan^{-1}\dfrac{3.5411\ldots}{2} = 60.5430\ldots°$

21. Answers will vary.

Test 18 Form A

1. Verbally: Horizontal dilation by a factor of 2.
   Equation: $g(x) = f(0.5x)$

2. The reference angle is 30°.

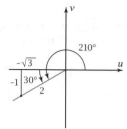

$$\cos 120° = -\frac{\sqrt{3}}{2}$$

3. $y = 5 + 2 \cos 3(\theta - 20°)$

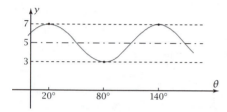

4. $\tan x = \dfrac{-0.6}{0.8} = -0.75$ 5. $\sec x = \dfrac{1}{0.8} = 1.25$

6. $\cos^2 x + \sin^2 x = 1$

7. $\cos(A - B) = \cos A \cos B + \sin A \sin B$

8. Sine is an odd function. $\sin(-A) = -\sin A$

9. $\cos 33° = \sin(90° - 33°) = \sin 57°$

10. $r^2 = s^2 + t^2 - 2st \cos R$

11. $\dfrac{r}{\sin R} = \dfrac{s}{\sin S}$ or $\dfrac{\sin R}{r} = \dfrac{\sin S}{s}$

12.

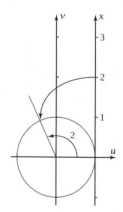

13. $2 \cdot \dfrac{180°}{\pi} = 114.5915...°$

14. $90° \cdot \dfrac{\pi}{180°} = \dfrac{\pi}{2}$ radians

15. Period = $2(11 - 3) = 16$
    Horizontal dilation = $\dfrac{16}{2\pi} = \dfrac{8}{\pi}$
    Equation: $y = 6 + 4 \cos \dfrac{\pi}{8}(x - 11)$ (Others possible.)

16. Amplitude = 4
    Period = 16
    Phase displacement = 11
    Sinusoidal axis location = 6

17. First high tide at 2:00 a.m. (the phase displacement)
    Depth = 7 ft (the upper bound)

18. Period = $2\pi \dfrac{5.7}{\pi} = 11.4$ h

19. Second high tide occurs one period later.
    $x = 2 + 11.4 = 13.4$, or 1:24 p.m.

20.

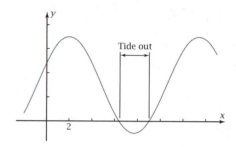

$3 + 4 \cos \dfrac{\pi}{5.7}(x - 2) = 0$

Numerical solution gives $x = 6.3886...$ or $9.0113....$
(Algebraic solution can also be used.) Tide is out between
6:23 and 9:01 a.m.

21. $\arcsin 0.3 = 17.4576...° + 360°n$ or $162.5423...° + 360°n$

22. $\arccos(-0.9) = \pm 2.6905... + 2\pi n$

23. $\arctan 3 = 71.5650...° + 180°n$
    $= 71.5650..., 251.5650...°,$ or $432.5650...°$

24. Sines are never more than 1, so there is no value of $\arcsin 3$.

25. $y = \tan^{-1} x$ (thick) is a reflection of $y = \tan x$ across the
    line $y = x$ (dashed).

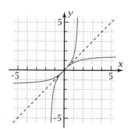

26. $\cot x + \tan x = \dfrac{\cos x}{\sin x} + \dfrac{\sin x}{\cos x}$
    $= \dfrac{\cos^2 x}{\cos x \sin x} + \dfrac{\sin^2 x}{\cos x \sin x}$
    $= \dfrac{\cos^2 x + \sin^2 x}{\cos x \sin x}$
    $= \dfrac{1}{\cos x \sin x}$, Q.E.D.

27. Proof:
$$\cos x(\sec x - \cos x) = \cos x \sec x - \cos^2 x$$
$$= 1 - \cos^2 x$$
$$= \sin^2 x$$
$\therefore \cos x(\sec x - \cos x) = \sin^2 x$, Q.E.D.

28. Proof:
$$\cos(90° - \theta) = \cos 90° \cos \theta + \sin 90° \sin \theta$$
$$= 0 \cdot \cos \theta + 1 \cdot \sin \theta$$
$$= \sin \theta$$
$\therefore \cos(90° - \theta) = \sin \theta$, Q.E.D.

29.

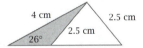

$x^2 = 20^2 + 30^2 - 2(20)(30) \cos 140° = 2219.2533...$
$x = 47.1089... \approx 47.1$ cm

30. Area $= \dfrac{1}{2}(20)(30) \sin 140° = 192.8362... \approx 192.8$ cm^2

31.

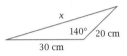

The largest angle, A, is opposite the longest side.
$100^2 = 50^2 + 70^2 - 2(50)(70) \cos A$
$\cos A = \dfrac{50^2 + 70^2 - 100^2}{2(50)(70)} = \dfrac{-2600}{7000}$
$A = \cos^{-1} -\dfrac{26}{70} = 111.8037...° \approx 111.8°$

32. $s = (0.5)(50 + 70 + 100) = 110$
Area $= \sqrt{110(60)(40)(10)} = \sqrt{2,640,000} = 1,624.8076...$
$\approx 1,624.8$ ft^2
(You can check this with the area formula in Problem 30.)

33.

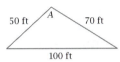

34. Let $x =$ length of third side.
$2.5^2 = x^2 + 4^2 - 2(x)(4) \cos 26°$
$x^2 - (8 \cos 26°)x + 9.75 = 0$
By quadratic formula, $x = 5.3771...$ or $1.8132...$
≈ 5.4 cm or 1.8 cm.

35. The 20-unit vector is translated so that its tail is at the head of the 30-unit vector. The resultant sum goes from the beginning of the first to the end of the second.

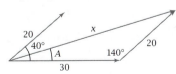

The triangle is congruent to the one in Problem 29.
Therefore, $x = 47.1089...$.
$20^2 = 30^2 + 47.1089...^2 - 2(30)(47.1089...) \cos A$
$\cos A = \dfrac{30^2 + 47.1089...^2 - 20^2}{2(30)(47.1089...)} = 0.9620...$
$A = \cos^{-1} 0.9620... = 15.8365...°$
Vector ≈ 47.1 units at an angle of $15.8°$.

36.

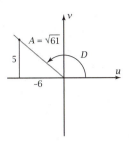

$A = \sqrt{(-6)^2 + 5^2} = \sqrt{61}$
$D = \arctan\left(\dfrac{-5}{6}\right) = -39.8055...° + 180°n = 140.1944...°$
$y = \sqrt{61} \cos(\theta - 140.1944...°)$

37. Only one graph shows up because the two graphs are identical.

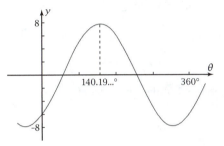

38. $f(g(2)) = f(6)$, and 6 is not in the domain of f. So $f(g(2))$ is undefined.

39.

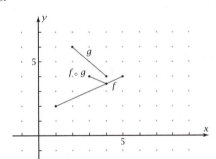

40. Domain: $3 \leq x \leq 4$

41.

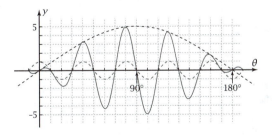

42. Equation: $y = 4 \sin 3\theta \sin 33\theta$

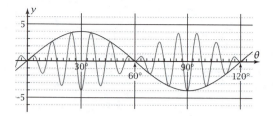

43. Equation: $y = 4 \cos x + 2 \sin 12x$

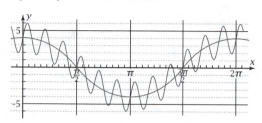

44. Answers will vary.

Test 18 Form B

1. Verbally: Horizontal dilation by a factor of 2.
   Equation: $g(x) = f(0.5x)$

2. The reference angle is 60°.

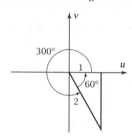

   $\cos 300° = \dfrac{1}{2}$

3. $y = 2 + 3 \cos 2(\theta - 30°)$

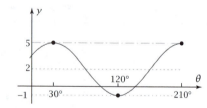

4. $\cot x = \dfrac{0.8}{-0.6} = -\dfrac{4}{3}$

5. $\csc x = \dfrac{1}{-0.6} = -\dfrac{5}{3}$

6. $\cos^2 x + \sin^2 x = 1$

7. $\cos(A + B) = \cos A \cos B - \sin A \sin B$

8. Cosine is an even function. $\cos(-A) = \cos A$

9. $\sin 20° = \cos(90° - 20°) = \cos 70°$

10. $a^2 = b^2 + c^2 - 2bc \cos A$

11. $\dfrac{a}{\sin A} = \dfrac{b}{\sin B}$ or $\dfrac{\sin A}{a} = \dfrac{\sin B}{b}$

12.

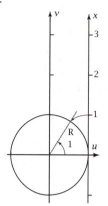

13. $2 \cdot \dfrac{180°}{\pi} = 114.5915...°$

14. $45° \cdot \dfrac{\pi}{180°} = \dfrac{\pi}{4}$

15. Period = $2(10 - 4) = 12$
    Horizontal dilation $= \dfrac{12}{2\pi} = \dfrac{6}{\pi}$
    Equation: $y = 4 + 3 \cos \dfrac{\pi}{6}(x - 10)$ (Others possible.)

16. Amplitude = 3
    Period = 12
    Phase displacement = 10
    Sinusoidal axis location = 4

17. First high tide at 5:00 a.m. (the phase displacement)
    Depth = 5 ft (the upper bound)

18. Period $p = 2\pi \cdot \dfrac{4.8}{\pi} = 9.6$ h

19. Second high tide occurs one period later.
    $x = 5 + 9.6 = 14.6$, or 2:36 p.m.

20.

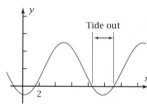

    $y = 2 + 3 \cos\left(\dfrac{\pi}{4.8}(x - 5)\right)$
    Numerical solution gives $x = 8.5149...$ or $11.0850....$
    (Algebraic solution can also be used.)
    Tide is out between 8:31 and 11:05 a.m.

21. $\arccos 0.3 = \pm 72.5423...° + 360°n$

22. $\arcsin -0.9 = -1.1197... + 2\pi n$ or $\pi - (-1.1197...) + 2\pi n$
    $= 4.2613... + 2\pi n$

23. $\arctan 2 = 63.4349...° + 180°n$
    $= 63.4349..., 243.4349...°$, or $423.4349...°$

24. Sines are never more than 1, so there is no value of arcsin 4.

25. $y = \tan^{-1} x$ (thick) is a reflection of $y = \tan x$ across the line $y = x$ (dashed).

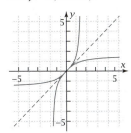

26. $\csc x - \sin x = \dfrac{1}{\sin x} - \dfrac{\sin x}{\sin x} \cdot \sin x$

$= \dfrac{1}{\sin x} - \dfrac{\sin^2 x}{\sin x}$

$= \dfrac{1 - \sin^2 x}{\sin x}$

$= \dfrac{\cos^2 x}{\sin x}$

$= \dfrac{\cos x}{\sin x} \cdot \cos x$

$= \cot x \cos x$, Q.E.D.

27. Proof:
$\sin x(\csc x - \sin x)$
$= \sin x \csc x - \sin^2 x$
$= 1 - \sin^2 x$
$= \cos^2 x$
$\therefore \sin x(\csc x - \sin x) = \cos^2 x$, Q.E.D.

28. Proof:
$\sin (90° - \theta)$
$= \sin 90° \cos \theta - \cos 90° \sin \theta$
$= 1 \cdot \cos \theta - 0 \cdot \sin \theta$
$= \cos \theta$
$\therefore \sin (90° - \theta) = \cos \theta$, Q.E.D.

29.

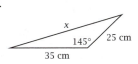

$x^2 = 25^2 + 35^2 - 2(25)(35) \cos 145° = 3283.5160...$
$x = 57.3019... \approx 57.3$ cm

30. Area $= \dfrac{1}{2}(25)(35) \sin 145° = 250.9396...$ cm^2

31.

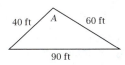

The largest angle, A, is opposite the longest side.
$90^2 = 40^2 + 60^2 - 2(40)(60) \cos A$
$\cos A = \dfrac{40^2 + 60^2 - 90^2}{2(40)(60)} = \dfrac{-2900}{4800}$
$A = \cos^{-1} -\dfrac{29}{48} = 127.1688...° \approx 127.2°$

32. $s = (0.5)(40 + 60 + 90) = 95$
Area $= \sqrt{95(55)(35)(5)} = \sqrt{914,375} = 956.2295...$ ft$^2 \approx 956.2$ ft^2
(You can check this with the area formula in Problem 30.)

33.

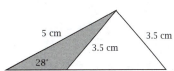

34. Let x = length of third side.
$3.5^2 = x^2 + 5^2 - 2(x)(5) \cos 28°$
$x^2 - (10 \cos 28°)x + 12.75 = 0$
By quadratic formula, $x = 1.8186...$ or $7.0108...$
≈ 1.8 cm or 7.0 cm.

35. The 25-unit vector is translated so that its tail is at the head of the 35-unit vector. The resultant sum goes from the beginning of the first to the end of the second.

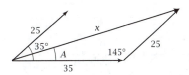

The triangle is congruent to the one in Problem 29.
Therefore, $x = 57.3019...$.
$25^2 = 35^2 + 57.3019...^2 - 2(35)(57.3019...) \cos A$
$\cos A = \dfrac{35^2 + 57.3019...^2 - 25^2}{2(35)(57.3019...)} = 0.96818...$
$A = \cos^{-1} 0.96818... = 14.4918...°$
Vector ≈ 57.3 units at an angle of $14.5°$.

36.

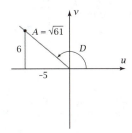

$A = \sqrt{(-5)^2 + 6^2} = \sqrt{61}$
$D = \arctan\left(\dfrac{6}{-5}\right) = -50.1944...° + 180°n = 129.8055...°$
$y = \sqrt{61} \cos (\theta - 129.8055...°)$

37. Only one graph shows up because the two graphs are identical.

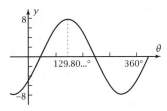

38. $f(g(4)) = f(8)$, and 8 is not in the domain of f. So $f(g(4))$ is undefined.

39.

40. Domain: $2 \le x \le 3$

41.

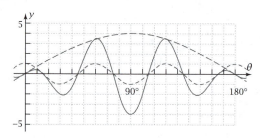

42. Equation: $y = -5 \sin 3\theta \sin 33\theta$

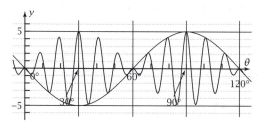

43. Equation: $y = 2 \cos x + 3 \sin 9x$

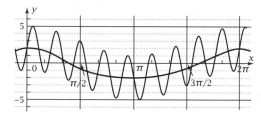

44. Answers will vary.

Test 19 Form A

1. Exponential function
   Increasing
   Concave up

2. Power function
   Increasing
   Concave down

3. Quadratic function
   Decreasing, then increasing
   Concave up

4. Power function
   Decreasing
   Concave up

5. $W = kL^3$

6. Boa weighs $5^3 = 125$ times as much as rattler.

7. Boa has $2 \cdot 5^2 = 50$ ft^2 of skin.

8. Power functions have the multiply-multiply property.

9. Exponential functions have the add-multiply property.

10. Exponential function. Each time 3 is added to x, $f(x)$ is multiplied by $\frac{1}{4}$.

11. $f(15) = \frac{1}{4}f(12) = \frac{1}{4}(25) = 6.25$

12.

t(s)	h(ft)	1st	2nd
2	166		
		> 50	
3	216		> −32
		> 18	
4	234		> −32
		> −14	
5	220		> −32
		> −46	
6	174		

The second differences are constant.

13. $h = at^2 + bt + c$. Use the first three points.
    $4a + 2b + c = 166$
    $9a + 3b + c = 216$
    $16a + 4b + c = 234$

    $$\begin{bmatrix} 4 & 2 & 1 \\ 9 & 3 & 1 \\ 16 & 4 & 1 \end{bmatrix}^{-1} \begin{bmatrix} 166 \\ 216 \\ 234 \end{bmatrix} = \begin{bmatrix} -16 \\ 130 \\ -30 \end{bmatrix}$$

    Equation is $h = -16t^2 + 130t - 30$.

14. Rocket hits the ground when $h = 0$.
    $-16t^2 + 130t - 30 = 0$
    By quadratic formula, $t = 0.2377...$ or $7.8872....$
    The rocket hits at about 7.9 s.
    (The smaller value is out of the domain, $t \ge 2$.)

15. $y = kx^n$
    $5.0 = k(4^n)$
    $7.5 = k(9^n)$
    $\frac{7.5}{5.0} = \frac{k(9^n)}{k(4^n)} = (9/4)^n$
    $\log 1.5 = \log 2.25^n = n \log 2.25$
    $n = \frac{\log 1.5}{\log 2.25} = 0.5$
    $5.0 = k(4^{0.5}) = 2k$
    $k = 2.5$
    Equation is $y = 2.5x^{0.5}$.

16. The equation fits all points exactly.

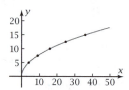

17. $y = 2.5(100^{0.5}) = 25$ gal/min
    Extrapolation

18. $20 = 2.5x^{0.5}$
    $8 = x^{0.5}$
    $x = 64$ psi
    Extrapolation

19. If x increases from 4 to 16, y increases from 5 to 10.
    If x increases from 9 to 36, y increases from 7.5 to 15.

20. Add-multiply pattern. Adding 3 to x multiplies y by $\frac{1}{4}$.
    Exponential function

21. General equation is $f(x) = ab^x$.
    $1600 = ab^3$
    $25 = ab^{12}$
    $\frac{25}{1600} = \frac{ab^{12}}{ab^3} = b^9$
    $b = \left(\frac{25}{1600}\right)^{1/9} = 0.6299...$
    $1600 = a(0.6299...)^3$
    $a = \frac{1600}{0.6299...^3} = 6400$
    Equation is $f(x) = 6400(0.6299...)^x$

22. $f(6) = 6400(0.6299...)^6 = 400$, which agrees with table.

23. y is increasing at a decreasing rate as x increases.

24. Proof:
$y_1 = ax_1^n$
$y_2 = ax_2^n$
$y_2 = a(cx_1)^n$
$y_2 = c^n(ax_1^n)$
$y_2 = c^n y_1 = ky_1$, where $k = c^n$, Q.E.D.

25. Answers will vary.

Test 19 Form B

1. Quadratic function
   Increasing, then decreasing
   Concave down

2. Exponential function
   Increasing
   Concave up

3. Power function
   Decreasing
   Concave up

4. Power function
   Increasing
   Concave down

5. $W = kL^3$

6. Weight is $2700 \left(\dfrac{1}{3}\right)^3 = 100$ lb.

7. Girth is directly proportional to length, so the girth is
   $9 \left(\dfrac{1}{3}\right) = 3$ ft.

8. Power functions have the multiply-multiply property.

9. Exponential functions have the add-multiply property.

10. Exponential function. Each time 4 is added to x, $f(x)$ is multiplied by $\frac{1}{5}$.

11. $f(20) = \dfrac{1}{5}f(16) = \dfrac{1}{5}(16) = 3.2$

12.

t(s)	h(ft)	1st	2nd
1	84		
		> 132	
3	216		> −128
		> 4	
5	220		> −128
		> −124	
7	96		

   The second differences are constant.

13. $h = at^2 + bt + c$. Use the second three points.
    $9a + 3b + c = 216$
    $25a + 5b + c = 220$
    $49a + 7b + c = 96$
    $$\begin{bmatrix} 9 & 3 & 1 \\ 25 & 5 & 1 \\ 49 & 7 & 1 \end{bmatrix}^{-1} \begin{bmatrix} 216 \\ 220 \\ 96 \end{bmatrix} = \begin{bmatrix} -16 \\ 130 \\ -30 \end{bmatrix}$$
    Equation is $h = -16t^2 + 130t - 30$.

14. Rocket hits the ground when $h = 0$.
    $-16t^2 + 130t - 30 = 0$
    By quadratic formula, $t = 0.2377...$ or $7.8872...$.
    The rocket hits at about 7.9 s.
    (The smaller value is out of the domain, $t \geq 1$.)

15. $y = kx^n$
    $1.004 = k(1^n)$
    $k = 1.004$
    $0.709 = 1.004(0.5^n)$
    $\dfrac{0.709}{1.004} = 0.5^n$
    $n = \dfrac{\log\left(\dfrac{0.709}{1.004}\right)}{\log 0.5}$
    $n = 0.50190...$
    $n \approx 0.5$
    $y = 1.004\sqrt{x}$

16. The equation fits all points exactly.

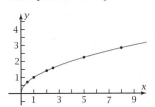

17. $y = 1.004(4^{0.5}) = 2.008$ s
    Interpolation

18. $4 = 1.004x^{0.5}$
    $x = 15.8727...$ m
    Extrapolation

19. If x increases from 0.5 to 1, y increases from 0.709 to 1.004.
    If x increases from 1 to 2, y increases from 1.004 to 1.420.

20. Add-multiply pattern. Adding 4 to x multiplies y by $\frac{1}{5}$.
    Exponential function

21. General equation is $f(x) = ab^x$.
    $2000 = ab^4$
    $16 = ab^{16}$
    $\dfrac{16}{2000} = b^{12}$
    $b = 0.008^{1/12}$
    $b = 0.6687...$
    $a = \dfrac{2000}{0.6687...^4} = 10,000$
    $y = 10,000(0.6687...^x)$

22. $f(8) = 1000(0.66878...)^8 = 400$, which agrees with table.

23. y is increasing at a decreasing rate as x increases.

24. Proof:
    $y_1 = ax_1^n$
    $y_2 = ax_2^n$
    $y_2 = a(cx_1)^n$
    $y_2 = c^n(ax_1^n)$
    $y_2 = c^n y_1 = ky_1$, where $k = c^n$, Q.E.D.

25. Answers will vary.

Test 20 Form A

1. $m^p = y$

2. $\log_9 y = x$

3. $\log_{10} 100 = 2$ because $10^2 = 100$.

4. $\log(xy) = \log x + \log y$

5. $\log \dfrac{x}{y} = \log x - \log y$

6. $\log x^y = y \cdot \log x$

7. $5^x = 13$
   $\ln 5^x = \ln 13$
   $x \cdot \ln 5 = \ln 13$
   $x = \dfrac{\ln 13}{\ln 5}$
   $\therefore \log_5 13 = \dfrac{\ln 13}{\ln 5}$

8. Change-of-base property

9. $\log 8$

10. $\ln 3$

11. $5 \cdot \ln 7$

12. $\log 42$

13. $y = \ln x$ is a reflection of $y = e^x$ across the line $y = x$.

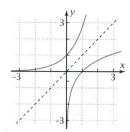

14. As x becomes very large, e^{-x} gets close to zero. So y gets close to $\frac{5}{1+0}$, which equals 5.

15. By the multiply–add pattern of logarithmic functions, multiplying x by 5 adds 4 to y. So when $x = 10 \cdot 5 = 50$, $y = 17 + 4 = 21$. The point is (50, 21).

16. $13 = a + b \ln 2$
    $\underline{17 = a + b \ln 10}$
    $\ \ 4 = b \ln 10 - b \ln 2$
    $\ \ 4 = b(\ln 10 - \ln 2) = b \ln 5$
    $b = \dfrac{4}{\ln 5} = 2.4853...$
    $13 = a + 2.4853... \ln 2$
    $a = 13 - 2.4853... \ln 2 = 11.2772...$
    Equation is $y = 11.2772... + 2.4853... \ln x$.

17. $y = 11.2772... + 2.4853... \ln 50 = 21$, which checks.

18. $e^{-3x} = 0.001$
    $\ln(e^{-3x}) = \ln 0.001$
    $-3x = \ln 0.001$
    $x = \dfrac{\ln 0.001}{-3} = 2.3205...$

19. $\log_6(x - 1) + \log_6(x + 4) = 2$
    $\log_6(x^2 + 3x - 4) = 2$
    $x^2 + 3x - 4 = 6^2$
    $x^2 + 3x - 40 = 0$
    $x = 5$ or $x = -8$
    Checking these solutions, only $x = 5$ works.
    $x = 5$

20. Logistic function

21. $y = \dfrac{1200}{1 + 150e^{-0.5x}}$, showing a horizontal asymptote at $y = 1200$.

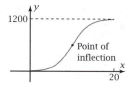

22. See the graph in Problem 21. The point of inflection is at $y = 600$, halfway between the two asymptotes.

23. $x = 0$: $y = \dfrac{1200}{1 + 150e^0} = 7.9470... \approx 8$ students

24. $x = 15$: $y = \dfrac{1200}{1 + 150e^{-7.5}} = 1108.0714... \approx 1108$ students
    The rate is decreasing because the graph is concave down at $x = 15$.

25. 1200 students, the location of the upper asymptote

26. Answers will vary.

Test 20 Form B

1. $a^b = y$

2. $\log_{16} y = x$

3. $\log_8 64 = 2$ because $8^2 = 64$.

4. $\log(xy) = \log x + \log y$

5. $\log \dfrac{x}{y} = \log x - \log y$

6. $\log x^y = y \cdot \log x$

7. $13^x = 5$
   $\ln 13^x = \ln 5$
   $x \cdot \ln 13 = \ln 5$
   $x = \dfrac{\ln 5}{\ln 13}$
   $\therefore \log_{13} 5 = \dfrac{\ln 5}{\ln 13}$

8. Change-of-base property

9. $\log 18$

10. $\ln 4$

11. $7 \cdot \ln 5$

12. $\log 9$

Precalculus with Trigonometry: Assessment Resources
© 2007 Key Curriculum Press

13. $y = e^x$ is a reflection of $y = \ln x$ across the line $y = x$.

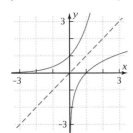

14. As x becomes very large, e^{-x} gets close to zero. So y gets close to $\frac{3}{1+0}$, which equals 3.

15. By the multiply-add pattern of logarithmic functions, multiplying x by 2 adds 4 to y. So when $x = 10 \cdot 2 = 20$, $y = 18 + 4 = 22$. The point is (20, 22).

16. $14 = a + b \ln 5$
$\underline{18 = a + b \ln 10}$
$\ \ 4 = b \ln 10 - b \ln 5$
$\ \ 4 = b(\ln 10 - \ln 5) = b \ln 2$
$b = \dfrac{4}{\ln 2} = 5.7707...$
$14 = a + 5.7707... \ln 5$
$a = 14 - 5.7707... \ln 5 = 4.7122...$
Equation is $y = 4.7122... + 5.7707... \ln x$.

17. $y = 4.7122... + 5.7707... \ln 20 = 22$, which checks.

18. $e^{-3x} = 0.01$
$\ln(e^{-3x}) = \ln 0.01$
$-3x = \ln 0.01$
$x = \dfrac{\ln 0.01}{-3} = 1.5350...$

19. $\log_6(x+1) + \log_6(x-4) = 1$
$\log_6(x^2 - 3x - 4) = 1$
$x^2 - 3x - 4 = 6$
$x^2 - 3x - 10 = 0$
$x = 5$ or $x = -2$
Checking these solutions, only $x = 5$ works.
$x = 5$

20. Logistic function

21. $y = \dfrac{1000}{1 + 100e^{-0.5x}}$, showing a horizontal asymptote at $y = 1000$.

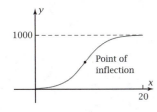

Point of inflection

22. See the graph in Problem 21. The point of inflection is at $y = 500$, halfway between the two asymptotes.

23. $x = 0$: $y = \dfrac{1000}{1 + 100e^0} = 9.9009... \approx 10$ students

24. $x = 15$: $y = \dfrac{1000}{1 + 100e^{-7.5}} = 947.5902 \approx 948$
≈ 948 students
The rate is decreasing because the graph is concave down at $x = 15$.

25. 1000 students, the location of the upper asymptote

26. Answers will vary.

Test 21 Form A

1. • Exponential: $y = ab^x$
   • Power: $y = ax^b$
   • Logarithmic: $y = a + b \ln x$
   • Logistic: $y = \dfrac{c}{1 + ae^{bx}}$

2.

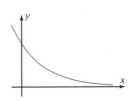

3.

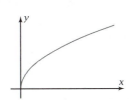

4.

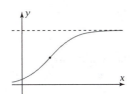

5. The base is 2 because $\log_b 2 = 1$.

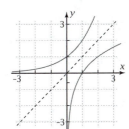

6. $\ln 35$

7. $\log 7$

8. $7 \ln 4$

9. $\log_p j = n$

10. $g(x) = e^{(x-4)} = e^x \cdot e^{-4}$
So $g(x) = ke^x$, where $k = e^{-4}$.

11. • Quadratic: constant-second-differences
    • Power: multiply-multiply
    • Logarithmic: multiply-add

12. The pattern is add-multiply.
$f(11 + 3) = 2 f(11)$
$f(14) = 52$

13. $x = 3$: $y = 9.8\dfrac{1}{3^2} = 1.0888...$ m/s^2

$x = 9$: $y = 1.0888...\dfrac{1}{3^2} = 0.1209...$ m/s^2

14. $y = \dfrac{k}{x^2}$

$9.8 = \dfrac{k}{1^2}$

$k = 9.8$

Equation is $y = \dfrac{9.8}{x^2}$

15. $x = 63$: $y = \dfrac{9.8}{63^2} = 0.002469\ldots$ m/s^2

16.

x	$f(x)$	Diff. 1	Diff. 2
3	36.7	−9.2	2.4
5	27.5	−6.8	2.4
7	20.7	−4.4	2.4
9	16.3	−2.0	
11	14.3		

The second differences are constant, 2.4.

17. $f(x) = ax^2 + bx + c$
$9a + 3b + c = 36.7$
$25a + 5b + c = 27.5$
$49a + 7b + c = 20.7$

$$\begin{bmatrix} 9 & 3 & 1 \\ 25 & 5 & 1 \\ 49 & 7 & 1 \end{bmatrix}^{-1} \begin{bmatrix} 36.7 \\ 27.5 \\ 20.7 \end{bmatrix} = \begin{bmatrix} 0.3 \\ -7 \\ 55 \end{bmatrix}$$

Equation is $f(x) = 0.3x^2 - 7x + 55$.

18. Concave up (because the x^2-coefficient is positive)

19. $0.3x^2 - 7x + 55 = 36.7$
$0.3x^2 - 7x + 18.3 = 0$
By quadratic formula, $x = 3$ or $20.3333\ldots$.
The other value is $20.3333\ldots$.

20. $L(1) = 2$, $L(3) = 7.4930\ldots$, $L(9) = 12.9861\ldots$
The x-values increase by multiplying by 3.
The $L(x)$-values increase by adding $5.4930\ldots$.
Therefore, the values have the multiply-add property.

21. $2 + 5 \ln x = 10$
$5 \ln x = 8$
$\ln x = 1.6$
$x = e^{1.6} = 4.9530\ldots$

22. A logistic function is reasonable because the temperature rises slowly at first, then faster, then levels off at the temperature of the water heater. So the graph is similar in shape to a logistic function graph, meaning that a logistic function is a reasonable model.

23. $c = 70$, the vertical dilation
$2 = \dfrac{70}{1 + ae^0}$ and $15 = \dfrac{70}{1 + ae^{-10b}}$
$2 + 2a = 70$ and $15 + 15ae^{-10b} = 70$
$2a = 68$ and $15ae^{-10b} = 55$
From the first equation, $a = 34$. Substituting 34 for a into the second equation,
$510e^{-10b} = 55$
$-10b = \ln \dfrac{55}{510}$
$b = 0.2227\ldots$
Equation is $T(x) = \dfrac{70}{1 + 34e^{-0.2227\ldots x}}$

24. By solver, $T(x) = 35$ for $x = 15.8340\ldots$.

25. Answers will vary.

Test 21 Form B

1. • Exponential: $y = ab^x$
   • Power: $y = ax^b$
   • Logarithmic: $y = a + b \ln x$
   • Logistic: $y = \dfrac{c}{1 + ae^{bx}}$

2.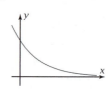

3.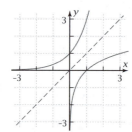

4.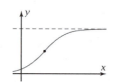

5. The base is 3 because $\log_b 3 = 1$.

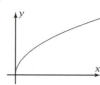

6. $\ln 24$

7. $\log 7$

8. $4 \ln 7$

9. $\log_q r = m$

10. $g(x) = e^{(x-2)} = e^x \cdot e^{-2}$
So $g(x) = ke^x$, where $k = e^{-2}$.

11. • Linear: add-add
    • Power: multiply-multiply
    • Exponential: add-multiply

12. The pattern is add-multiply.
$f(9 + 4) = 0.5f(9)$
$f(13) = 11$

13. $x = 50/2 = 25\%$: $y = 13 + 13 = 26$ ft
$x = 25/2 = 12.5\%$: $y = 26 + 13 = 39$ ft

14. $y = a + b \log x$
$0 = a + b \log 100$
$13 = a + b \log 50$
$a = b \log 50 - b \log 100$
$13 = b \log (0.5)$
$b = \dfrac{13}{\log 0.5} = -43.1850...$
$13 = a - 43.1850... \log 50$
$a = 13 + 43.1850... \log 50 = 86.3701...$
$y = 86.3701... - 43.1850 \log x$

15. $y(1) = 86.3701...$ ft

16.

x	$f(x)$	Diff. 1	Diff. 2
1	25	60	-32
5	85	28	-32
9	113	-4	-32
13	109	-36	
17	73		

The second differences are constant, −32.

17. $f(x) = ax^2 + bx + c$
$a + b + c = 25$
$25a + 5b + c = 85$
$81a + 9b + c = 113$
$$\begin{bmatrix} 1 & 1 & 1 \\ 25 & 5 & 1 \\ 81 & 9 & 1 \end{bmatrix}^{-1} \begin{bmatrix} 25 \\ 85 \\ 113 \end{bmatrix} = \begin{bmatrix} -1 \\ 21 \\ 5 \end{bmatrix}$$
Equation is $f(x) = -x^2 + 21x + 5$.

18. Concave down (because the x^2-coefficient is negative)

19. $-x^2 + 21x + 5 = 25$
$-x^2 + 21x - 20 = 0$
By quadratic formula, $x = 1$ or 20. The other value is 20.

20. $L(1) = 5$, $L(3) = 7.1972...$, $L(9) = 9.3944...$
The x-values increase by multiplying by 3.
The $L(x)$-values increase by adding 2.1972....
Therefore, the values have the multiply–add property.

21. $5 + 2 \ln x = 8$
$2 \ln x = 3$
$\ln x = 1.5$
$x = e^{1.5} = 4.4816...$

22. A logistic function is reasonable because the population rises slowly at first, then faster, then levels off at the maximum population allowed for the island. So the graph is similar in shape to a logistic function graph, meaning that a logistic function is a reasonable model.

23. $c = 460$, the vertical dilation (maximum sustainable population)
$75 = \dfrac{460}{1 + ae^{-6b}}$
$153 = \dfrac{460}{1 + ae^{-12b}}$
$75 + 75ae^{-6b} = 460$
$153 + 153ae^{-12b} = 460$
$75ae^{-6b} = 385$
$153ae^{-12b} = 307$
$\dfrac{75ae^{-6b}}{153ae^{-12b}} = \dfrac{385}{307}$
$e^{6b} = \dfrac{385}{307} \cdot \dfrac{153}{75}$

$b = 0.1565...$
$a = \dfrac{385}{75\, e^{-6(0.1565...)}} = 13.1326...$
$y = \dfrac{460}{1 + 13.1326...e^{-0.1565t}}$

24. By solver, $P(x) = 230$ for $x = 16.4482...$

25. Answers will vary.

Test 22 Form A

1. • Quadratic: $y = ax^2 + bx + c$
   • Power: $y = ax^b$

2. • f: logistic
   • g: logarithmic

3. • Exponential: add–multiply
   • Quadratic: constant-second-differences

4. Exponential function

5. The inverse function (and $y = x$)

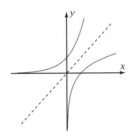

6.

x	y	$\hat{y}$	Resid.	(Resid.)^2
1	16	17.5	−1.5	2.25
3	16	13.5	2.5	6.25
5	9	9.5	−0.5	0.25
7	5	5.5	−0.5	0.25

$SS_{res} = 9.00$

7. For any other linear function, SS_{res} would be greater because SS_{res} for the regression line is the smallest possible.

8.

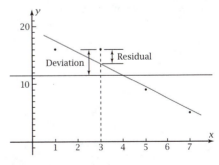

9. $r^2 = \dfrac{89 - 9}{89} = \dfrac{80}{89} = 0.8988...$

10. Use the negative square root because y is decreasing as x increases.

11. *Residual* is the adjective form of *residue*, meaning "what is left over."

12. Add 3 to x and multiply y by 2.

x	y
3	17
6	34
9	68
12	136

13. $y = ab^x$

$17 = ab^3$

$34 = ab^6$

$\dfrac{34}{17} = \dfrac{ab^6}{ab^3}$

$2 = b^3$

$b = 2^{1/3} = 1.2599\ldots$ (Store as B.)

$17 = a \cdot 1.2599\ldots^3$

$a = \dfrac{17}{1.2599\ldots^3} = 8.5$

Equation is $y = 8.5(1.2599\ldots^x)$.

14. $x = 12$:

$y = 8.5(1.2599\ldots^{12}) = 136$, which checks.

15. $x = 4.7$:

$y = 8.5(1.2599\ldots^{4.7}) = 25.1786\ldots$

The calculation involves interpolation because 4.7 is within the interval [3, 6] determined by the two given x-values.

16.

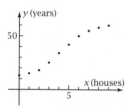

- Pattern: S-shaped, as is a logistic function graph
- Endpoint: The number of houses will level off at the maximum number that can be sustained by the community.

17. Equation is $y = \dfrac{67.5622\ldots}{1 + 5.8229\ldots e^{-0.4482\ldots x}}$

$x = 12$: $y = 65.7941\ldots \approx 66$ houses

18. The limit of y as x approaches infinity is 67.5622…, meaning that there can ultimately be about 68 houses.

19. Table, $\hat{y}$ from regression equation, res $= (y - \hat{y})$ as they would appear in lists on the grapher.

Year	Houses	$\hat{y}$	(Resid.)^2
0	13	9.90…	9.59…
1	15	14.31…	0.46…
2	18	20.01…	4.05…
3	25	26.83…	3.36…
4	34	34.30…	0.09…
5	42	41.72…	0.07…
6	50	48.41…	2.52…
7	55	53.93…	1.13…
8	58	58.17…	0.02…
9	60	61.24…	1.55…
		$SS_{\text{res}} =$	22.8971…

20. By linear regression, equation is $y_1 = 0.29x + 20.78$.

$r = 0.9989\ldots$

21. r close to 1 suggests that the linear function fits well.

22. $SS_{\text{res}} = \sum(y - y_1)^2 = 1.436$

23. The residuals follow a pattern, showing that the linear function leaves out something (specifically, the fact that as the water warms up, more of the input heat is lost to the surroundings rather than being used to warm the water further, as indicated by the slight concave down curvature of the graph in Problem 25).

x	$y - y_1$	x	$y - y_1$
10	−0.58	60	0.42
20	−0.28	70	0.12
30	0.02	80	−0.08
40	0.42	90	−0.18
50	0.62	100	−0.48

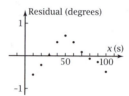

24. By quadratic regression, the equation is

$y_2 = -0.0004924\ldots x^2 + 0.05416\ldots x - 1.0833\ldots$

25. $y_3 = y_1 + y_2$, with original data

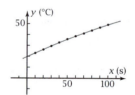

26. $SS_{\text{res}} = \sum(y - y_3)^2 = 0.1556\ldots$

This value of SS_{res} is smaller than the 1.436 for y_1 because the quadratic function takes out some more of the deviations.

27. By quadratic regression on the original data,

$y_4 = -0.0004924\ldots x^2 + 0.3441\ldots x + 19.6966\ldots$

y_4 and y_3 coincide exactly.

28. Answers will vary.

Test 22 Form B

1. • Logarithmic: $y = a + b \log_c x$
   • Exponential: $y = ab^x$

2. • f: logistic
   • g: quadratic

3. • Power: multiply–multiply
   • Exponential: add–multiply

4. Logarithmic function

Precalculus with Trigonometry: Assessment Resources
© 2007 Key Curriculum Press

5. The inverse function (and $y = x$)

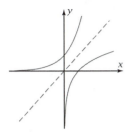

6.

x	y	$\hat{y}$	Resid.	(Resid.)^2
2	8	7.9	0.1	0.01
4	10	11.8	−1.8	3.24
6	19	15.7	3.3	10.89
8	18	19.6	−1.6	2.56

$$SS_{res} = 16.7$$

7. For any other linear function, SS_{res} would be greater because SS_{res} for the regression line is the smallest possible.

8.

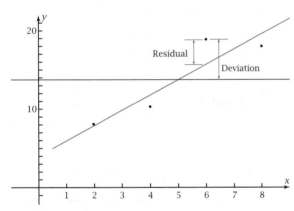

9. $r^2 = \dfrac{92.75 - 16.7}{92.75} = \dfrac{76.05}{92.75} = 0.8199...$

10. Use the positive square root because y is increasing as x increases.

11. *Residual* is the adjective form of *residue*, meaning "what is left over."

12. Add 4 to x and multiply y by 1.5.

x	y
4	12
8	18
12	27

13. $y = ab^x$
$12 = ab^4$
$18 = ab^8$
$\dfrac{18}{12} = \dfrac{ab^8}{ab^4}$
$1.5 = b^4$
$1.1066... = b$ (Store as *B*.)
$a = \dfrac{12}{1.1066...^4} = 8$
$y = 8(1.1066...^x)$

14. $x = 12$:
$y = 8(1.1066...^{12}) = 27$, which checks.

15. $x = 5.2$:
$y = 8(1.1066...^{5.2}) = 13.5521...$
The calculation involves interpolation because 5.2 is within the interval [4, 8] determined by the two given x-values.

16.

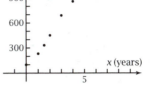

- Pattern: *S*-shaped, as is a logistic function graph
- Endpoint: The number of rabbits will level off at the maximum number that can be sustained by the ecosystem.

17. Equation is $y = \dfrac{1000}{1 + 8.99219...e^{-0.9998...x}}$
$x = 12$: $y = 999.953... \approx 1000$ rabbits

18. The limit of y as x approaches infinity is 1000, meaning that there can ultimately be about 1000 rabbits.

19. Table, $\hat{y}$ from regression equation, res = $(y - \hat{y})$ as they would appear in lists on the grapher.

Year	Rabbits	$\hat{y}$	(Resid.)^2
0	100	100.07...	0.006...
1	232	232.09...	0.008...
2	451	450.97...	0.0004...
3	691	690.63...	0.130...
4	858	858.50...	0.255...
5	943	942.82...	0.030...
6	978	978.17...	0.030...
7	992	991.85...	0.020...
8	997	996.98...	0.0001...
9	999	998.88...	0.012...

$$SS_{res} = 0.494440...$$

20. By linear regression, equation is $y_1 = 0.29x + 17.23$.
$r = 0.9989667...$

21. r close to 1 suggests that the linear function fits well.

22. $SS_{res} = \sum(y - y_1)^2 = 1.436$

23. The residuals follow a pattern, showing that the linear function leaves out something (specifically, the fact that as the water warms up, more of the input heat is lost to the surroundings rather than being used to warm the water further, as indicated by the slight concave down curvature of the graph in Problem 25).

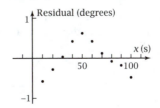

24. By quadratic regression, the equation is
$y_2 = -0.0004924\ldots x^2 + 0.0590\ldots x - 1.3664\ldots$

25. $y_3 = y_1 + y_2$, with original data

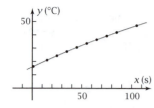

26. $SS_{res} = \Sigma(y - y_3)^2 = 0.1556\ldots$
This value of SS_{res} is smaller than the 1.436 for y_1 because the quadratic function takes out some more of the deviations.

27. By quadratic regression on the original data,
$y_4 = -0.0004924\ldots x^2 + 0.3490\ldots x + 15.8635\ldots$
y_4 and y_3 coincide exactly.

28. Answers will vary.

Test 23 Form A

1. Random experiment

2. Sample space

3. 1 favorable outcome, so $P = \frac{1}{36}$.

4. 11 favorable outcomes, so $P = \frac{11}{36}$.

5. Total is 6: 5 favorable outcomes
Double: 6 favorable outcomes
A double is more probable.

6.

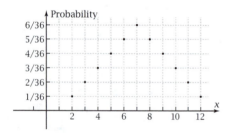

7. n(cookie *or* candy) = 13 + 20 = 33 ways

8. n(cookie *and then* candy) = 13 · 20 = 260 ways

9. n(cookie *and then* cookie) = 13 · 12 = 156 ways

10. A permutation considers the way the elements selected from the set are arranged. A combination considers just which elements are selected, not the arrangement.

11. $_{50}P_3 = 50 \cdot 49 \cdot 48 = 117,600$ permutations

12. $_{50}C_3 = \dfrac{50!}{3!\,47!} = \dfrac{50 \cdot 49 \cdot 48}{6} = 19,600$ combinations

13. $_{50}C_3 = {}_{50}C_{47}$ because there are just as many ways to select 3 elements of 50 to be in a given group as there are to select 47 elements not to be in that group.

14. $_{10}P_{10} = 10! = 3,628,800$ ways

15. $_{10}P_3 = 10 \cdot 9 \cdot 8 = 720$ ways

16. $_{10}C_3 = \dfrac{10!}{3!\,7!} = \dfrac{10 \cdot 9 \cdot 8}{6} = 120$ groups

17. n(3 girls and 2 boys) = $_6C_3 \cdot {}_4C_2 = 20 \cdot 6 = 120$ ways

18. $_{10}C_5 = 252$ ways

19. P(3 girls and 2 boys) = $\dfrac{120}{252} = \dfrac{10}{21} = 0.4761\ldots \approx 47.62\%$

20. $n(A) \cdot n(B) = x \cdot 6 = 6x$

21. $6x = 10!$
$x = \dfrac{10!}{6} = 604,800$ permutations

22. $n = \dfrac{9!}{4!} = 15,120$ permutations

23. $n = \dfrac{11!}{4!\,4!\,2!} = 34,650$ permutations

24. Answers will vary.

Test 23 Form B

1. Random experiment

2. Sample space

3. 1 favorable outcome, so $P = \frac{1}{36}$.

4. 11 favorable outcomes, so $P = \frac{11}{36}$.

5. Total is 6: 5 favorable outcomes
Double: 6 favorable outcomes
A double is more probable.

6.

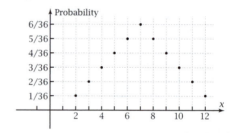

7. n(game *or* movie) = 15 + 30 = 45 ways

8. n(game *and then* movie) = 15 · 30 = 450 ways

9. n(movie *and then* movie) = 30 · 29 = 870 ways

10. A permutation considers the way the elements selected from the set are arranged. A combination considers just which elements are selected, not the arrangement.

11. $_{40}P_5 = 40 \cdot 39 \cdot 38 \cdot 37 \cdot 36 = 78,960,960$ permutations

12. $_{40}C_5 = \dfrac{40!}{5!\,35!} = \dfrac{40 \cdot 39 \cdot 38 \cdot 37 \cdot 36}{5!} = 658,008$ combinations

13. $_{40}C_5 = {}_{40}C_{35}$ because there are just as many ways to select 5 elements of 40 to be in a given group as there are to select 35 elements not to be in that group.

14. $_{12}P_{12} = 12! = 479,001,600$ ways

15. $_{12}P_7 = 12 \cdot 11 \cdot 10 \cdot 9 \cdot 8 \cdot 7 \cdot 6 = 3,991,680$ ways

16. $_{12}C_7 = \dfrac{12!}{7!\,5!} = \dfrac{12 \cdot 11 \cdot 10 \cdot 9 \cdot 5}{120} = 792$ groups

17. n(3 flutists and 2 drummers) = $_8C_3 \cdot {}_4C_2 = 56 \cdot 6 = 336$ ways

18. $_{12}C_5 = 792$ ways

19. P(3 flutists and 2 drummers) $= \dfrac{336}{792} = \dfrac{14}{33} = 0.4242 \approx 42.42\%$

20. $n(A) \cdot n(B) = x \cdot 24 = 24x$

21. $24x = 9!$

$x = \dfrac{9!}{24} = 15{,}120$ permutations

22. $n = \dfrac{9!}{4!} = 15{,}120$ permutations

23. $n = \dfrac{9!}{2!\,2!\,4!} = 3{,}780$ permutations

24. Answers will vary.

Test 24 Form A

1. $_6P_4 = 6 \cdot 5 \cdot 4 \cdot 3 = 360$ permutations

2. $_{10}C_7 = \dfrac{10!}{7!\,3!}$

3. Combinations. It is the same group no matter how you arrange the group members.

4. Permutations. It is a different arrangement if the same students are assigned different problems.

5. $P(X \text{ and } Y) = (0.6)(0.7) = 0.42$, or 42%

6. $P(X \text{ or } Y) = P(X) + P(Y) - P(X \text{ and } Y)$
$= 0.6 + 0.7 - 0.42 = 0.88$, or 88%

7. $P(\text{no rain}) = 1 - 0.6 = 0.4$, or 40%

8. • $P(3) = 0.6^3 = 0.216$, or 21.6%
   • $P(2) = {}_3C_2(0.4)(0.6^2) = 3(0.4)(0.36)$
     $= 0.432 = 43.2\%$

9. The answers are the fourth and third terms, respectively, of the binomial expansion.

10. $E = (0.02)(100) + (0.08)(2) + (0.90)(-3)$
    $= 2 + 0.16 - 2.7 = -0.54$
    On the average, you lose 54 cents each time you play.

11. $P(\text{larger}) = 1 - (0.1 + 0.4 + 0.3 + 0.15) = 0.05$, or 5%

12. $E = 0.1(25) + 0.4(10) + 0.3(10) + 0.15(0) + 0.05(50)$
    $= 12$, or \$12.00

13. $P(T \text{ and } F) = (0.7)(0.6) = 0.42$, or 42%

14. $P(T \text{ or } F) = 0.7 + 0.6 - (0.7)(0.6) = 0.88$, or 88%

15. $P(T \text{ and not } F) = (0.7)(1 - 0.6) = 0.28$, or 28%

16. $P(\text{not } T \text{ and not } F) = (1 - 0.7)(1 - 0.6) = 0.12$, or 12%

17. $_7C_3 = \dfrac{7!}{3!\,4!} = 35$

18. Term $= {}_7C_3\, a^4 b^3 = 35a^4 b^3$

19. $n = \dfrac{7!}{3!\,4!} = 35$ permutations

20. All three problems involve the fraction $\frac{7!}{(3!\,4!)}$.

21. $P(\text{not stop}) = 1 - 0.4 = 0.6$, or 60%

22. $P(7 \text{ stops}) = 0.4^7 = 0.0016384$

23. $P(0 \text{ stops}) = 0.6^7 = 0.0279936$

24. $P(3 \text{ stops}) = {}_7C_3\,(0.6)^4(0.4)^3 = 0.290304 \approx 29\%$

25.

x	$P(x)$
0	0.0279936
1	0.1306368
2	0.2612736
3	0.2903040
4	0.1935360
5	0.0774144
6	0.0172032
7	0.0016384

26.

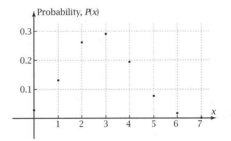

27.

No.	P units	$P(x) \cdot (P \text{ units})$
0	100	2.799360
1	90	11.757312
2	60	15.676416
3	10	2.903040
4	-20	-3.870720
5	-50	-3.870720
6	-70	-1.204224
7	-100	-0.163840
		$E = 24.026624$

28. Answers will vary.

Test 24 Form B

1. $_5P_3 = 5 \cdot 4 \cdot 3 = 60$ permutations

2. $_{11}C_6 = \dfrac{11!}{6!\,5!}$

3. Combinations. It is the same group no matter how you arrange the group members.

4. Permutations. It is a different arrangement if the same students are assigned different problems.

5. $P(X \text{ and } Y) = (0.4)(0.3) = 0.12$, or 12%

6. $P(X \text{ or } Y) = P(X) + P(Y) - P(X \text{ and } Y)$
$= 0.4 + 0.3 - 0.12 = 0.58$, or 58%

7. $P(\text{no test}) = 1 - 0.3 = 0.7$, or 70%

8. • $P(3) = 0.3^3 = 0.027$, or 2.7%
   • $P(2) = {}_3C_2(0.7)(0.3^2) = 3(0.7)(0.09)$
     $= 0.189 = 18.9\%$

9. The answers are the fourth and third terms, respectively, of the binomial expansion.

10. $E = (0.04)(100) + (0.06)(4) + (0.90)(-5)$
$= 4 + 0.24 - 4.5 = -0.26$
On the average, you lose 26 cents each time you play.

11. $P(\text{other}) = 1 - (0.4 + 0.25 + 0.1 + 0.15) = 0.1$, or 10%

12. $E = 0.4(20) + 0.25(25) + 0.1(0) + 0.15(30) + 0.1(50)$
$= 23.75$, or \$23.75

13. $P(T \text{ and } F) = (0.3)(0.4) = 0.12$, or 12%

14. $P(T \text{ or } F) = 0.3 + 0.4 - (0.3)(0.4) = 0.58$, or 58%

15. $P(T \text{ and not } F) = (0.3)(1 - 0.4) = 0.18$, or 18%

16. $P(\text{not } T \text{ and not } F) = (1 - 0.3)(1 - 0.4) = 0.42$, or 42%

17. $_6C_4 = \dfrac{6!}{4! \, 2!} = 15$

18. Term $= {}_6C_4 \, a^2b^4 = 15a^2b^4$

19. $n = \dfrac{6!}{4! \, 2!} = 15$ permutations

20. All three problems involve the fraction $\frac{6!}{(4! \, 2!)}$.

21. $P(\text{not make an A}) = 1 - 0.7 = 0.3$, or 30%

22. $P(6 \text{ A's}) = 0.7^6 = 0.117649$

23. $P(0 \text{ A's}) = 0.3^6 = 0.000729$

24. $P(4 \text{ A's}) = {}_6C_4 \, (0.3)^2(0.7)^4 = 0.324135 \approx 32\%$

25.

x	$P(x)$
0	0.000729
1	0.010206
2	0.059535
3	0.18522
4	0.324135
5	0.302526
6	0.117649

26.

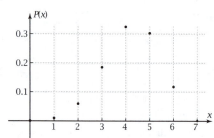

27.

No.	\$	$P(x) \cdot (\$)$
0	-100	-0.0729
1	50	0.5103
2	60	3.5721
3	70	12.965
4	80	25.931
5	90	27.227
6	100	11.765

$E = 81.89794$, or about \$82.00

28. Answers will vary.

Test 25 Form A

1. • Exponential: $y = ab^x$
   • Power: $y = ax^b$
   • Logarithmic: $y = a + b \log_c x$

2. Logistic (e.g.)   Quadratic (e.g.)

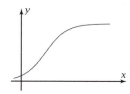   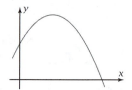

3. • Exponential: add-multiply
   • Power: multiply-multiply

4.

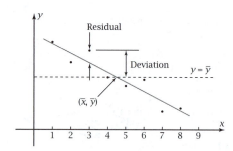

5. $\bar{x} = \dfrac{1}{8}(1 + 2 + 3 + 4 + 5 + 6 + 7 + 8) = 4.5$
Graph, Problem 4, showing the point $(\bar{x}, \bar{y})$.

6. See the graph in Problem 4, showing the regression line. The residual at $x = 3$ is smaller than the deviation there. (Regression equation is $y = -0.7949\ldots x + 7.9377\ldots$)

7. At $x = 3$, $\hat{y} = -2(3) + 13 = 7$.
Residual $= 5 - 7 = -2$

8. For any other line the sum of the squares of the residuals will be greater than 19 because SS_{res} for the regression line is the minimum possible.

9. $r^2 = \dfrac{100 - 19}{100} = \dfrac{81}{100} = 0.81$

10. $_{30}C_6 = \dfrac{30!}{6! \, 24!}$

11. $P(A \text{ or } B) = P(A) + P(B) - p(A \text{ and } B)$
$= 0.9 + 0.8 - (0.9)(0.8) = 0.98$, or 98%

12. • $P(\text{not } C) = 1 - p(C) = 1 - 0.3 = 0.7$
    • $E = 0.3(10) + 0.7(-2) = \$1.60$

13. Multiply-multiply. Multiplying x by 2 multiplies y by 7. Power functions have this property.

14. $y = ax^b$
$14 = a \cdot 12^b$
$98 = a \cdot 24^b$
$\dfrac{98}{14} = \dfrac{a \cdot 24^b}{a \cdot 12^b}$
$7 = 2^b$
$b \log 2 = \log 7$
$b = \dfrac{\log 7}{\log 2} = 2.8073\ldots$
$14 = a \cdot 12^{2.8073\ldots}$

$a = 0.01307...$
$y = 0.01307...x^{2.8073...}$
  $y(29) = 166.7068...$, which is close to 170.
  $y(34) = 260.5482...$, which is close to 260.
  $y(37) = 330.3559...$, which is close to 330.

15. By power regression, $y = 0.01302...x^{2.8095...}$
    The correlation coefficient $r = 0.9999917...$ is close to 1, indicating a very good fit.

16. $y(4) = 0.6402... \approx 0.64$ lb
    You use extrapolation.

17. The pattern is increasing, concave up, and has a positive y-intercept. Eventually, the weight Emma can lift will approach a maximum, indicating that a logistic function is more reasonable.

18. By logistic regression, $y = \dfrac{138.8805...}{1 + 12.5654...e^{0.3222...x}}$
    $y(15) = 126.2528... \approx 126$ lb

19.

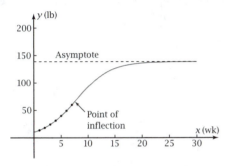

20. Limit $= 138.8805... \approx 139$ lb

21. $\hat{h} = 2.6224...p + 8.0666...$
    $r = 0.99987...$, which is close to 1, indicating that the linear function fits quite well.

22. $\hat{h}(20) = 60.5151... \approx 60.5$ cm
    This is less than twice 34.1 because only the rim of each flower pot adds to the height of the stack. The h-intercept, 8.0666..., is added only once.

23. The fact that the residuals follow a definite pattern indicates that the linear function leaves out something that influences the height of the stack.

p	$\hat{h}$
1	$-0.1890...$
2	$-0.1115...$
3	$0.0660...$
4	$0.1436...$
5	$0.1212...$
6	$0.0987...$
7	$0.0763...$
8	$0.0539...$
9	$-0.0684...$
10	$-0.1909...$

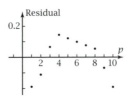

24. The graph of h will be concave down. The residuals show that the actual points are below the line at the beginning and end of the interval and above the line in the middle. This fact indicates that the stack height increases at a slower rate as more pots are added, possibly because the weight of added pots pushes the lower pots closer together.

25. $y = \log_7 41$
    $7^y = 41$
    $\log 7^y = \log 41$
    $y \log 7 = \log 41$
    $y = \dfrac{\log 41}{\log 7} = 1.9083...$
    (Note that $\left(\frac{\ln 41}{\ln 7}\right)$ gives the same answer.)

26. $5^{2x} = 157$
    $\log 5^{2x} = \log 157$
    $2x \log 5 = \log 157$
    $x = \dfrac{\log 157}{2 \log 5} = 1.5708...$

27. $\log_8 91 = \dfrac{\ln 91}{\ln 8} = 2.1692...$

28. $f(1) = 0$ because $e^0 = 1$.
    $f(4) = 1.3862...$, $f(6) = 1.7917...$, and $f(24) = 3.1780...$.
    Therefore, $f(4) + f(6) = f(24)$.

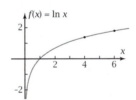

29. $P(\text{no rain}) = 1 - 0.3 = 0.7$, or 70%

30. $P_1(2) = {}_5C_2 \cdot 0.3^2 \cdot 0.7^3 = 0.3807$ (exactly) $= 30.87\%$

31. Using the binomial series program, the probabilities are shown in the table.

x	$P_1(x)$
0	0.16807
1	0.36015
2	0.30870
3	0.13230
4	0.02835
5	0.00243

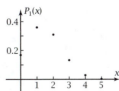

32.

x	$P_2(x)$
1	$1 - 0.7 = 0.3$
2	$1 - 0.7^2 = 0.51$
3	$1 - 0.7^3 = 0.657$
4	$1 - 0.7^4 = 0.7599$
5	$1 - 0.7^5 = 0.83193$

33. The pattern increases toward 1 as x gets large.
(Note that this is not a probability distribution.)

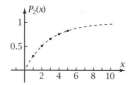

34. $_{68}P_5 = 68 \cdot 67 \cdot 66 \cdot 65 \cdot 64 = 1{,}250{,}895{,}360$ (Wow!)

35. $P(A \text{ and } B) = 0.8 \cdot 0.6 = 0.48$, or 48%

36. $P(A \text{ or } B) = P(A) + P(B) - P(A \text{ and } B)$
$= 0.8 + 0.6 - 0.48 = 0.92$, or 92%

37. $P(\text{not } B) = 1 - 0.6 = 0.4$
$P(A \text{ and not } B) = 0.8 \cdot 0.4 = 0.32$, Q.E.D.

38. $P(B \text{ and not } A) = 0.6 \cdot (1 - 0.8) = 0.12$, or 12%

39. $E = 0.48(200) + (0.32 + 0.12)(30)$
$+ (0.2 \cdot 0.4)(-100) = \$101.20$

40. Answers will vary.

Test 25 Form B

1. • Quadratic: $y = ax^2 + bx + c$
   • Exponential: $y = ab^x$
   • Logarithmic: $y = a + b \log_c x$

2. Power (e.g.)   Logistic (e.g.)

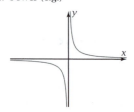   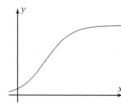

3. • Logarithmic: multiply-add
   • Power: multiply-multiply

4.

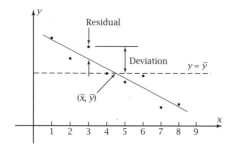

5. $\bar{x} = \dfrac{1}{8}(1 + 2 + 3 + 4 + 5 + 6 + 7 + 8) = 4.5$

Graph, Problem 4, showing the point $(\bar{x}, \bar{y})$.

6. See the graph in Problem 4, showing the regression line.
The residual at $x = 3$ is smaller than the deviation there.
(Regression equation is $y = -0.7949...x + 7.9377....$)

7. At $x = 3$, $\hat{y} = -2(3) + 13 = 7$.
Residual $= 5 - 7 = -2$

8. For any other line the sum of the squares of the residuals
will be greater than 19 because SS_{res} for the regression line is
the minimum possible.

9. $r^2 = \dfrac{100 - 19}{100} = \dfrac{81}{100} = 0.81$

10. $_{20}C_5 = \dfrac{20!}{5! \ 15!}$

11. $P(A \text{ or } B) = P(A) + P(B) - p(A \text{ and } B)$
$= 0.7 + 0.8 - (0.7)(0.8) = 0.94$, or 94%

12. • $P(\text{not } C) = 1 - p(C) = 1 - 0.4 = 0.6$
   • $E = 0.4(20) + 0.6(-4) = \$5.60$

13. Multiply-multiply. Multiplying x by 2 multiplies y by 8. Power
functions have this property.

14. $y = ax^b$
$600 = a \cdot 10^b$
$4800 = a \cdot 20^b$
$\dfrac{4800}{600} = \dfrac{a \cdot 20^b}{a \cdot 10^b}$
$8 = 2^b$
$b = 3$
$600 = a \cdot 10^3$
$a = 0.6$
$y = 0.6x^3$
$y(25) = 9375$, which is close to 9340.
$y(30) = 16{,}200$, which is close to 16,000.
$y(35) = 25{,}725$, which is close to 25,600.

15. By power regression, $y = 0.6035...x^{2.9970...}$
The correlation coefficient $r = 0.9999996998...$ is close to 1,
indicating a very good fit.

16. $y(32) = 19{,}576.5206... \approx 19{,}577$ lb
You use interpolation.

17. The pattern is increasing, concave up, and has a positive
y-intercept. Eventually, the weight Emma can lift will
approach a maximum, indicating that a logistic function is
more reasonable.

18. By logistic regression, $y = \dfrac{138.8805...}{1 + 12.5654...e^{0.3222...x}}$
$y(15) = 126.2528... \approx 126$ lb

19.

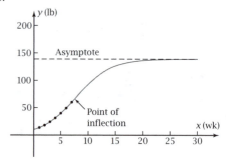

20. Limit $= 138.8805... \approx 139$ lb

Precalculus with Trigonometry: Assessment Resources
© 2007 Key Curriculum Press

21. $\hat{h} = 2.6224\ldots c + 8.4666\ldots$
$r = 0.99987\ldots$, which is close to 1, indicating that the linear function fits quite well.

22. $\hat{h}(20) = 60.915\ldots \approx 60.9$ cm
This is less than twice 34.69 because only the rim of each cup adds to the height of the stack. The h-intercept, $8.4666\ldots$, is added only once.

23. The fact that the residuals follow a definite pattern indicates that the linear function leaves out something that influences the height of the stack.

c	$\hat{h}$
1	$-0.1890\ldots$
2	$-0.1115\ldots$
3	$0.0660\ldots$
4	$0.1436\ldots$
5	$0.1212\ldots$
6	$0.0987\ldots$
7	$0.0763\ldots$
8	$0.0539\ldots$
9	$-0.0684\ldots$
10	$-0.1909\ldots$

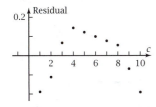

24. The graph of h will be concave down. The residuals show that the actual points are below the line at the beginning and end of the interval and above the line in the middle. This fact indicates that the stack height increases at a slower rate as more cups are added, possibly because the weight of added cups pushes the lower cups closer together.

25. $y = \log_6 35$
$6^y = 35$
$\log 6^y = \log 35$
$y \log 6 = \log 35$
$y = \dfrac{\log 35}{\log 6} = 1.9842\ldots$
(Note that $\left(\dfrac{\ln 35}{\ln 6}\right)$ gives the same answer.)

26. $4^{3x} = 291$
$\log 4^{3x} = \log 291$
$3x \log 4 = \log 291$
$x = \dfrac{\log 291}{3 \log 4} = 1.3641\ldots$

27. $\log_9 78 = \dfrac{\ln 78}{\ln 9} = 1.9828\ldots$

28. $f(1) = 0$ because $e^0 = 1$.
$f(2) = 0.6931\ldots$, $f(5) = 1.6094\ldots$, and $f(10) = 2.3025\ldots$.
Therefore, $f(2) + f(5) = f(10)$.

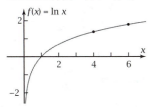

29. $P(\text{no sleet}) = 1 - 0.8 = 0.2$, or 20%

30. $P_1(2) = {}_5C_2 \cdot 0.8^2 \cdot 0.2^3 = 0.0512$ (exactly) = 5.12%

31. Using the binomial series program, the probabilities are shown in the table.

x	$P_1(x)$
0	0.00032
1	0.0064
2	0.0512
3	0.2048
4	0.4096
5	0.32768

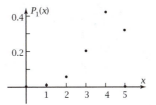

32.

x	$P_2(x)$
1	$1 - 0.8 = 0.2$
2	$1 - 0.8^2 = 0.36$
3	$1 - 0.8^3 = 0.488$
4	$1 - 0.8^4 = 0.5904$
5	$1 - 0.8^5 = 0.67232$

33. The pattern increases toward 1 as x gets large. (Note that this is not a probability distribution.)

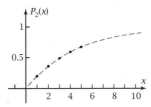

34. ${}_{58}P_4 = 58 \cdot 57 \cdot 56 \cdot 55 = 10{,}182{,}480$ (Wow!)

35. $P(A \text{ and } B) = 0.7 \cdot 0.5 = 0.35$, or 35%

36. $P(A \text{ or } B) = P(A) + P(B) - P(A \text{ and } B)$
$= 0.7 + 0.5 - 0.35 = 0.85$, or 85%

37. $P(\text{not } B) = 1 - 0.5 = 0.5$
$P(A \text{ and not } B) = 0.7 \cdot 0.5 = 0.35$, Q.E.D.

38. $P(B \text{ and not } A) = 0.5 \cdot (1 - 0.7) = 0.15$, or 15%

39. $E = 0.35(200) + (0.35 + 0.15)(30)$
$+ (0.3 \cdot 0.5)(-100) = \$70.00$

40. Answers will vary.

Test 26 Form A

1.

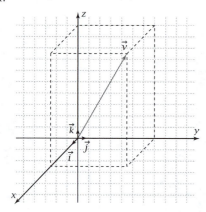

2. Graph, showing $\vec{i}, \vec{j}$, and $\vec{k}$ in Problem 1.

3.

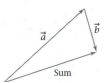

4.

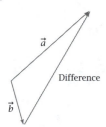

5. $\vec{a} \cdot \vec{b} = (5)(2)(-0.3) = -3$

6. $\vec{m} \cdot \vec{r} = (5)(2) + (3)(-8) + (7)(3) = 7$

7.

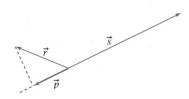

8.

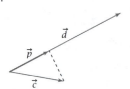

9. $\vec{p} = p\vec{u} = 10\left(\dfrac{1}{3}\vec{i} + \dfrac{2}{3}\vec{j} - \dfrac{2}{3}\vec{k}\right) = \dfrac{10}{3}\vec{i} + \dfrac{20}{3}\vec{j} - \dfrac{20}{3}\vec{k}$

10. $|\vec{a}| = \sqrt{5^2 + 3^2 + 7^2} = \sqrt{83} = 9.1104...$
    $|\vec{b}| = \sqrt{2^2 + 8^2 + 3^2} = \sqrt{77} = 8.7749...$

11. $\vec{a} \cdot \vec{b} = (5)(2) + (3)(-8) + (7)(3) = 7$

12. $\sqrt{83}\sqrt{77}\cos\theta = 7$
    $\cos\theta = \dfrac{7}{\sqrt{83}\sqrt{77}} = 0.0875...$
    $\theta = 84.9766...°$

13. $p = |\vec{a}|\cos\theta = \sqrt{83}\cos 84.9766...° = 0.7977...$

14. $p = \dfrac{\vec{a} \cdot \vec{b}}{|\vec{b}|} = \dfrac{7}{\sqrt{77}} = 0.7977...$, which agrees with Problem 13.

15. $\vec{u} = \dfrac{2}{\sqrt{77}}\vec{i} - \dfrac{8}{\sqrt{77}}\vec{j} + \dfrac{3}{\sqrt{77}}\vec{k}$

16. $\vec{p} = p\vec{u} = \dfrac{14}{77}\vec{i} - \dfrac{56}{77}\vec{j} + \dfrac{21}{77}\vec{k}$
    $= 0.1818...\vec{i} - 0.7272...\vec{j} + 0.2727...\vec{k}$

17. $\vec{r} = \vec{e} + \vec{m} = 2\vec{i} - 2\vec{j} + \vec{k}$
    $|\vec{r}| = \sqrt{2^2 + (-2)^2 + 1^2} = 3$ lb

18. $\vec{r} \cdot \vec{m} = 2(32) - 2(38) + 1(51) = 39$
    Angle is acute because the dot product is positive.

19.

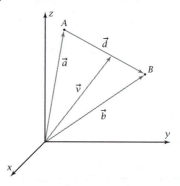

20. See the graph in Problem 19, showing $\vec{d}$.
    $\vec{d} = (80 - 37)\vec{i} + (19 - 50)\vec{j} + (22 - 18)\vec{k}$
    $= 43\vec{i} - 31\vec{j} + 4\vec{k}$

21. See the graph in Problem 19, showing $\vec{v}$.
    $\vec{v} = \vec{a} + 0.6\vec{d}$
    $= 37\vec{i} + 50\vec{j} + 18\vec{k} + 0.6(43\vec{i} - 31\vec{j} + 4\vec{k})$
    $= 62.8\vec{i} + 31.4\vec{j} + 20.4\vec{k}$

22. Answers will vary.

Test 26 Form B

1.

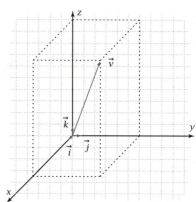

2. Graph, showing $\vec{i}, \vec{j}$, and $\vec{k}$ in Problem 1.

3.

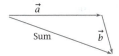

Sum

4.

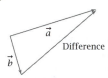

Difference

5. $\vec{a} \cdot \vec{b} = (7)(3)(-0.4) = -8.4$

6. $\vec{m} \cdot \vec{r} = (4)(5) + (3)(-6) + (7)(1) = 9$

7.

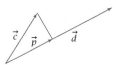

8.

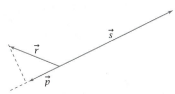

9. $\vec{p} = p\vec{u} = 12\left(\frac{2}{3}\vec{i} + \frac{1}{3}\vec{j} - \frac{2}{3}\vec{k}\right) = 8\vec{i} + 4\vec{j} - 8\vec{k}$

10. $|\vec{a}| = \sqrt{4^2 + 6^2 + 5^2} = \sqrt{77} = 8.7749...$
$|\vec{b}| = \sqrt{3^2 + 10^2 + 7^2} = \sqrt{158} = 12.5698...$

11. $\vec{a} \cdot \vec{b} = (4)(3) + (6)(-10) + (5)(7) = -13$

12. $\sqrt{77}\sqrt{158} \cos \theta = -13$
$\cos \theta = \frac{-13}{\sqrt{77}\sqrt{158}} = -0.1178...$
$\theta = 96.7686...°$

13. $p = |\vec{a}| \cos \theta = \sqrt{77} \cos 96.7686...° = -1.0342...$

14. $p = \frac{\vec{a} \cdot \vec{b}}{|\vec{b}|} = \frac{-13}{\sqrt{158}} = -1.0342...$, which agrees with Problem 13.

15. $\vec{u} = \frac{3}{\sqrt{158}}\vec{i} - \frac{10}{\sqrt{158}}\vec{j} + \frac{7}{\sqrt{158}}\vec{k}$

16. $\vec{p} = p\vec{u} = \frac{-39}{158}\vec{i} + \frac{130}{158}\vec{j} - \frac{91}{158}\vec{k}$
$= -0.2468...\vec{i} + 0.8227...\vec{j} - 0.5759...\vec{k}$

17. $\vec{r} = \vec{e} + \vec{m} = 2\vec{i} - 2\vec{j} + \vec{k}$
$|\vec{r}| = \sqrt{2^2 + (-2)^2 + 1^2} = 3$ lb

18. $\vec{r} \cdot \vec{m} = 2(32) - 2(38) + 1(51) = 39$
Angle is acute because the dot product is positive.

19.

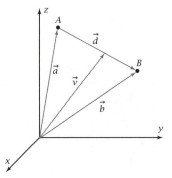

20. See the graph in Problem 19, showing $\vec{d}$.
$\vec{d} = (75 - 35)\vec{i} + (18 - 55)\vec{j} + (24 - 20)\vec{k}$
$= 40\vec{i} - 37\vec{j} + 4\vec{k}$

21. See the graph in Problem 19, showing $\vec{v}$.
$\vec{v} = \vec{a} + 0.7\vec{d}$
$= 35\vec{i} + 55\vec{j} + 20\vec{k} + 0.7(40\vec{i} - 37\vec{j} + 4\vec{k})$
$= 63\vec{i} - 29.1\vec{j} + 22.8\vec{k}$

22. Answers will vary.

Test 27 Form A

1. $\vec{a} \cdot \vec{b} = |\vec{a}||\vec{b}| \cos \theta$

2. $\vec{a} \times \vec{b}$ is a vector with these properties.
   - $\vec{a} \times \vec{b}$ is normal to both $\vec{a}$ and $\vec{b}$.
   - $|\vec{a} \times \vec{b}| = |\vec{a}||\vec{b}| \sin \theta$
   - The right-hand rule determines the direction.

3. • Dot product is also called scalar product.
   • Cross product is also called vector product.

4. $\vec{i} \cdot \vec{i} = |\vec{i}||\vec{i}| \cos 0° = 1 \cdot 1 \cdot 1 = 1$
$\vec{i} \cdot \vec{j} = |\vec{i}||\vec{j}| \cos 90° = 1 \cdot 1 \cdot 0 = 0$

5. $|\vec{i} \times \vec{i}| = |\vec{i}||\vec{i}| \sin 0° = 1 \cdot 1 \cdot 0 = 0$
$\therefore \vec{i} \times \vec{i}$ is the zero vector.
$|\vec{i} \times \vec{j}| = |\vec{i}||\vec{j}| \sin 90° = 1 \cdot 1 \cdot 1 = 1$
$\therefore \vec{i} \times \vec{j}$ is a unit vector perpendicular to $\vec{i}$ and $\vec{j}$, as are $\vec{k}$ and $-\vec{k}$. By the right-hand rule, $\vec{i} \times \vec{j} = \vec{k}$.

6. $\vec{a} \cdot \vec{b} = (1\vec{i} + 2\vec{j} + 3\vec{k}) \cdot (6\vec{i} + 5\vec{j} + 4\vec{k})$
$= 6(\vec{i} \cdot \vec{i}) + 5(\vec{i} \cdot \vec{j}) + 4(\vec{i} \cdot \vec{k})$
$+ 12(\vec{j} \cdot \vec{i}) + 10(\vec{j} \cdot \vec{j}) + 8(\vec{j} \cdot \vec{k})$
$+ 18(\vec{k} \cdot \vec{i}) + 15(\vec{k} \cdot \vec{j}) + 12(\vec{k} \cdot \vec{k})$
$= 6(1) + 5(0) + 4(0)$
$+ 12(0) + 10(1) + 8(0)$
$+ 18(0) + 15(0) + 12(1)$
$= 6 + 0 + 0$
$+ 0 + 10 + 0$
$+ 0 + 0 + 12$
$= 28$

It is called the inner product because only the numbers on the main diagonal ("inside" the array) contribute to the dot product, not the zeros on the outside of the array.

7. $1x + 2y + 3z = D$
$1(9) + 2(8) + 3(7) = D$
$D = 46$
Equation is $1x + 2y + 3z = 46$

8. $\vec{v}_1 = -4\vec{i} + 4\vec{j} + 6\vec{k}$ and
$\vec{v}_2 = -\vec{i} + 10\vec{j} + 2\vec{k}$

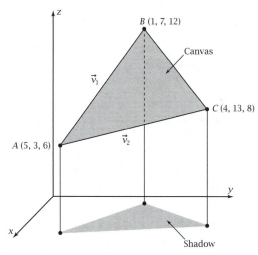

9. $|\vec{v}_1| = \sqrt{4^2 + 4^2 + 6^2} = \sqrt{68} = 8.2462...$

10. $|\vec{v}_2| = \sqrt{1^2 + 10^2 + 2^2} = \sqrt{105} = 10.2469...$

11. $\vec{v}_1 \cdot \vec{v}_2 = 4 + 40 + 12 = 56$

12. $\vec{v}_1 \times \vec{v}_2 = -52\vec{i} + 2\vec{j} - 36\vec{k}$ (by calculator program)

13. $|\vec{v}_1||\vec{v}_2| \cos A = 56$

$\cos A = \dfrac{56}{\sqrt{68}\sqrt{105}} = 0.6627...$

$A = 48.4913...°$ (Store as A.)

14. $|\vec{v}_1 \times \vec{v}_2| = \sqrt{52^2 + 2^2 + 36^2} = \sqrt{4004} = 63.2771...$
$|\vec{v}_1||\vec{v}_2| \sin A = \sqrt{68}\sqrt{105} \sin 48.4913...° = 63.2771...$
The answers are equal, Q.E.D.

15. $\vec{v}_1 \cdot (\vec{v}_1 \times \vec{v}_2) = (-4)(-52) + (4)(2) + (6)(-36) = 0$
$\therefore \vec{v}_1$ is perpendicular to $\vec{v}_1 \times \vec{v}_2$, Q.E.D.

16. Area $= \dfrac{1}{2}|\vec{v}_1||\vec{v}_2| \sin A = \dfrac{1}{2}|\vec{v}_1 \times \vec{v}_2|$

$= \dfrac{1}{2}(63.2771...) = 31.6385... = 31.6$ ft

17. $\vec{n} = \vec{v}_1 \times \vec{v}_2 = -52\vec{i} + 2\vec{j} - 36\vec{k}$

18. $-52x + 2y - 36z = D$
$-52(5) + 2(3) - 36(6) = D$
$-470 = D$
Equation is $-52x + 2y - 36z = -470$

19. $-52(3) + 2(8) - 36z = -470$
$-36z = -330$
$z = 9.1666... \approx 9.17$ ft

20. Substitute 0 for x and for z.
$2y = -470$
$y = -235$

21. Answers will vary.

Test 27 Form B

1. $\vec{a} \cdot \vec{b} = |\vec{a}||\vec{b}| \cos \theta$

2. $\vec{a} \times \vec{b}$ is a vector with these properties.
   • $\vec{a} \times \vec{b}$ is normal to both $\vec{a}$ and $\vec{b}$.
   • $|\vec{a} \times \vec{b}| = |\vec{a}||\vec{b}| \sin \theta$
   • The right-hand rule determines the direction.

3. • Dot product is also called scalar product.
   • Cross product is also called vector product.

4. $\vec{i} \cdot \vec{i} = |\vec{i}||\vec{i}| \cos 0° = 1 \cdot 1 \cdot 1 = 1$
$\vec{i} \cdot \vec{j} = |\vec{i}||\vec{j}| \cos 90° = 1 \cdot 1 \cdot 0 = 0$

5. $|\vec{j} \times \vec{j}| = |\vec{j}||\vec{j}| \sin 0° = 1 \cdot 1 \cdot 0 = 0$
$\therefore \vec{j} \times \vec{j}$ is the zero vector.
$|\vec{j} \times \vec{k}| = |\vec{j}||\vec{k}| \sin 90° = 1 \cdot 1 \cdot 1 = 1$
$\therefore \vec{j} \times \vec{k}$ is a unit vector perpendicular to $\vec{j}$ and $\vec{k}$, as are $\vec{i}$ and $-\vec{i}$. By the right-hand rule, $\vec{j} \times \vec{k} = \vec{i}$.

6. $\vec{a} \cdot \vec{b} = (4\vec{i} + 5\vec{j} + 6\vec{k}) \cdot (3\vec{i} + 2\vec{j} + 1\vec{k})$
$= 12(\vec{i} \cdot \vec{i}) + 8(\vec{i} \cdot \vec{j}) + 4(\vec{i} \cdot \vec{k})$
$\quad + 15(\vec{j} \cdot \vec{i}) + 10(\vec{j} \cdot \vec{j}) + 5(\vec{j} \cdot \vec{k})$
$\quad + 18(\vec{k} \cdot \vec{i}) + 12(\vec{k} \cdot \vec{j}) + 6(\vec{k} \cdot \vec{k})$
$= 12(1) + 8(0) + 4(0)$
$\quad + 15(0) + 10(1) + 5(0)$
$\quad + 18(0) + 12(0) + 6(1)$
$= 12 + 0 + 0$
$\quad + 0 + 10 + 0$
$\quad + 0 + 0 + 6$
$= 28$

It is called the inner product because only the numbers on the main diagonal ("inside" the array) contribute to the dot product, not the zeros on the outside of the array.

7. $4x + 5y + 6z = D$
$4(1) + 5(2) + 6(3) = D$
$D = 32$
Equation is $4x + 5y + 6z = 32$

8. $\vec{v}_1 = -3\vec{i} + 4\vec{j} + 7\vec{k}$ and
$\vec{v}_2 = -\vec{i} + 10\vec{j} + 2\vec{k}$

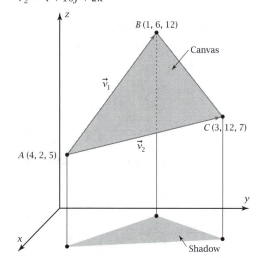

9. $|\vec{v}_1| = \sqrt{3^2 + 4^2 + 7^2} = \sqrt{74} = 8.6023...$

10. $|\vec{v}_2| = \sqrt{1^2 + 10^2 + 2^2} = \sqrt{105} = 10.2469...$

11. $\vec{v}_1 \cdot \vec{v}_2 = 3 + 40 + 14 = 57$

12. $\vec{v}_1 \times \vec{v}_2 = -62\vec{i} - 1\vec{j} - 26\vec{k}$ (by calculator program)

13. $|\vec{v}_1||\vec{v}_2| \cos A = 57$

$\cos A = \dfrac{57}{\sqrt{74}\sqrt{105}} = 0.6466...$

$A = 49.7110...°$ (Store as A.)

14. $|\vec{v}_1 \times \vec{v}_2| = \sqrt{62^2 + 1^2 + 26^2} = \sqrt{4521} = 67.2383...$
$|\vec{v}_1||\vec{v}_2|\sin A = \sqrt{74}\sqrt{105}\sin 49.7110...° = 67.2383...$
The answers are equal, Q.E.D.

15. $\vec{v}_1 \cdot (\vec{v}_1 \times \vec{v}_2) = (-3)(-62) + (4)(-1) + (7)(-26) = 0$
$\therefore \vec{v}_1$ is perpendicular to $\vec{v}_1 \times \vec{v}_2$, Q.E.D.

16. $\text{Area} = \frac{1}{2}|\vec{v}_1||\vec{v}_2|\sin A = \frac{1}{2}|\vec{v}_1 \times \vec{v}_2|$
$= \frac{1}{2}(67.2383...) = 33.6191... \approx 33.6 \text{ ft}$

17. $\vec{n} = \vec{v}_1 \times \vec{v}_2 = -62\vec{i} - 1\vec{j} - 26\vec{k}$

18. $-62x - 1y - 26z = D$
$-62(4) - 1(2) - 26(5) = D$
$-380 = D$
Equation is $-62x - 1y - 26z = -380$

19. $-62(3) - 1(8) - 26z = -380$
$-26z = -186$
$z = 7.1538... \approx 7.15 \text{ ft}$

20. Substitute 0 for x and for z.
$-1y = -380$
$y = 380$

21. Answers will vary.

Test 28 Form A

1. By definition, $\vec{a} \cdot \vec{b} = |\vec{a}||\vec{b}|\cos\theta$.
Therefore, $\theta = \arccos\dfrac{\vec{a} \cdot \vec{b}}{|\vec{a}||\vec{b}|}$.
Because $\arccos x = \cos^{-1} x$ for angles between 0° and 180°, θ can be found using inverse cosine from the calculator.

2. By definition, $|\vec{a} \times \vec{b}| = |\vec{a}||\vec{b}|\sin\theta$.
Therefore, $\theta = \arcsin\dfrac{|\vec{a} \cdot \vec{b}|}{|\vec{a}||\vec{b}|}$.
However, $\arcsin x = 180° - \sin^{-1} x$ for x between 90° and 180°, so to get the correct answer, you would have to know beforehand whether θ is obtuse or acute.

3. $\vec{u} = -\dfrac{\vec{b}}{|\vec{b}|}$

4. • $\vec{n} = 3\vec{i} + 4\vec{j} + 5\vec{k}$
   • $3(0) + 4y + 5(0) = 60$
   $4y = 60 \Rightarrow y = 15$

5.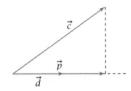

6. $\vec{v} = 5\vec{i} + 3\vec{j} + 7\vec{k}$

7. $\vec{r} = (5 + 6)\vec{i} + (3 + 9)\vec{j} + (7 + 2)\vec{k}$
$= 11\vec{i} + 12\vec{j} + 9\vec{k}$
Point is (11, 12, 9).

8.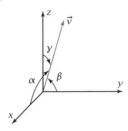

9. $0.6^2 + 0.7^2 + \cos^2\gamma = 1$
$\cos^2\gamma = 1 - 0.36 - 0.49 = 0.15$
$\cos\gamma = \sqrt{0.15}$

10. $3(6) + 2(8) + 5(4) = 54$
So (6, 8, 4) is on the plane.
$3(13) + 2(18) + 5(5) = 100 \neq 54$
So (13, 18, 5) is not on the plane.

11. $\vec{n} = 3\vec{i} + 2\vec{j} + 5\vec{k}$

12. $\vec{v} = (13 - 6)\vec{i} + (18 - 8)\vec{j} + (5 - 4)\vec{k}$
$= 7\vec{i} + 10\vec{j} + \vec{k}$

13. $\vec{n} \cdot \vec{v} = (3)(7) + (2)(10) + (5)(1) = 46$
$|\vec{n}| = \sqrt{3^2 + 2^2 + 5^2} = \sqrt{38}$
$|\vec{v}| = \sqrt{7^2 + 10^2 + 1^2} = \sqrt{150}$
$\cos\theta = \dfrac{46}{\sqrt{38}\sqrt{150}} = 0.6092...$
$\theta = 52.4621...°$

14. $p = |\vec{v}|\cos\theta = \sqrt{150}\cos 52.4621...° = 7.4621...$
or $p = \dfrac{\vec{n} \cdot \vec{v}}{|\vec{n}|} = \dfrac{46}{\sqrt{38}} = 7.4621...$

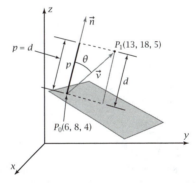

15. See the graph in Problem 14, showing distance d perpendicular to the plane. Vector $\vec{v}$ is the diagonal of a rectangle with opposite sides p and d, which explains why $p = d$.

16. If $d = 0$, then $\vec{r} = 5\vec{i} + 3\vec{j} + 7\vec{k}$.
So point (5, 3, 7) is on the line.

17. From the given equation, $\vec{u} = \frac{6}{11}\vec{i} + \frac{9}{11}\vec{j} + \frac{2}{11}\vec{k}$.
$|\vec{u}| = \sqrt{\left(\frac{6}{11}\right)^2 + \left(\frac{9}{11}\right)^2 + \left(\frac{2}{11}\right)^2} = \sqrt{\frac{121}{121}} = 1$
$\therefore \vec{u}$ is a unit vector, Q.E.D.

18. $\overrightarrow{P_0P_1} = (13 - 5)\vec{i} + (15 - 3)\vec{j} + (11 - 7)\vec{k}$
$= 8\vec{i} + 12\vec{j} + 4\vec{k}$

19. $\overrightarrow{P_0P_1} \cdot \vec{u} = 8\left(\frac{6}{11}\right) + 12\left(\frac{9}{11}\right) + 4\left(\frac{2}{11}\right) = \frac{164}{11}$

$\left|\overrightarrow{P_0P_1}\right| = \sqrt{8^2 + 12^2 + 4^2} = \sqrt{224}$

$\cos\theta = \dfrac{\frac{164}{11}}{\sqrt{224}\sqrt{1}} = 0.9961\ldots$

$\theta = \cos^{-1} 0.9961\ldots = 5.0256\ldots°$

20. Graph, showing p and θ in a right triangle.

$p = \left|\overrightarrow{P_0P_1}\right| \sin\theta = \sqrt{224}\sin 5.0256\ldots° = 1.3111\ldots$

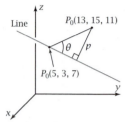

21. By calculator program,

$\overrightarrow{P_0P_1} \times \vec{u} = -\frac{12}{11}\vec{i} + \frac{8}{11}\vec{j} + 0\vec{k}$

22. $\left|\overrightarrow{P_0P_1} \times \vec{u}\right| = \sqrt{\left(\frac{12}{11}\right)^2 + \left(\frac{8}{11}\right)^2 + 0^2} = 1.3111\ldots$

Both lengths equal 1.3111....

$\therefore p = \left|\overrightarrow{P_0P_1} \times \vec{u}\right|$

23. By trigonometry, $p = \left|\overrightarrow{P_0P_1}\right| \sin\theta$.

By definition, $\left|\overrightarrow{P_0P_1} \times \vec{u}\right| = \left|\overrightarrow{P_0P_1}\right| |\vec{u}| \sin\theta$.

Because $|\vec{u}| = 1$, the two quantities are equal.

$\therefore p = \left|\overrightarrow{P_0P_1} \times \vec{u}\right|$, Q.E.D.

24. Answers will vary.

Test 28 Form B

1. By definition, $\vec{a} \cdot \vec{b} = |\vec{a}||\vec{b}| \cos\theta$.

Therefore, $\theta = \arccos\dfrac{\vec{a} \cdot \vec{b}}{|\vec{a}||\vec{b}|}$.

Because $\arccos x = \cos^{-1} x$ for angles between $0°$ and $180°$, θ can be found using inverse cosine from the calculator.

2. By definition, $|\vec{a} \times \vec{b}| = |\vec{a}||\vec{b}| \sin\theta$.

Therefore, $\theta = \arcsin\dfrac{|\vec{a} \cdot \vec{b}|}{|\vec{a}||\vec{b}|}$.

However, $\arcsin x = 180° - \sin^{-1} x$ for x between $90°$ and $180°$, so to get the correct answer, you would have to know beforehand whether θ is obtuse or acute.

3. $\vec{u} = -\dfrac{\vec{b}}{|\vec{b}|}$

4. • $\vec{n} = 6\vec{i} + 8\vec{j} + 10\vec{k}$

• $6(0) + 8y + 10(0) = 120$
$8y = 120 \Rightarrow y = 15$

5.

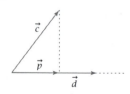

6. $\vec{v} = 1\vec{i} + 2\vec{j} + 3\vec{k}$

7. $\vec{r} = (1+3)\vec{i} + (2+6)\vec{j} + (3+2)\vec{k}$
$= 4\vec{i} + 8\vec{j} + 5\vec{k}$
Point is $(4, 8, 5)$.

8.

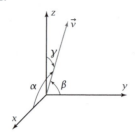

9. $0.3^2 + 0.6^2 + \cos^2\gamma = 1$
$\cos^2\gamma = 1 - 0.09 - 0.36 = 0.55$
$\cos\gamma = \sqrt{0.55}$

10. $6(6) + 4(8) + 10(4) = 108$
So $(6, 8, 4)$ is on the plane.
$6(13) + 4(18) + 10(5) = 200 \ne 108$
So $(13, 18, 5)$ is not on the plane.

11. $\vec{n} = 6\vec{i} + 4\vec{j} + 10\vec{k}$

12. $\vec{v} = (13-6)\vec{i} + (18-8)\vec{j} + (5-4)\vec{k}$
$= 7\vec{i} + 10\vec{j} + \vec{k}$

13. $\vec{n} \cdot \vec{v} = (6)(7) + (4)(10) + (10)(1) = 92$
$|\vec{n}| = \sqrt{6^2 + 4^2 + 10^2} = \sqrt{152}$
$|\vec{v}| = \sqrt{7^2 + 10^2 + 1^2} = \sqrt{150}$
$\cos\theta = \dfrac{92}{\sqrt{152}\sqrt{150}} = 0.6092$
$\theta = 52.4621\ldots°$

14. $p = |\vec{v}| \cos\theta = \sqrt{150}\cos 52.4621\ldots° = 7.4621\ldots$

or $p = \dfrac{\vec{n} \cdot \vec{v}}{|\vec{n}|} = \dfrac{92}{\sqrt{152}} = 7.4621\ldots$

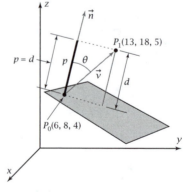

15. See the graph in Problem 14, showing distance d perpendicular to the plane. Vector $\vec{v}$ is the diagonal of a rectangle with opposite sides p and d, which explains why $p = d$.

16. If $d = 0$, then $\vec{r} = 5\vec{i} + 3\vec{j} + 7\vec{k}$.
So point $(5, 3, 7)$ is on the line.

17. From the given equation, $\vec{u} = \frac{3}{7}\vec{i} + \frac{6}{7}\vec{j} + \frac{2}{7}\vec{k}$.

$|\vec{u}| = \sqrt{\left(\frac{3}{7}\right)^2 + \left(\frac{6}{7}\right)^2 + \left(\frac{2}{7}\right)^2} = \sqrt{\left(\frac{9}{49}\right) + \left(\frac{36}{49}\right) + \left(\frac{4}{49}\right)}$

$= \sqrt{\frac{49}{49}} = 1$

$\therefore \vec{u}$ is a unit vector, Q.E.D.

18. $\overrightarrow{P_0P_1} = (13 - 5)\vec{i} + (15 - 3)\vec{j} + (11 - 7)\vec{k}$
    $= 8\vec{i} + 12\vec{j} + 4\vec{k}$

19. $\overrightarrow{P_0P_1} \cdot \vec{u} = 8\left(\dfrac{3}{7}\right) + 12\left(\dfrac{6}{7}\right) + 4\left(\dfrac{2}{7}\right) = \dfrac{104}{7}$

$|\overrightarrow{P_0P_1}| = \sqrt{8^2 + 12^2 + 4^2} = \sqrt{224}$

$\cos\theta = \dfrac{\frac{104}{7}}{\sqrt{224}\sqrt{1}} = 0.9926...$

$\theta = \cos^{-1} 0.9926... = 6.9345...°$

20. Graph, showing p and θ in a right triangle.
    $p = |\overrightarrow{P_0P_1}| \sin\theta = \sqrt{224} \sin 6.9345...° = 1.8070...$

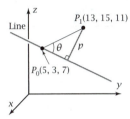

21. By calculator program,
    $\overrightarrow{P_0P_1} \times \vec{u} = 0\vec{i} - \dfrac{4}{7}\vec{j} + \dfrac{12}{7}\vec{k}$

22. $|\overrightarrow{P_0P_1} \times \vec{u}| = \sqrt{\left(\dfrac{4}{7}\right)^2 + \left(\dfrac{12}{7}\right)^2} = \sqrt{\dfrac{160}{49}} = 1.8070...$

Both lengths equal 1.8070....
$\therefore p = |\overrightarrow{P_0P_1} \times \vec{u}|$

23. By trigonometry, $p = |\overrightarrow{P_0P_1}| \sin\theta$.
    By definition, $|\overrightarrow{P_0P_1} \times \vec{u}| = |\overrightarrow{P_0P_1}| |\vec{u}| \sin\theta$.
    Because $|\vec{u}| = 1$, the two quantities are equal.
    $\therefore p = |\overrightarrow{P_0P_1} \times \vec{u}|$, Q.E.D.

24. Answers will vary.

Test 29 Form A

1. $\begin{bmatrix} 5 & 8 \\ 3 & 2 \end{bmatrix} + \begin{bmatrix} 4 & 6 \\ 1 & 9 \end{bmatrix} = \begin{bmatrix} 9 & 14 \\ 4 & 11 \end{bmatrix}$

2. $\begin{bmatrix} 2 & 3 & -1 \\ 5 & 4 & 2 \end{bmatrix} \begin{bmatrix} 6 & 2 \\ 3 & 0 \\ 1 & -3 \end{bmatrix} = \begin{bmatrix} 20 & 7 \\ 44 & 4 \end{bmatrix}$

3. In matrix multiplication, you take the dot product of a row in the first matrix with a column in the second matrix.

4. The matrices are commensurate for multiplication because there are the same number of elements in the rows of the first matrix as there are in the columns of the second matrix.

5. Dilation by a factor of 0.9 (90% reduction)
   Rotation of −30° (30° clockwise)
   x-translation of 2
   y-translation of 4

6.

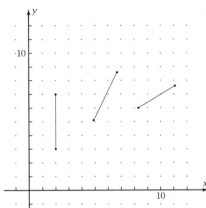

7. The images will spiral around and approach a fixed point.

8. The matrix is 4×5.

9. $[D] = \begin{bmatrix} 2 & 4 & 6 & 4 \\ 4 & 1 & 4 & 5 \\ 1 & 1 & 1 & 1 \end{bmatrix}$

10. $[E] \approx \begin{bmatrix} 3.8 & 6.2 & 7.3 & 5.3 \\ 5.9 & 3.8 & 6.9 & 7.3 \\ 1 & 1 & 1 & 1 \end{bmatrix}$

11.

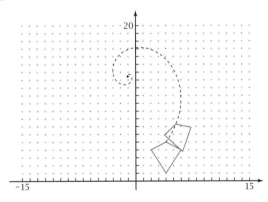

12. Graph, Problem 11, showing the path followed by the top point in the pre-image.

13. Fixed point is $(-1.0356..., 13.4599...)$.
    - Raise $[A]$ to a high power, say $[A]^{200}$, and look at the translation part of the answer.
    - Multiply $[A]^{200} [D]$ and see that the coordinates of all the points in the image are the same as the fixed point.

14. The fixed point is the same, $(-1.0356..., 13.4599...)$.

15. The new fixed point is $(4.0616..., 14.8936...)$.

16. $\begin{bmatrix} (0.9 \cos 15°)X + (0.9 \cos 105°)Y + 4 \\ (0.9 \sin 15°)X + (0.9 \sin 105°)Y + 1 \\ 1 \end{bmatrix}$

17. The answer matrix will be $\begin{bmatrix} X \\ Y \\ 1 \end{bmatrix}$.

18. $(0.9 \cos 15°)X + (0.9 \cos 105°)Y + 4 = X$
$(0.9 \sin 15°)X + (0.9 \sin 105°)Y + 1 = Y$
$(0.9 \cos 15° - 1)X + (0.9 \cos 105°)Y = -4$
$(0.9 \sin 15°)X + (0.9 \sin 105° - 1)Y = -1$

$$\begin{bmatrix} (0.9 \cos 15° - 1) & (0.9 \cos 105°) \\ (0.9 \sin 15°) & (0.9 \sin 105° - 1) \end{bmatrix}^{-1} \begin{bmatrix} -4 \\ -1 \end{bmatrix} = \begin{bmatrix} 4.0616... \\ 14.8936... \end{bmatrix}$$

Fixed point is (4.0616..., 14.8936...).

19. Answers will vary.

Test 29 Form B

1. $\begin{bmatrix} 3 & 2 \\ 8 & 5 \end{bmatrix} + \begin{bmatrix} 7 & 6 \\ 9 & 1 \end{bmatrix} = \begin{bmatrix} 10 & 8 \\ 17 & 6 \end{bmatrix}$

2. $\begin{bmatrix} 5 & 4 & 2 \\ 3 & 2 & -1 \end{bmatrix} \begin{bmatrix} 3 & 1 \\ 6 & 0 \\ 2 & -1 \end{bmatrix} = \begin{bmatrix} 43 & 3 \\ 19 & 4 \end{bmatrix}$

3. In matrix multiplication, you take the dot product of a row in the first matrix with a column in the second matrix.

4. The matrices are commensurate for multiplication because there are the same number of elements in the rows of the first matrix as there are in the columns of the second matrix.

5. Dilation by a factor of 0.7 (70% reduction)
Rotation of −70° (70° clockwise)
x-translation of 3
y-translation of 5

6.

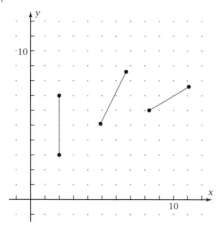

7. The images will spiral around and approach a fixed point.

8. The matrix is 3 × 4.

9. $[D] = \begin{bmatrix} 2 & 4 & 6 & 4 \\ 4 & 1 & 4 & 5 \\ 1 & 1 & 1 & 1 \end{bmatrix}$

10. $[E] \approx \begin{bmatrix} 3.8 & 6.2 & 7.3 & 5.3 \\ 5.9 & 3.8 & 6.9 & 7.3 \\ 1 & 1 & 1 & 1 \end{bmatrix}$

11.

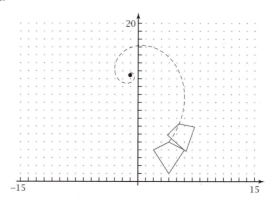

12. Graph, Problem 11, showing the path followed by the top point in the pre-image.

13. Fixed point is (−1.0356..., 13.4599...).
   • Raise [A] to a high power, say $[A]^{200}$, and look at the translation part of the answer.
   • Multiply $[A]^{200} [D]$ and see that the coordinates of all the points in the image are the same as the fixed point.

14. The fixed point is the same, (−1.0356..., 13.4599...).

15. The new fixed point is (−10.4339..., 27.3179...).

16. $\begin{bmatrix} (0.9 \cos 15°)X + (0.9 \cos 105°)Y + 5 \\ (0.9 \sin 15°)X + (0.9 \sin 105°)Y + 6 \\ 1 \end{bmatrix}$

17. The answer matrix will be $\begin{bmatrix} X \\ Y \\ 1 \end{bmatrix}$.

18. $(0.9 \cos 15°)X + (0.9 \cos 105°)Y + 5 = X$
$(0.9 \sin 15°)X + (0.9 \sin 105°)Y + 6 = Y$
$(0.9 \cos 15° - 1)X + (0.9 \cos 105°)Y = -5$
$(0.9 \sin 15°)X + (0.9 \sin 105° - 1)Y = -6$

$$\begin{bmatrix} (0.9 \cos 15° - 1) & (0.9 \cos 105°) \\ (0.9 \sin 15°) & (0.9 \sin 105° - 1) \end{bmatrix}^{-1} \begin{bmatrix} -5 \\ -6 \end{bmatrix} = \begin{bmatrix} -10.4339... \\ 27.3179... \end{bmatrix}$$

Fixed point is (−10.4339..., 27.3179...).

19. Answers will vary.

Test 30 Form A

1. $[M][M]^{-1} = \begin{bmatrix} 1 & 0 & 0 \\ 0 & 1 & 0 \\ 0 & 0 & 1 \end{bmatrix}$, the 3 × 3 identity matrix.

2. $\begin{bmatrix} 4 & 2 & 3 \\ -1 & 5 & 2 \end{bmatrix} \begin{bmatrix} 3 & -2 \\ 1 & 5 \\ 4 & 0 \end{bmatrix} = \begin{bmatrix} 26 & 2 \\ 10 & 27 \end{bmatrix}$

3. For the first product, the number of elements in the rows of the first matrix is the same as the number of elements in the columns of the second matrix, namely, 3.
For the second product, there are three elements in the rows of the first matrix but only two elements in the columns of the second matrix.

4. $[A] = \begin{bmatrix} 0.7 \cos 50° & 0.7 \cos 140° & 10 \\ 0.7 \sin 50° & 0.7 \sin 140° & -6 \\ 0 & 0 & 1 \end{bmatrix}$

Precalculus with Trigonometry: Assessment Resources
© 2007 Key Curriculum Press

5.

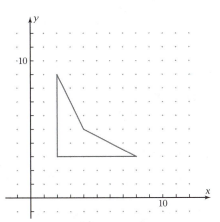

6. The images will spiral around counterclockwise, getting smaller and approaching a fixed point.

7. $N = 5$ and $r = \dfrac{1}{3}$.

8. In the seventh iteration, there will be 5^7 images.

9. In the right triangle with angle θ marked, a is the leg adjacent to θ. Segment b is equal to the leg opposite angle θ. The hypotenuse is 8, the length of the smaller square's side. Thus, $a = 8 \cos \theta$ and $b = 8 \sin \theta$, Q.E.D.

10. $8 \cos \theta + 8 \sin \theta = 10$
Solving numerically for θ close to zero gives $\theta = 17.1144\ldots°$.
Store as A.

11. The dilation is $\dfrac{8}{10} = 0.8$.
$$[A] = \begin{bmatrix} 0.8 \cos A & 0.8 \cos(90° + A) & 0 \\ 0.8 \sin A & 0.8 \sin(90° + A) & 0 \\ 0 & 0 & 1 \end{bmatrix}$$

12. Several iterations are shown.

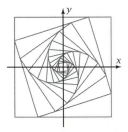

13. Two images of different size that are self-similar to the entire wave are circled.

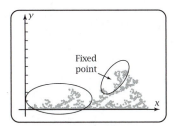

14. Dilation by a factor of 0.5
Rotation by 30°
x-translation of 7 spaces
y-translation of 0 spaces

15. Raise $[A]^{100}$. The answer is
$$\begin{bmatrix} 0.0000\ldots & 0.0000\ldots & 10.3363\ldots \\ 0.0000\ldots & 0.0000\ldots & 4.5575\ldots \\ 0 & 0 & 1 \end{bmatrix}$$
Fixed point is $(10.3363\ldots, 4.5575\ldots)$.

16. Graph, Problem 13, showing that the fixed point is at the "crest" of the wave. (Note that each of the infinite number of points in a strange attractor is the fixed point for an infinite sequence of the transformations used to generate that attractor.)

17. $D = \dfrac{\log N}{\log \left(\frac{1}{r} \right)} = \dfrac{\log 3}{\log 2} = 1.5849\ldots$ dimensional
(These are the other two transformation matrices mentioned in the problem. Both rotations are 0°.)
$$\begin{bmatrix} 0.5 & 0 & 0 \\ 0 & 0.5 & 0 \\ 0 & 0 & 1 \end{bmatrix} \text{ and } \begin{bmatrix} 0.5 & 0 & 7 \\ 0 & 0.5 & 0 \\ 0 & 0 & 1 \end{bmatrix}$$

18. Fractal figure, or just "fractal"

19. Strange attractor

20. Answers will vary.

Test 30 Form B

1. $[M][M]^{-1} = \begin{bmatrix} 1 & 0 \\ 0 & 1 \end{bmatrix}$, the 2×2 identity matrix.

2. $\begin{bmatrix} 3 & -2 \\ 1 & 5 \\ 4 & 0 \end{bmatrix} \begin{bmatrix} 4 & 2 \\ -1 & 5 \end{bmatrix} = \begin{bmatrix} 14 & -4 \\ -1 & 27 \\ 16 & 8 \end{bmatrix}$

3. For the first product, the number of elements in the rows of the first matrix is the same as the number of elements in the columns of the second matrix, namely, 2.
For the second product, there are two elements in the rows of the first matrix but three elements in the columns of the second matrix.

4. $[A] = \begin{bmatrix} 0.8 \cos(-40°) & 0.8 \cos 50° & -10 \\ 0.8 \sin(-40°) & 0.8 \sin 50° & 6 \\ 0 & 0 & 1 \end{bmatrix}$

5.

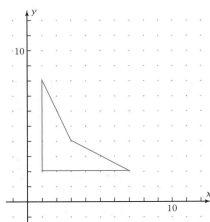

6. The images will spiral around clockwise, getting smaller and approaching a fixed point.

7. $N = 5$ and $r = \dfrac{1}{3}$.

8. In the seventh iteration, there will be 5^7 images.

9. In the right triangle with angle θ marked, a is the leg adjacent to θ. Segment b is equal to the leg opposite angle θ. The hypotenuse is 8, the length of the smaller square's side. Thus, $a = 8 \cos \theta$ and $b = 8 \sin \theta$, Q.E.D.

10. $8 \cos \theta + 8 \sin \theta = 10$
Solving numerically for θ close to zero gives $\theta = 17.1144...°$. Store as A.

11. The dilation is $\dfrac{8}{10} = 0.8$.

$$[A] = \begin{bmatrix} 0.8\cos A & 0.8\cos(90° + A) & 0 \\ 0.8\sin A & 0.8\sin(90° + A) & 0 \\ 0 & 0 & 1 \end{bmatrix}$$

12. Several iterations are shown.

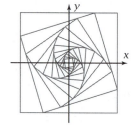

13. Two images of different size that are self-similar to the entire wave are circled.

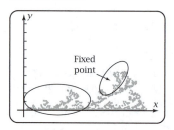

14. Dilation by a factor of 0.5
Rotation by 30°
x-translation of 7 spaces
y-translation of 0 spaces

15. Raise $[A]^{100}$. The answer is

$$\begin{bmatrix} 0.0000... & 0.0000... & 10.3363... \\ 0.0000... & 0.0000... & 4.5575... \\ 0 & 0 & 1 \end{bmatrix}$$

Fixed point is $(10.3363..., 4.5575...)$.

16. Graph, Problem 13, showing that the fixed point is at the "crest" of the wave. (Note that each of the infinite number of points in a strange attractor is the fixed point for an infinite sequence of the transformations used to generate that attractor.)

17. $D = \dfrac{\log N}{\log\left(\frac{1}{r}\right)} = \dfrac{\log 3}{\log 2} = 1.5849...$ dimensional

(These are the other two transformation matrices mentioned in the problem. Both rotations are 0°.)

$$\begin{bmatrix} 0.5 & 0 & 0 \\ 0 & 0.5 & 0 \\ 0 & 0 & 1 \end{bmatrix} \text{ and } \begin{bmatrix} 0.5 & 0 & 7 \\ 0 & 0.5 & 0 \\ 0 & 0 & 1 \end{bmatrix}$$

18. Fractal figure, or just "fractal"

19. Strange attractor

20. Answers will vary.

Test 31 Form A

1. a: Major radius (semimajor axis)
   b: Minor radius (semiminor axis)
   c: Focal radius
   d: Directrix radius

2.

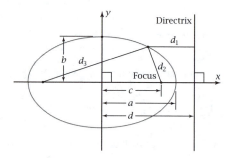

3. • $d_2 = ed_1$
   • $d_2 + d_3 = 2a$
   • $a^2 = b^2 + c^2$
   • $c = ea$ or $\dfrac{c}{a} = e$
   • $a = ed$ or $\dfrac{a}{d} = e$

4. • Opens in the y-direction. (The y^2-term is positive.)
   • Center is at the point $(2, -1)$.
   • Asymptote slopes: $m = \pm\dfrac{3}{5} = \pm 0.6$

5.

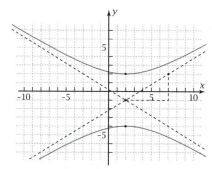

6. Paraboloid   7. Ellipsoid

8. Hyperboloid of one sheet

9. Center at point (2, 4), *x*-radius 5, *y*-radius 3

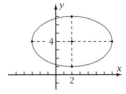

10. $a = 5$ and $b = 3$, so $c^2 = 5^2 - 3^2 = 16$.
    Focal radius is $c = 4$.
    Eccentricity $= \dfrac{c}{a} = \dfrac{4}{5} = 0.8$

11. $x = 2 + 5 \cos t$
    $y = 4 + 3 \sin t$

12. $\left(\dfrac{x-2}{5}\right)^2 + \left(\dfrac{y-4}{3}\right)^2 = 1$
    $\dfrac{(x-2)^2}{25} + \dfrac{(y-4)^2}{9} = 1$
    $9(x^2 - 4x + 4) + 25(y^2 - 8y + 16) = 225$
    $9x^2 - 36x + 36 + 25y^2 - 200y + 400 = 225$
    $9x^2 + 25y^2 - 36x - 200y + 211 = 0$

13. The graph is an ellipse because the squared terms are the same sign but have different coefficients. (And there is no *xy*-term.)

14. Graph of $9x^2 - 16y^2 = 144$ on the grapher, using the CONIC program, agrees with the given figure.

15. $\dfrac{9x^2 + 16y^2}{144} = \dfrac{144}{144}$
    $\dfrac{x^2}{16} + \dfrac{y^2}{9} = 1$ or $\left(\dfrac{x}{4}\right)^2 + \left(\dfrac{y}{3}\right)^2 = 1$
    x-radius = 4, *y*-radius = 3

16. Slopes are $\pm\dfrac{y\text{-radius}}{x\text{-radius}} = \pm\dfrac{3}{4} = \pm 0.75$.

17. *x*-radius, $a = 4$, is the transverse radius.
    y-radius, $b = 3$, is the conjugate radius.

18. Measure the diagonal by marking off on a piece of paper. The length is 5 units, equal to the focal radius, *c*.

19. $c^2 = a^2 + b^2$

20. Eccentricity: $e = \dfrac{c}{a} = \dfrac{5}{4} = 1.25$

21. Directrix radius: $a = ed \Rightarrow d = \dfrac{a}{e} = \dfrac{4}{1.25} = 3.2$

22. Transverse radius $a = 2$, and conjugate radius $b = 6$.

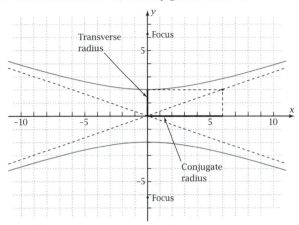

23. $c^2 = a^2 + b^2 = 2^2 + 6^2 = 40$
    $c = \sqrt{40} = 6.3245...$
    See the graph in Problem 22, showing the two foci.

24. False. The transverse axis goes from center to vertex and may be longer or shorter than, or the same length as, the conjugate axis. (Note: The conjugate axis is the transverse axis of the conjugate hyperbola, the hyperbola with the same center and asymptotes but opening in the other direction.)

25. $x = 6 \tan t$
    $y = 2 \sec t$

26. Center at point (−3, 2), *x*-radius 4, *y*-radius 7

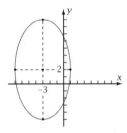

27. $x = -3 + 4 \cos t$ and $y = 2 + 7 \sin t$
    $\dfrac{x+3}{4} = \cos t$ and $\dfrac{y-2}{7} = \sin t$
    $\left(\dfrac{x+3}{4}\right)^2 = \cos^2 t$ and $\left(\dfrac{y-2}{7}\right)^2 = \sin^2 t$
    $\left(\dfrac{x+3}{4}\right)^2 + \left(\dfrac{y-2}{7}\right)^2 = \cos^2 t + \sin^2 t$
    $\left(\dfrac{x+3}{4}\right)^2 + \left(\dfrac{y-2}{7}\right)^2 = 1$
    (Note: This is the standard form of the Cartesian equation of an ellipse.)

28. Answers will vary.

Test 31 Form B

1. a: Major radius (semimajor axis)
   b: Minor radius (semiminor axis)
   c: Focal radius
   d: Directrix radius

2.

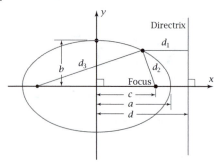

3. • $d_2 = ed_1$

   • $d_2 + d_3 = 2a$

   • $a^2 = b^2 + c^2$

   • $c = ea$ or $\dfrac{c}{a} = e$

   • $a = ed$ or $\dfrac{a}{d} = e$

4. • Opens in the x-direction. (The x^2-term is positive.)

   • Center is at the point $(-2, 1)$.

   • Asymptote slopes: $m = \pm\dfrac{5}{3} = \pm1.666...$

5.

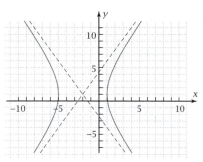

6. Paraboloid

7. Ellipsoid

8. Hyperboloid of one sheet

9. Center at point $(4, 2)$, x-radius 3, y-radius 5

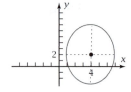

10. $a = 5$ and $b = 3$, so $c^2 = 5^2 - 3^2 = 16$.
    Focal radius is $c = 4$.
    Eccentricity $= \dfrac{c}{a} = \dfrac{4}{5} = 0.8$

11. $x = 4 + 3\cos t$
    $y = 2 + 5\sin t$

12. $\left(\dfrac{x-4}{3}\right)^2 + \left(\dfrac{y-2}{5}\right)^2 = 1$
    $\dfrac{(x-4)^2}{9} + \dfrac{(y-2)^2}{25} = 1$
    $25(x^2 - 8x + 16) + 9(y^2 - 4y + 4) = 225$
    $25x^2 - 400x + 400 + 9y^2 - 36y + 16 = 225$
    $25x^2 + 9y^2 - 400x - 36y + 211 = 0$

13. The graph is an ellipse because the squared terms are the same sign but have different coefficients. (And there is no xy-term.)

14. Graph of $16x^2 - 9y^2 = 144$ on the grapher, using the CONIC program, agrees with the given figure.

15. $\dfrac{16x^2 - 9y^2}{144} = \dfrac{144}{144}$
    $\dfrac{x^2}{9} - \dfrac{y^2}{16} = 1$ or $\left(\dfrac{x}{3}\right)^2 - \left(\dfrac{y}{4}\right)^2 = 1$
    x-radius = 3, y-radius = 4

16. Slopes are $\pm\dfrac{y\text{-radius}}{x\text{-radius}} = \pm\dfrac{4}{3} = \pm1.333...$.

17. x-radius, $a = 3$, is the transverse radius.
    y-radius, $b = 4$, is the conjugate radius.

18. Measure the diagonal by marking off on a piece of paper. The length is 5 units, equal to the focal radius, c.

19. $c^2 = a^2 + b^2$

20. Eccentricity: $e = \dfrac{c}{a} = \dfrac{5}{3} = 1.666...$

21. Directrix radius: $a = ed \Rightarrow d = \dfrac{a}{e} = \dfrac{3}{\left(\frac{5}{3}\right)} = 1.8$

22. Transverse radius $a = 2$, and conjugate radius $b = 6$.

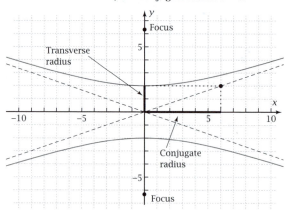

23. $c^2 = a^2 + b^2 = 2^2 + 6^2 = 40$
    $c = \sqrt{40} = 6.3245...$
    See the graph in Problem 22, showing the two foci.

Precalculus with Trigonometry: Assessment Resources
© 2007 Key Curriculum Press

24. False. The transverse axis goes from center to vertex and may be longer or shorter than, or the same length as, the conjugate axis. (Note: The conjugate axis is the transverse axis of the conjugate hyperbola, the hyperbola with the same center and asymptotes but opening in the other direction.)

25. $x = 6 \tan t$
$y = 2 \sec t$

26. Center at point $(-4, 3)$, x-radius 6, y-radius 4

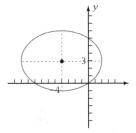

27. $x = -4 + 6 \cos t$ and $y = 3 + 4 \sin t$
$$\frac{x + 4}{6} = \cos t \text{ and } \frac{y - 3}{4} = \sin t$$
$$\left(\frac{x + 4}{6}\right)^2 = \cos^2 t \text{ and } \left(\frac{y - 3}{4}\right)^2 = \sin^2 t$$
$$\left(\frac{x + 4}{6}\right)^2 + \left(\frac{y - 3}{4}\right)^2 = \cos^2 t + \sin^2 t$$
$$\left(\frac{x + 4}{6}\right)^2 + \left(\frac{y - 3}{4}\right)^2 = 1$$
(Note: This is the standard form of the Cartesian equation of an ellipse.)

28. Answers will vary.

Test 32 Form A

1. The xy-term rotates the graph (without changing the intercepts).

2. Discriminant $= B^2 - 4AC$

3. If $B = 0$, then the discriminant equals $-4AC$. If A and C have opposite signs, as they do for a hyperbola, then $-4AC$ will be a positive number. Thus, a positive discriminant indicates a hyperbola.

4. $B^2 - 4AC = (-6)^2 - 4(1)(9) = 0$
Therefore, the graph will be a parabola.

5.

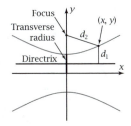

6. The hyperbola opens in the y-direction.

7.

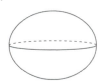

8. $\frac{c}{a} = e \Rightarrow c = ae = (10)(2) = 20$
Graph, Problem 7, showing the focus at a point twice as far from the center as the vertex.

9. $\frac{a}{d} = e \Rightarrow d = \frac{a}{e} = \frac{10}{2} = 5$
Graph, Problem 7, showing the directrix halfway between the center and the vertex.

10. Graph, Problem 7, showing point (x, y) on the hyperbola and distances d_1 and d_2.
By the definition of eccentricity, $d_2 = 2d_1$.

11. $y = 4 - 0.7^2 = 3.51$
Volume $= \pi(0.7^2)(3.51) = 5.4032... \approx 5.4 \text{ cm}^3$

12. $y = 4 - 1^2 = 3$
Volume $= \pi(1^2)(3) = 9.4247... \approx 9.42 \text{ cm}^3$

13. Volume $= \pi x^2 y = \pi x^2(4 - x^2)$
Maximum volume of $12.5663...$ at $x = 1.4142...$.
(Exact values: $x = \sqrt{2}$, volume $= 4\pi$)

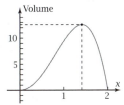

14. If you substitute 0 for x or for y in the second equation to find an intercept, the xy-term is zero, leaving the same equation as on the left. So the intercepts will be the same for the two graphs.

15. $B^2 - 4AC = 5^2 - 4(1)(4) = 9 > 0$
Because the discriminant is positive, the graph will be a hyperbola. The rule that the graph is an ellipse if the squared terms have the same sign works only if the xy-term is zero.

16. Ellipse and rotated hyperbola. (Note that the intercepts are the same for both graphs.)

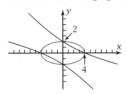

17. Major axis $= 2a = 156 + 128 = 284$ million mi
Major radius $= a = \frac{284}{2} = 142$ million mi

18. Focal radius $= c = 142 - 128 = 14$ million mi
$b^2 = a^2 - c^2 = 142^2 - 14^2 = 19{,}968$
Minor radius $b = 141.3081... \approx 141.31$ million mi
Eccentricity $= \frac{c}{a} = \frac{14}{142} = 0.09859...$

19. Equation is $\left(\frac{x - 14}{142}\right)^2 + \left(\frac{y}{141.3081...}\right)^2 = 1$.

20. The angle is $90°$ when $x = 0$.
$$\left(\frac{0 - 14}{142}\right)^2 + \left(\frac{y}{141.3081...}\right)^2 = 1$$
$$\frac{y^2}{19{,}968} = 1 - \frac{196}{20{,}164}$$
$$y^2 = 19{,}773.9051...$$
$$y = \pm 140.6197..., \text{ or about } 140.62 \text{ million mi}$$

21. $d = \dfrac{a}{e} = \dfrac{142}{\left(\frac{14}{142}\right)} = 1440.2857...$

1440.2857... ± 14 = 1454.2857... or 1426.2857...
The directrices are about 1454.29 and 1426.29 million mi from the Sun.

22. $x = 14 + 142 \cos t$
$y = 141.3081... \sin t$
The graph agrees with the given figure.

23. Answers will vary.

Test 32 Form B

1. The xy-term rotates the graph (without changing the intercepts).

2. Discriminant $= B^2 - 4AC$

3. If $B = 0$, then the discriminant equals $-4AC$. If A and C have the same signs, as they do for an ellipse or a circle, then $-4AC$ will be a negative number. Thus, a negative discriminant indicates an ellipse or a circle.

4. $B^2 - 4AC = (6)^2 - 4(1)(9) = 0$
Therefore, the graph will be a parabola.

5.

6. The hyperbola opens in the y-direction.

7.
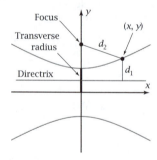

8. $\dfrac{c}{a} = e \Rightarrow c = ae = (10)(2) = 20$
Graph, Problem 7, showing the focus at a point twice as far from the center as the vertex.

9. $\dfrac{a}{d} = e \Rightarrow d = \dfrac{a}{e} = \dfrac{10}{2} = 5$
Graph, Problem 7, showing the directrix halfway between the center and the vertex.

10. Graph, Problem 7, showing point (x, y) on the hyperbola and distances d_1 and d_2.
By the definition of eccentricity, $d_2 = 2d_1$.

11. $y = 9 - 0.7^2 = 8.51$
Volume $\pi(0.7)^2(8.51) = 13.1001...$ cm³

12. $y = 9 - 1^2 = 8$
Volume $\pi(1)^2(8) = 25.1327...$ cm³

13. Volume $\pi x^2 y = \pi x^2(9 - x^2)$
Maximum volume of 63.6172... at $x = 2.1213....$

(Exact values: $x = \sqrt{\dfrac{9}{2}}$, volume $= \dfrac{81}{4}\pi$)

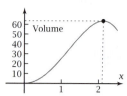

14. If you substitute 0 for x or for y in the second equation to find an intercept, the xy-term is zero, leaving the same equation as on the left. So the intercepts will be the same for the two graphs.

15. $B^2 - 4AC = 5^2 - 4(4)(1) = 9 > 0$
Because the discriminant is positive, the graph will be a hyperbola. The rule that the graph is an ellipse if the squared terms have the same sign works only if the xy-term is zero.

16. Ellipse and rotated hyperbola. (Note that the intercepts are the same for both graphs.)

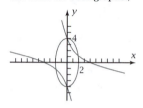

17. $a = \dfrac{5000 + 50}{2} = 2525$ million mi
$c = 2525 - 50 = 2475$ million mi
$e = \dfrac{c}{a} = \dfrac{99}{101} = 0.9801...$

18. $b = \sqrt{a^2 - c^2} = 500$ million mi
center $(c, 0) = (2475, 0)$
Equation is $\left(\dfrac{x - 2475}{2525}\right)^2 + \left(\dfrac{y}{500}\right)^2 = 1$, with x and y in million mi.

19. $(2)(500) = 1000$ million mi

20. $\left(\dfrac{0 - 2475}{2525}\right)^2 + \left(\dfrac{y}{500}\right)^2 = 1$
$y^2 = 9802.9604... \Rightarrow y = 99$ million mi

21. $d = \dfrac{a^2}{c} \approx 2576$ million mi from the center, or
2576 − 2475 = 101 million mi from the Sun, that is, at $x = -101$.

22. $x = 2475 + 2525 \cos t$
$y = 500 \sin t$

23. Answers will vary.

Precalculus with Trigonometry: Assessment Resources
© 2007 Key Curriculum Press

Test 33 Form A

1. (5, 230°)   (−3, 150°)

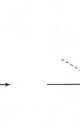

2. e.g., (5, 430°)   3. e.g., (5, −290°)

4. e.g., (−5, 250°)   5. e.g., (−5, −110°)

6. $(2 + 7i)(5 + 4i) = 10 + 43i + 28i^2 = -18 + 43i$

7. (Equation is $r = -2 + 7 \sin(\theta + 60 \cos \theta)$, a sinusoid with a variable phase displacement.)

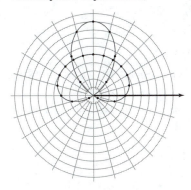

8. $(10 \text{ cis } 200°)(2 \text{ cis } 50°) = 20 \text{ cis } 250°$

9. $\dfrac{10 \text{ cis } 200°}{2 \text{ cis } 50°} = 5 \text{ cis } 150°$

10. $(2 \text{ cis } 40°)^3 = 8 \text{ cis } 120°$

11. From graph, $r \approx 6.5$.

12. $\theta \approx 90°$ and $\theta \approx 270°$

13. Substitute 0° and 180° for θ and solve for a and b.
    At $\theta = 0°$, $r = 8$. At $\theta = 180°$, $r = 2$.
    $8 = a + b \cos 0° \Rightarrow 8 = a + b$
    $2 = a + b \cos 180° \Rightarrow 2 = a - b$
    $10 = 2a \Rightarrow a = 5$
    $6 = 2b \Rightarrow b = 3$
    Equation is $r = 5 + 3 \cos \theta$.

14. Point on spiral is at $\theta = 450°$.

15. The point is not a solution to the system of equations because the two curves are not at this point for the same value of θ. (For the rose, $r = -7$, and for the spiral, $r = 7$ at this point.)

16. $\theta \approx 374°$

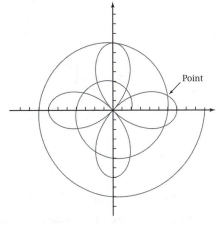

17. By solver, $\theta = 374.1981...°$.

18. $z = -6 + 2i \Rightarrow r = |z| = \sqrt{36 + 4} = \sqrt{40}$
    $\theta = \arctan \dfrac{2}{-6} = -18.4349...° + 180°n = 161.5650...°$
    $\therefore z = \sqrt{40} \text{ cis } 161.5650...°$

19. $5 \text{ cis } 120° = 5(\cos 120° + i \sin 120°) = -2.5 + 4.3301...i$

20. $(64 \text{ cis } 150°)^{1/3} = [64 \text{ cis } (150° + 360°n)]^{1/3}$
    $= 4 \text{ cis } (50° + 120°n) = 4 \text{ cis } 50°, 4 \text{ cis } 170°, 4 \text{ cis } 290°$

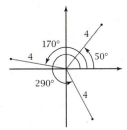

21. $z_1 z_2 = (2 + 7i)(5 + 4i) = -18 + 43i$

22. $|z_1| = \sqrt{4 + 49} = \sqrt{53}$
    $|z_2| = \sqrt{25 + 16} = \sqrt{41}$
    $|z_1 z_2| = \sqrt{(-18)^2 + 43^2} = \sqrt{2173}$
    $\sqrt{53}\sqrt{41} = \sqrt{2173}$
    $\therefore |z_1 z_2| = |z_1||z_2|$, Q.E.D.

23. Modulus

24. $r = \dfrac{6}{3 - 2 \cos \theta}$
    $3r - 2r \cos \theta = 6$
    $3\sqrt{x^2 + y^2} - 2x = 6$
    $3\sqrt{x^2 + y^2} = 2x + 6$
    $9(x^2 + y^2) = 4x^2 + 24x + 36$
    $9x^2 + 9y^2 = 4x^2 + 24x + 36$
    $5x^2 + 9y^2 - 24x - 36 = 0$
    $\therefore$ the graph is an ellipse because the x^2- and y^2-coefficients have the same sign but are unequal (and there is no x-term).

25. Answers will vary.

1.   (4, 240°)   (−2, 120°)

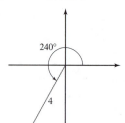

16. $\theta \approx 195°$

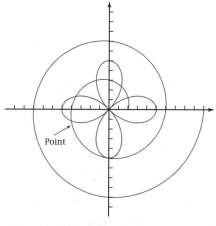

2. e.g., (4, 420°)   3. e.g., (4, −300°)

4. e.g., (−4, 240°)   5. e.g., (−4, −120°)

6. $(3 + 5i)(2 + 3i) = 6 + 19i + 15i^2 = -9 + 19i$

7. (Equation is $r = -1 + 5\sin(\theta + 60\cos\theta)$, a sinusoid with a variable phase displacement.)

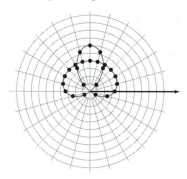

8. $(8 \text{ cis } 150°)(4 \text{ cis } 100°) = 32 \text{ cis } 250°$

9. $\dfrac{8 \text{ cis } 150°}{4 \text{ cis } 100°} = 2 \text{ cis } 50°$

10. $(3 \text{ cis } 40°)^4 = 81 \text{ cis } 160°$

11. From graph, $r \approx 4.0$.

12. $\theta \approx 90°$ and $\theta \approx 270°$

13. Substitute 0° and 180° for θ and solve for a and b.
     At $\theta = 0°$, $r = 5$. At $\theta = 180°$, $r = 1$.
     $5 = a + b\cos 0° \Rightarrow 5 = a + b$
     $1 = a + b\cos 180° \Rightarrow 1 = a - b$
     $6 = 2a \Rightarrow a = 3$
     $4 = 2b \Rightarrow b = 2$
     Equation is $r = 3 + 2\cos\theta$.

14. Point on spiral is at $\theta = 270°$.

15. The point is not a solution to the system of equations because the two curves are not at this point for the same value of θ. (For the rose, $r = -5$, and for the spiral, $r = 5$ at this point.)

17. By solver, $\theta = 196.5941...°$.

18. $z = -4 + 2i \Rightarrow r = |z| = \sqrt{16 + 4} = \sqrt{20}$
     $\theta = \arctan\dfrac{2}{-4} = -26.5650...° + 180°n$
     $\therefore z = \sqrt{20} \text{ cis } 153.4349...°$

19. $4 \text{ cis } 135° = 4(\cos 135° + i\sin 135°) = -2.8284... + 2.8284...i$

20. $(27 \text{ cis } 120°)^{1/3} = [27 \text{ cis }(120° + 360°n)]^{1/3}$
     $= 3 \text{ cis }(40° + 120°n) = 3 \text{ cis } 40°, 3 \text{ cis } 160°, 3 \text{ cis } 280°$

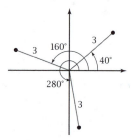

21. $z_1 z_2 = (3 + 5i)(2 + 3i) = -9 + 19i$

22. $|z_1| = \sqrt{9 + 25} = \sqrt{34}$
     $|z_2| = \sqrt{4 + 9} = \sqrt{13}$
     $|z_1 z_2| = \sqrt{81 + 361} = \sqrt{442}$
     $\sqrt{34}\sqrt{13} = \sqrt{442}$
     $\therefore |z_1 z_2| = |z_1||z_2|$, Q.E.D.

23. Modulus

24. $r = \dfrac{6}{1 + \cos\theta}$
     $r + r\cos\theta = 6$
     $\sqrt{x^2 + y^2} + x = 6$
     $\sqrt{x^2 + y^2} = 6 - x$
     $x^2 + y^2 = 36 - 12x + x^2$
     $y^2 + 12x - 36 = 0$
     $\therefore$ the graph is a parabola because there is just one squared term (and there is no xy-term).

25. Answers will vary.

Test 34 Form A

1. $x = -8 + 4t$
   $y = 19 + 2t$

2. $x = -8 + 4(10) = 32$
   $y = 19 + 2(10) = 39$
   He is at his 32-yard line, 39 yards from the right sideline.

3. $60 = -8 + 4t \Rightarrow t = 17$ s

4. $y = 19 + 2(17) = 53$ yd
   He is just barely in bounds.

5.

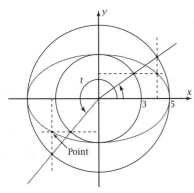

6. Angle t, adjacent leg x, hypotenuse 5 (the radius of the big circle)
   $\dfrac{x}{5} = \cos t \Rightarrow x = 5 \cos t$

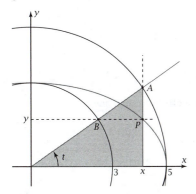

7. Angle t, opposite leg y, and hypotenuse 3 (the radius of the small circle)
   $\dfrac{y}{3} = \sin t \Rightarrow y = 3 \sin t$

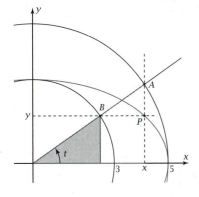

8. $\dfrac{x}{5} = \cos t \Rightarrow \left(\dfrac{x}{5}\right)^2 = \cos^2 t$

   $\dfrac{y}{3} = \sin t \Rightarrow \left(\dfrac{y}{3}\right)^2 = \sin^2 t$

   $\left(\dfrac{x}{5}\right)^2 + \left(\dfrac{y}{3}\right)^2 = \cos^2 t + \sin^2 t$

   $\left(\dfrac{x}{5}\right)^2 + \left(\dfrac{y}{3}\right)^2 = 1$

   This is the equation of an ellipse centered at the origin with x-radius 5 and y-radius 3, as in the given figure.

9. Center of big, moving circle is at the point
   $(6 \cos 0.9, 6 \sin 0.9) = (3.7296\ldots, 4.6999\ldots)$.

10. arc length = (radius)(angle in radians)
    From small circle, $a = (2)(0.9) = 1.8$ units.
    In big circle, $1.8 = (4)(A) \Rightarrow A = 0.45$ radians.

11. For t, if parallel lines are cut by a transversal, then corresponding angles are congruent.
    For a, vertical angles are congruent.
    $\theta = 0.9 + 0.45 = 1.35$ radians

12. x = horizontal displacement from origin to center of big circle plus horizontal displacement from center of big circle to P.
    $x = 6 \cos 0.9 + 4 \cos 1.35 = 4.6056\ldots$
    Similarly, $y = 6 \sin 0.9 + 4 \sin 1.35 = 8.6028\ldots$.
    P has coordinates $(4.6056\ldots, 8.6028\ldots)$.
    On the graph, P has approximate coordinates $(4.6, 8.6)$, which agree with the numerical answers.

13. $\theta = t + A$ and $A = 0.5t$, so $\theta = 1.5t$.

14. $x = 6 \cos t + 4 \cos \theta$
    $y = 6 \sin t + 4 \sin \theta$
    Equations as functions of t alone are
    $x = 6 \cos t + 4 \cos 1.5t$
    $y = 6 \sin t + 4 \sin 1.5t$

15. Two revolutions are needed for t because after one revolution, θ has only completed half a cycle.
    Equations of the small circle are
    $x = 2 \cos t$
    $y = 2 \sin t$

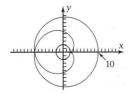

16. Answers will vary.

Test 34 Form B

1. $v_x = 6 \cos 55° = 3.4414\ldots$ ft/s
   $v_y = 6 \sin 55° = 4.9149\ldots$ ft/s

2. $x = 263 + 6t \cos 55° = 263 + 3.4414\ldots t$
   $y = 107 + 6t \sin 55° = 107 + 4.9149\ldots t$

3. $y = 0$ ft $\Rightarrow t = \dfrac{-107}{6 \sin 55°} = 21.7704\ldots$ s
   About 22 seconds before $t = 0$ s.

4. $x = 263 + 6\left(\dfrac{-170}{6 \sin 55°}\right) \cos 55° = 188.0777\ldots$ ft

5.

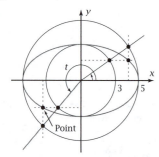

6. Angle t, adjacent leg x, hypotenuse 5 (the radius of the big circle)

$$\frac{x}{5} = \cos t \Rightarrow x = 5 \cos t$$

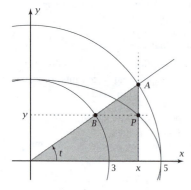

7. Angle t, opposite leg y, and hypotenuse 3 (the radius of the small circle)

$$\frac{y}{3} = \sin t \Rightarrow y = 3 \sin t$$

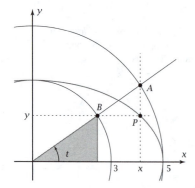

8. $\dfrac{x}{5} = \cos t \Rightarrow \left(\dfrac{x}{5}\right)^2 = \cos^2 t$

$\dfrac{y}{3} = \sin t \Rightarrow \left(\dfrac{y}{3}\right)^2 = \sin^2 t$

$\left(\dfrac{x}{5}\right)^2 + \left(\dfrac{y}{3}\right)^2 = \cos^2 t + \sin^2 t$

$\left(\dfrac{x}{5}\right)^2 + \left(\dfrac{y}{3}\right)^2 = 1$

This is the equation of an ellipse centered at the origin with x-radius 5 and y-radius 3, as in the given figure.

9. The points should lie on the serpentine.

10. $\tan t = \dfrac{5}{x} \Leftrightarrow x = 5 \cot t$

Let A be the distance from the origin to the point on the circle. Using a right triangle with right angle at A and hypotenuse 10, $|A| = 10 \cos t$.
Because $y = |A| \sin t$, $y = 10 \cos t \sin t = 5 \sin 2t$.
So $x = 5 \cot t$, $y = 5 \sin 2t$.

11. The graph agrees.

12. $x(0.35) = 5 \cot 0.35 = 13.6975...$
$y(0.35) = 5 \sin 0.70 = 3.2210...$

13. Answers will vary.

Test 35 Form A

1. $\dfrac{x}{r} = \dfrac{\text{adjacent}}{\text{hypotenuse}} = \cos\theta \Rightarrow x = r\cos\theta$

$\dfrac{y}{r} = \dfrac{\text{opposite}}{\text{hypotenuse}} = \sin\theta \Rightarrow y = r\sin\theta$

By the Pythagorean theorem, $x^2 + y^2 = r^2$.

2.

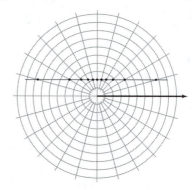

3. $r = \dfrac{2}{\sin\theta} \Rightarrow r\sin\theta = 2 \Rightarrow y = 2$

This is the equation of a horizontal line, Q.E.D.

4. $r = \dfrac{2}{\sin(\theta - 40°)}$

5. $(10 \text{ cis } 60°)(2 \text{ cis } 40°) = 20 \text{ cis } 100°$

6. $\dfrac{10 \cos 60°}{2 \text{ cis } 40°} = 5 \text{ cis } 20°$

7. De Moivre's theorem

8. $[8 \text{ cis } (-30°)]^{1/3} = [8 \text{ cis } (-30° + 360n°)]^{1/3}$
$= 2 \text{ cis } (-10° + 120n°)$
$= 2 \text{ cis } (-10°), 2 \text{ cis } 110°, 2 \text{ cis } 230°$

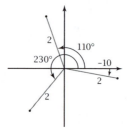

9. The graph agrees with the given figure.

10. The point is in the fourth quadrant because r is negative.

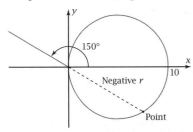

11. For θ between 180° and 360°, the graph is retracing itself but with r the opposite sign.

12. $r = 10 \cos \theta$
$r^2 = 10r \cos \theta$
$x^2 + y^2 = 10x$
$x^2 + y^2 - 10x = 0$
The graph is a circle because x^2 and y^2 have equal coefficients (and there is no xy-term).

13. In each case, the distance between the curve and the line $y = 2$ measures 7 units. (For the angle in Quadrant III, measure back to the line, as shown.)

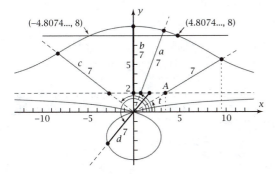

14. Let x_1 and x_2 be the lengths of the two segments. For x_1 use the right triangle with opposite leg 2. For x_2 use the right triangle with hypotenuse 7. In both triangles, an acute angle equals t degrees.
$\dfrac{x_1}{2} = \cot t$ and $\dfrac{x_2}{7} = \cos t$
$x_1 = 2 \cot t$ and $x_2 = 7 \cos t$
$x = 2 \cot t + 7 \cos t$

15. Let y_1 and y_2 be the lengths of the two segments. Use the same triangles as in Problem 14.
$y_1 = 2$ and $y_2 = 7 \sin t$
$y = 2 + 7 \sin t$

16. The grapher plot agrees with the given graph. (Use a fairly small t-step.)

17. $(x^2 + y^2)(y - 2)^2 = 49y^2$
$(x^2 + 64)(8 - 2)^2 = 49(64)$
$x^2 + 64 = \dfrac{49(64)}{36}$
$x^2 = 23.1111\ldots$
$x = \pm 4.8074\ldots$
See the graph in Problem 13, showing that a horizontal line at $y = 8$ cuts the curve at about ±4.8.

18. Answers will vary.

Test 35 Form B

1. $\dfrac{x}{r} = \dfrac{\text{adjacent}}{\text{hypotenuse}} = \cos \theta \Rightarrow x = r \cos \theta$
$\dfrac{y}{r} = \dfrac{\text{opposite}}{\text{hypotenuse}} = \sin \theta \Rightarrow y = r \sin \theta$
By the Pythagorean theorem, $x^2 + y^2 = r^2$.

2.

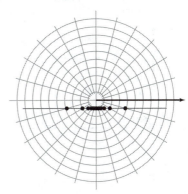

3. $r = \dfrac{-1}{\sin \theta} \Rightarrow r \sin \theta = -1 \Rightarrow y = -1$
This is the equation of a horizontal line, Q.E.D.

4. $r = \dfrac{-1}{\sin(\theta - 50°)}$

5. $(12 \operatorname{cis} 60°)(4 \operatorname{cis} 20°) = 48 \operatorname{cis} 80°$

6. $\dfrac{12 \cos 60°}{4 \operatorname{cis} 20°} = 3 \operatorname{cis} 40°$

7. De Moivre's theorem

8. $[27 \operatorname{cis}(-30°)]^{1/3} = [27 \operatorname{cis}(-30° + 360n°)]^{1/3}$
$= 3 \operatorname{cis}(-10° + 120n°)$
$= 3 \operatorname{cis}(-10°),\ 3 \operatorname{cis} 110°,\ 3 \operatorname{cis} 230°$

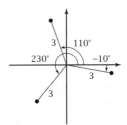

9. The graph agrees with the given figure.

10. The point is in the fourth quadrant because r is negative.

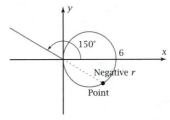

11. For θ between 180° and 360°, the graph is retracing itself but with r the opposite sign.

12. $r = 6 \cos \theta$
$r^2 = 6r \cos \theta$
$x^2 + y^2 = 6x$
$x^2 + y^2 - 6x = 0$
The graph is a circle because x^2 and y^2 have equal coefficients (and there is no xy-term).

13. In each case, the distance between the curve and the line $y = 2$ measures 7 units. (For the angle in Quadrant III, measure back to the line, as shown.)

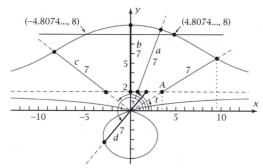

14. Let x_1 and x_2 be the lengths of the two segments.
For x_1 use the right triangle with opposite leg 2.
For x_2 use the right triangle with hypotenuse 7.
In both triangles, an acute angle equals t radians.
$\dfrac{x_1}{2} = \cot t$ and $\dfrac{x_2}{7} = \cos t$
$x_1 = 2 \cot t$ and $x_2 = 7 \cos t$
$x = 2 \cot t + 7 \cos t$

15. Let y_1 and y_2 be the lengths of the two segments.
Use the same triangles as in Problem 14.
$y_1 = 2$ and $y_2 = 7 \sin t$
$y = 2 + 7 \sin t$

16. The grapher plot agrees with the given graph.
(Use a fairly small t-step.)

17. $(x^2 + y^2)(y - 2)^2 = 49y^2$
$(x^2 + 64)(8 - 2)^2 = 49(64)$
$x^2 + 64 = \dfrac{49(64)}{36}$
$x^2 = 23.1111\ldots$
$x = \pm 4.8074\ldots$
See the graph in Problem 13, showing that a horizontal line at $y = 8$ cuts the curve at about ± 4.8.

18. Answers will vary.

Test 36 Form A

1. 10, 30, <u>50</u>, <u>70</u>   2. 10, 30, <u>90</u>, <u>270</u>

3. Sequence: 5, 15, 45, . . .
Series: $5 + 15 + 45 + \cdots$

4. $8 + 13 + 18 + \cdots$

5. $6 - 2 = 4$ and $12 - 6 = 6$, so it's not arithmetic.
$\dfrac{6}{2} = 3$ and $\dfrac{12}{6} = 2$, so it's not geometric.

6. 1, 3, 1, 5, 1, 7, <u>1</u>, <u>9</u>
(Pattern: Two sequences merged, 1, 1, 1, 1, . . . and 3, 5, 7, 9, ...)

7. $2 + 6 + 12 + 20 + 30 + 42 + \underline{56} + \underline{72}$

8. Possible patterns:
Iterative: Add 4, add 6, add 8, add 10, add 12, add 14, . . .
Numeric: $1 \cdot 2 + 2 \cdot 3 + 3 \cdot 4 + 4 \cdot 5 + 5 \cdot 6 + \cdots$
Algebraic: $t_n = (n)(n + 1) = n^2 + n$

9. $d = 23 - 19 = 4$
Terms are $19 - 4 = \underline{15}$ and $23 + 4 = \underline{27}$.

10. 3, <u>6</u>, <u>12</u>, <u>24</u>, <u>48</u>, 96

11. $n = 6$

12. Geometric means

13. Women: \$25,000, \$26,250, \$27,562.5; geometric
Men: \$30,000, \$32,000, \$34,000; arithmetic

14. Women's salaries increase by \$1250 and \$1312.50.
Men's salaries increase \$2000 both years.
So men's salaries are increasing faster than women's.
(Note that women's salaries are increasing at an increasing rate, though!)

15. For $n = 25$:
Women's: $25,000(1.05)^{24} = 80,627.4985\ldots \approx \$80,627$
Men's: $30,000 + 24(2000) = \$78,000$
So women will be making about \$2,627 more!

16. $d = 32 - 19 = 13$

17. $t_{300} = 19 + (299)(13) = 3{,}906$

18. • $S_{300} = 150(19 + 3{,}906) = 588{,}750$ by formula
    • Enter $t_n = 19 + (n - 1)(13)$ in the y= menu.
      $S_{300} = 588{,}750$ by program
    • The formula is quicker. For the program, you must still enter the formula for t_n and then wait while it does the 300 iterations.

19. $7377 = 19 + (n - 1)(13)$
$7358 = (n - 1)(13)$
$566 = n - 1$
$n = 567$

20. Algebraically:
$1086 = \left(\dfrac{n}{2}\right)[19 + 19 + (n - 1)(13)]$
$2172 = 25n + 13n^2$
$13n^2 + 25n - 2172 = 0$
$n = 12$ or $-13.9230\ldots$
$n = 12$ terms

Numerically:
• Enter $t_n = 19 + (n - 1)(13)$ in the y= menu.
  Run the program, stopping when the partial sum is 972.
  Read $n = 12$ from the program display.
• Enter $S_n = \left(\dfrac{n}{2}\right)[19 + 19 + (n - 1)(13)]$ in the y= menu.
  Make a table of values, reading $n = 12$ when $S_n = 1086$.

21. $r = \dfrac{90}{100} = 0.9$

22. $t_{30} = 100(0.9^{29}) = 4.7101\ldots$

23. $28.2429 \approx 100(0.9^{n-1})$
$\log 0.282429 \approx (n - 1)\log 0.9$
$n - 1 \approx \dfrac{\log 0.282429\ldots}{\log 0.9} = 12.000018\ldots$
$n = 13$

24. $S_3 = 100 + 90 + 81 = 271$

25. $S_3 = 100 \cdot \dfrac{1 - 0.9^3}{1 - 0.9} = 271$, agreeing with Problem 24.

26. $S = \lim\limits_{n \to \infty} \left(100 \cdot \dfrac{1 - 0.9^n}{1 - 0.9} \right)$

$\quad = 100 \cdot \dfrac{1}{0.1} = 1000$

27. $S_4 = 2 + 5 + 10 + 17 = 34$

28. Answers will vary.

Test 36 Form B

1. 5, 25, <u>45</u>, <u>65</u>   2. 5, 25, <u>125</u>, <u>625</u>

3. Sequence: 10, 30, 90, . . .
   Series: $10 + 30 + 90 + \cdots$

4. $7 + 12 + 17 + \cdots$

5. $6 - 2 = 4$ and $24 - 6 = 18$, so it's not arithmetic.
   $\dfrac{6}{2} = 3$ and $\dfrac{24}{6} = 4$, so it's not geometric.

6. 1, 2, 1, 4, 1, 6, <u>1</u>, <u>8</u>
   (Pattern: Two sequences merged, 1, 1, 1, 1, . . .
   and 2, 4, 6, 8, ...)

7. $1 + 3 + 6 + 10 + 15 + 21 + \underline{28} + \underline{36}$

8. Possible patterns:
   Iterative: Add 2, add 3, add 4, add 5, add 6, add 7, . . .
   Algebraic: $t_n = 0.5(n)(n + 1) = 0.5n^2 + 0.5n$

9. $d = 27 - 22 = 5$
   Terms are $22 - 5 = \underline{17}$ and $27 + 5 = \underline{32}$.

10. $4 + 12 + 36 + 108 + 324$

11. $n = 5$

12. Geometric means

13. Women: \$30,000, \$31,200, \$32,448; geometric
    Men: \$35,000, \$36,600, \$38,200; arithmetic

14. Women's salaries increase by \$1200 and \$1248.
    Men's salaries increase \$1600 both years.
    So men's salaries are increasing faster than women's.
    (Note that women's salaries are increasing at an increasing
    rate, though!)

15. For $n = 25$:
    Women's: $30,000(1.04)^{24} = 76,899.1249\ldots \approx \$76,899$
    Men's: $35,000 + 24(1600) = \$73,400$
    So women will be making about \$3,499 more!

16. $d = 13 - 8 = 5$

17. $t_{300} = 8 + (299)(5) = 1{,}503$

18. • $S_{300} = 150(8 + 1{,}503) = 226{,}650$ by formula
    • Enter $t_n = 8 + (n - 1)(5)$ in the y= menu.
      $S_{300} = 226{,}650$ by program
    • The formula is quicker. For the program, you must still
      enter the formula for t_n and then wait while it does the
      300 iterations.

19. $1673 = 8 + (n - 1)(5)$
    $n = 334$

20. Algebraically:
    $4859 = \left(\dfrac{n}{2} \right)[8 + 8 + (n - 1)(5)]$
    $9718 = 11n + 5n^2$
    $5n^2 + 11n - 9718 = 0$
    $n = 43$ or -45.2
    $n = 43$ terms

    Numerically:
    • Enter $t_n = 8 + (n - 1)(5)$ in the y= menu.
      Run the program, stopping when the partial sum is 4859.
      Read $n = 43$ from the program display.

    • Enter $S_n = \left(\dfrac{n}{2} \right)[8 + 8 + (n - 1)(5)]$ in the y= menu.

      Make a table of values, reading $n = 43$ when $S_n = 4859$.

21. $r = \dfrac{75}{100} = 0.75$

22. $t_{30} = 100(0.75^{29}) = 0.02381\ldots$

23. $3.1676 = 100(0.75^{n-1})$
    $0.031676 = 0.75^{n-1}$
    $\dfrac{\log 0.031676}{\log 0.75} + 1 = n$
    $n = 13$

24. $S_3 = 100 + 75 + 56.25 = 231.25$

25. $S_3 = 100 \cdot \dfrac{1 - 0.75^3}{1 - 0.75} = 231.25$, agreeing with Problem 24.

26. $S_n = \lim\limits_{n \to \infty} \dfrac{100 \cdot (1 - 0.75^n)}{1 - 0.75}$

    $\quad = 100 \cdot \dfrac{1}{0.25} = 400$

27. $S_4 = 3 + 9 + 27 + 81 = 120$

28. Answers will vary.

Test 37 Form A

1. • Degree: 5
   • Real zeros: 3
   • Complex zeros: 2 (nonreal)
   • Leading coefficient sign: negative
   (Equation is $f(x) = -x^5 + 2x^4 + 19x^3 - 22x^2 - 118x + 120$.)

2. • Degree: 6
   • Real zeros: 4 (counting the double zero twice)
   • Complex zeros: 2 (nonreal)
   • Leading coefficient sign: positive
   (Equation is $f(x) = x^6 - 3x^5 - 12.75x^4 + 30.75x^3 + 32.75x^2 - 58.25x - 51$.)

3. All five extreme points and all four points of inflection. (Only
   one of each need be shown.)

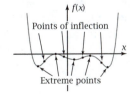

4. • Product of zeros: −30

   • Sum of pairwise products: −7

   • Sum of zeros: 5

5.
```
2 | 1   -5    -7    30
  |      2    -6   -26
  ---------------------
    1   -3   -13     4
```

6. • $f(2) = 4$

   • Remainder = 4

   • Remainder theorem

   • $\dfrac{f(x)}{x-2} = x^2 - 3x + 13 + \dfrac{4}{x-2}$

7. Real zero is $x = -5$.
   ($x = -5$ makes the factor $(x + 5)$ equal zero.)

8. $x^2 - 6x + 13 = 0$
   $x = \dfrac{6 \pm \sqrt{36 - 4(1)(13)}}{2} = 6 \pm \dfrac{\sqrt{-16}}{2} = 3 \pm 2i$
   Zeros are $3 + 2i$ and $3 - 2i$.

9. (Use ΔList feature on grapher.)

x	$f(x)$	Diff. 1	Diff. 2	Diff. 3
2	−14.6	4.2	2.4	−1.2
3	−10.4	6.6	1.2	−1.2
4	−3.8	7.8	0.0	−1.2
5	4.0	7.8	−1.2	
6	11.8	6.6		
7	18.4			

   ∴ third differences are constant, −1.2, Q.E.D.

10. General equation is $f(x) = ax^3 + bx^2 + cx + d$.
    Substitute the first four ordered pairs.
    $8a + 4b + 2c + d = -14.6$
    $27a + 9b + 3c + d = -10.4$
    $64a + 16b + 4c + d = -3.8$
    $125a + 25b + 5c + d = 4.0$
    $$\begin{bmatrix} 8 & 4 & 2 & 1 \\ 27 & 9 & 3 & 1 \\ 64 & 16 & 4 & 1 \\ 125 & 25 & 5 & 1 \end{bmatrix}^{-1} \begin{bmatrix} -14.6 \\ -10.4 \\ -3.8 \\ 4.0 \end{bmatrix} = \begin{bmatrix} -0.2 \\ 3 \\ -7 \\ -11 \end{bmatrix}$$
    Equation is $f(x) = -0.2x^3 + 3x^2 - 7x - 11$.

11. Cubic regression gives the same equation.

12. $f(-1) = -0.2(-1)^3 + 3(-1)^2 - 7(-1) - 11 = -0.8$
    Therefore, $x = -1$ is not a zero of $f(x)$.

13. The largest zero is between $x = 11$ and $x = 12$.
    Solving numerically, $f(x) = 0$ if $x = 11.5611\ldots$.

14. Third zero is $2 - i$ (the complex conjugate of $2 + i$).

15. • Sum is $3 + (2 + i) + (2 - i) = 7$.

    • Sum of pairwise products is
    $3(2 + i) + 3(2 - i) + (2 + i)(2 - i)$
    $= 6 + 3i + 6 - 3i + 4 - i^2 = 16 - (-1) = 17$.

    • Product is $3(2 + i)(2 - i) = 3(4 - i^2) = 15$.

16. Equation is $g(x) = x^3 - 7x^2 + 17x - 15$.

17.
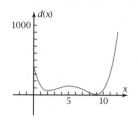

18. The $d(x)$-intercept shows that Ella was 405 km from Alderaan when she started the maneuver.

19. Using the Min feature, the closest Ella gets is
    $47.9782\ldots \approx 47.98$ km at $x = 2.1492\ldots \approx 2.15$ min.

20. The double zero is $x = 9$.

21. The spaceship just touches the surface, then rises again.

22. $d(2 + i) = (2 + i)^4 - 22(2 + i)^3 + 158(2 + i)^2 - 414(2 + i)$
    $+ 405 = 0$ (by complex-number arithmetic on calculator)
    (Can also be done by synthetic substitution.)

23. Other complex zero is $2 - i$.

24. Sum $= (2 + i) + (2 - i) + 9 + 9 = 22$, which is the opposite of the coefficient of the cubed term.

25. Answers will vary.

Test 37 Form B

1. • Degree: 5

   • Real zeros: 3

   • Complex zeros: 2 (nonreal)

   • Leading coefficient sign: positive
   (Equation is $f(x) = x^5 - 2x^4 - 19x^3 + 22x^2 + 118x - 120$.)

2. • Degree: 6

   • Real zeros: 4 (counting the double zero twice)

   • Complex zeros: 2 (nonreal)

   • Leading coefficient sign: negative
   (Equation is $f(x) = -x^6 + 3x^5 + 12.75x^4 - 30.75x^3 - 32.75x^2 + 58.25x + 51$.)

3. All five extreme points and all four points of inflection (Only one of each need be shown.)

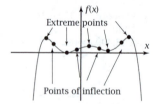

4. • Product of zeros: −8

   • Sum of pairwise products: −2

   • Sum of zeros: 5

5.
```
-2 | 1   -5    2    8
   |     -2   14  -32
   -------------------
     1   -7   16  -24
```

6. • $f(-2) = -24$

   • Remainder $= -24$

   • Remainder theorem

   • $\dfrac{f(x)}{x+2} = x^2 - 7x + 16 - \dfrac{24}{x+2}$

7. Real zero is $x = -1$.
   ($x = -1$ makes the factor $(x+1)$ equal zero.)

8. $x^2 - 4x + 13 = 0$
   $x = \dfrac{4 \pm \sqrt{16 - 52}}{2} = 2 \pm 3i$
   Zeros are $2 + 3i$ and $2 - 3i$.

9. (Use ΔList feature on grapher.)

x	$f(x)$	Diff. 1	Diff. 2	Diff. 3
2	25.4	−12.3	−4.6	1.8
3	13.1	−16.9	−2.8	1.8
4	−3.8	−19.7	−1.0	1.8
5	−23.5	−20.7	0.8	
6	−44.2	−19.9		
7	−64.1			

   ∴ third differences are constant, 1.8, Q.E.D.

10. General equation is $f(x) = ax^3 + bx^2 + cx + d$.
    Substitute the first four ordered pairs.
    $8a + 4b + 2c + d = 25.4$
    $27a + 9b + 3c + d = 13.1$
    $64a + 16b + 4c + d = -3.8$
    $125a + 25b + 5c + d = -23.5$
    $$\begin{bmatrix} 8 & 4 & 2 & 1 \\ 27 & 9 & 3 & 1 \\ 64 & 16 & 4 & 1 \\ 125 & 25 & 5 & 1 \end{bmatrix}^{-1} \begin{bmatrix} 25.4 \\ 13.1 \\ -3.8 \\ -23.5 \end{bmatrix} = \begin{bmatrix} 0.3 \\ -5.0 \\ 7.0 \\ 29.0 \end{bmatrix}$$
    Equation is $f(x) = 0.3x^3 - 5x^2 + 7x + 29$.

11. Cubic regression gives the same equation.

12. $f(4) = -3.8$
    Therefore, $x = 4$ is not a zero of $f(x)$.

13. The largest zero is between $x = 14$ and $x = 15$.
    Solving numerically, $f(x) = 0$ if $x = 14.6181\ldots$.

14. Third zero is $3 - i$ (the complex conjugate of $3 + i$).

15. • Sum is $2 + (3 + i) + (3 - i) = 8$.

    • Sum of pairwise products is
      $2(3 + i) + 2(3 - i) + (3 + i)(3 - i) = 22$.

    • Product is $2(3 + i)(3 - i) = 20$.

16. Equation is $g(x) = x^3 - 8x^2 + 22x - 20$.

17.

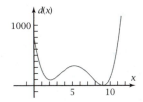

18. The $d(x)$-intercept shows that Ella was 810 km from Alderaan when she started the maneuver.

19. Using the Min feature, the closest Ella gets is $95.9564\ldots \approx 96.0$ km at $x = 2.1492\ldots \approx 2.15$ min.

20. The double zero is $x = 9$.

21. The spaceship just touches the surface, then rises again.

22. $d(2 + i) = 2(2 + i)^4 - 44(2 + i)^3 + 316(2 + i)^2 - 828(2 + i) + 810 = 0$ (by complex-number arithmetic on calculator)
    (Can also be done by synthetic substitution.)

23. Other complex zero is $2 - i$.

24. Sum $= (2 + i) + (2 - i) + 9 + 9 = 22$, which is one-half the opposite of the coefficient of the cubed term.

25. Answers will vary.

Test 38 Form A

1. • Degree: 5th

   • Real zeros: 3

   • Complex zeros: 2

   • Sign of leading coefficient: positive
   (Equation is $f(x) = x^5 + x^4 - 22x^3 + 2x^2 + 44x - 80$.)
   (Zeros are -5, -2, 4, $1 + i$, and $1 - i$.)

2. $y = \dfrac{1}{x}$

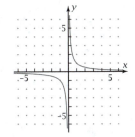

3. Horizontal translation by -2.

4. Vertical asymptote at $x = -2$.

5. $y = \dfrac{(x - 3)(x - 2)}{(x - 3)} = x - 2$, provided $x \ne 3$
   Removable discontinuity at $x = 3$

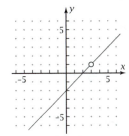

6. Zeros are -4, 3, 3.

7. • Sum: $-4 + 3 + 3 = 2$

   • Product: $(-4)(3)(3) = -36$

   • SPP: $(-4)(3) + (-4)(3) + (3)(3) = -15$

8. $b = -(2) = -2$, $c = +(-15) = -15$, $d = -(-36) = 36$
   Equation: $y = x^3 - 2x^2 - 15x + 36$

9.

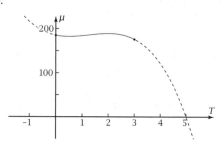

10. Use the Min and Max features to find the vertices.
Minimum: $\mu = 182.25$ at $T = 0.5$
Maximum: $\mu = 189$ at $T = 2$
At the endpoints, $\mu(0) = 185$ and $\mu(3) = 176$.
Therefore,

- Min, $\mu = 176$ centipoise at $T = 3(300°)$
- Max, $\mu = 189$ centipoise at $T = 2(200°)$

11. $\mu(5) = 0$ and $T = 5$ is out of the given domain.

12.
$$
\begin{array}{r|rrrr}
5 & -4 & 15 & -12 & 185 \\
& & -20 & -25 & -185 \\
\hline
& -4 & -5 & -37 & 0
\end{array}
$$

$\mu = (T - 5)(-4T^2 - 5T - 37) = -(T - 5)(4T^2 + 5T + 37)$
For $4T^2 + 5T + 37 = 0$, the discriminant is $5^2 - 4(4)(37) = -583$. Because the discriminant is negative, there are no real solutions. So μ has no other real zeros. This agrees with the fact that the graph of μ in Problem 9 crosses the T-axis only once.

13. The discontinuities at $x = 1$ and $x = 5$ are asymptotes because the numerator does not also equal zero at either of these values of x. Removable discontinuities occur only for the form $\frac{0}{0}$.

14. To find the zero, set the numerator equal to zero.
$5x - 13 = 0$
$x = 2.6$ (which agrees with the graph)

15. $y = \dfrac{5x - 13}{(x - 1)(x - 5)} = \dfrac{A}{x - 1} + \dfrac{B}{x - 5}$
$A = \dfrac{5(1) - 13}{1 - 5} = 2$ and $B = \dfrac{5(5) - 13}{5 - 1} = 3$
$\therefore y = \dfrac{2}{x - 1} + \dfrac{3}{x - 5}$

16. Slope of tangent line is $\frac{54}{8 - 2} = 9$.

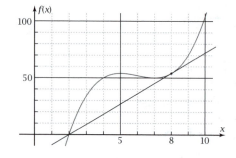

17. $m(x) = \dfrac{f(x) - 54}{x - 8} = \dfrac{x^3 - 18x^2 + 105x - 146 - 54}{x - 8}$
$m(x) = \dfrac{x^3 - 18x^2 + 105x - 200}{x - 8}$

$$
\begin{array}{r|rrrr}
8 & 1 & -18 & 105 & -200 \\
& & 8 & -80 & 200 \\
\hline
& 1 & -10 & 25 & 0
\end{array}
$$

$m(x) = \dfrac{(x - 8)(x^2 - 10x + 25)}{x - 8} = x^2 - 10x + 25, \ x \ne 8$

18. $\lim\limits_{x \to 8} m(x) = 8^2 - 10(8) + 25 = 9$, Q.E.D.

19. x-coordinate of point of tangency is 8, which equals the real part of $8 \pm 3i$. The slope of the tangent line is 9, whose square roots are ± 3, which equal the imaginary parts of $8 \pm 3i$.

20. The graph shows the tangent line.
The point of tangency is $(3, 8)$.
The slope of the tangent line is $\frac{8}{2} = 4$.
$\therefore$ zeros are $3 \pm 2i$.

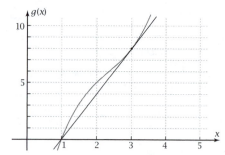

21. Answers will vary.

Test 38 Form B

1. • Degree: 5th

- Real zeros: 3

- Complex zeros: 2

- Sign of leading coefficient: negative

(Equation is $f(x) = -x^5 - x^4 + 22x^3 - 2x^2 - 44x + 80$.)
(Zeros are -5, -2, 4, $1 + i$, and $1 - i$.)

2. $y = \dfrac{1}{x}$

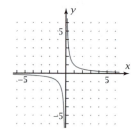

3. Horizontal translation by 3

4. Vertical asymptote at $x = 3$

5. $y = \dfrac{(x+2)(x+3)}{(x+3)} = x + 2$ provided $x \neq -3$

Removable discontinuity at $x = -3$

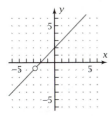

6. Zeros are $-4, 3, 3$.

7. • Sum: $-4 + 3 + 3 = 2$

• Product: $(-4)(3)(3) = -36$

• SPP: $(-4)(3) + (-4)(3) + (3)(3) = -15$

8. $b = -(2)(-1) = 2$, $c = +(-15)(-1) = 15$, $d = -(-36)(-1) = -36$

Equation: $y = -x^3 + 2x^2 + 15x - 36$

9.

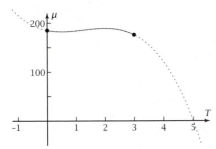

10. Use the Min and Max features to find the vertices.

Minimum: $\mu = 182.25$ at $T = 0.5$

Maximum: $\mu = 189$ at $T = 2$

At the endpoints, $\mu(0) = 185$ and $\mu(3) = 176$.

Therefore,

• Min, $\mu = 176$ centipoise at $T = 3(300°)$

• Max, $\mu = 189$ centipoise at $T = 2(200°)$

11. $\mu(5) = 0$ and $T = 5$ is out of the given domain.

12.
$$
\begin{array}{r|rrrr}
5 & -4 & 15 & -12 & 185 \\
  &   & -20 & -25 & -185 \\
\hline
  & -4 & -5 & -37 & 0
\end{array}
$$

$\mu = (T - 5)(-4T^2 - 5T - 37) = -(T - 5)(4T^2 + 5T + 37)$

For $4T^2 + 5T + 37 = 0$, the discriminant is $5^2 - 4(4)(37) = -583$.
Because the discriminant is negative, there are no real solutions. So μ has no other real zeros. This agrees with the fact that the graph of μ in Problem 9 crosses the T-axis only once.

13. The discontinuities at $x = 1$ and $x = 3$ are asymptotes because the numerator does not also equal zero at either of these values of x. Removable discontinuities occur only for the form $\frac{0}{0}$.

14. To find the zero, set the numerator equal to zero.

$10x - 26 = 0$

$x = 2.6$ (which agrees with the graph)

15. $y = \dfrac{10x - 26}{(x - 1)(x - 3)} = \dfrac{A}{x - 1} + \dfrac{B}{x - 3}$

$A = \dfrac{10(1) - 26}{1 - 3} = 8$ and $B = \dfrac{10(3) - 26}{3 - 1} = 2$

$\therefore y = \dfrac{8}{x - 1} + \dfrac{2}{x - 3}$

16. Slope of tangent line is $\frac{54}{8-2} = 9$.

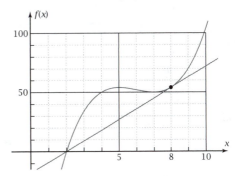

17. $m(x) = \dfrac{f(x) - 54}{x - 8} = \dfrac{x^3 - 18x^2 + 105x - 146 - 54}{x - 8}$

$m(x) = \dfrac{x^3 - 18x^2 + 105x - 200}{x - 8}$

$$
\begin{array}{r|rrrr}
8 & 1 & -18 & 105 & -200 \\
  &   & 8 & -80 & 200 \\
\hline
  & 1 & -10 & 25 & 0
\end{array}
$$

$m(x) = \dfrac{(x - 8)(x^2 - 10x + 25)}{x - 8} = x^2 - 10x + 25, \; x \neq 8$

18. $\lim\limits_{x \to 8} m(x) = 8^2 - 10(8) + 25 = 9$, Q.E.D.

19. x-coordinate of point of tangency is 8, which equals the real part of $8 \pm 3i$. The slope of the tangent line is 9, whose square roots are ± 3, which equal the imaginary parts of $8 \pm 3i$.

20. The graph shows the tangent line.
The point of tangency is $(3, 8)$.
The slope of the tangent line is $\frac{8}{2} = 4$.
$\therefore$ zeros are $3 \pm 2i$.

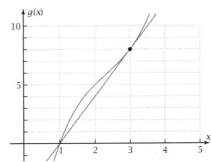

21. Answers will vary.

Test 39 Form A

1. $\vec{b} - \vec{a} = (\vec{i} + 4\vec{j} - 6\vec{k}) - (7\vec{i} - 2\vec{j} + 3\vec{k})$
   $= -6\vec{i} + 6\vec{j} - 9\vec{k}$

2. $|\vec{a}| = \sqrt{49 + 4 + 9} = \sqrt{62}$
   $|\vec{b}| = \sqrt{1 + 16 + 36} = \sqrt{53}$
   $\vec{a} \cdot \vec{b} = (7)(1) + (-2)(4) + (3)(-6) = -19$
   $\sqrt{62}\sqrt{53} \cos\theta = -19$
   $\cos\theta = -0.3314\ldots$
   $\theta = 109.3568\ldots°$

3. By program, $\vec{a} \times \vec{b} = 0\vec{i} + 45\vec{j} + 30\vec{k}$.
   $(\vec{a} \times \vec{b}) \cdot \vec{a} = (0)(7) + (45)(-2) + (30)(3) = 0$
   $\therefore (\vec{a} \times \vec{b})$ is perpendicular to $\vec{a}$, Q.E.D.

4. $0x + 45y + 30z = D$
   $0(3) + 45(4) + 30(5) = D$
   $D = 330$
   Equation is $0x + 45y + 30z = 330$ or $0x + 3y + 2z = 22$.

5. $|\vec{a} \times \vec{b}| = \sqrt{0 + 2025 + 900} = \sqrt{2925}$
   Area $= 0.5\sqrt{2925} = 27.0416...$

6. $p = |\vec{b}|\cos \theta = \sqrt{53} \cos 109.3568...°$
   $\qquad = -2.4130...$
   or: $p = \dfrac{\vec{a} \cdot \vec{b}}{|\vec{a}|} = \dfrac{-19}{\sqrt{62}} = -2.4130...$

7.

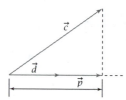

8. Fixed point is $(4, 1, 10)$.
   If $d = 21$, then $\vec{r} = 22\vec{i} + 7\vec{j} + 1\vec{k}$.
   Point is $(22, 7, 1)$.

9. $\vec{u} = \dfrac{6}{7}\vec{i} + \dfrac{2}{7}\vec{j} + \left(-\dfrac{3}{7}\right)\vec{k}$
   $|\vec{u}| = \sqrt{\dfrac{36}{49} + \dfrac{4}{49} + \dfrac{9}{49}} = \sqrt{\dfrac{49}{49}} = 1$
   $\therefore \vec{u}$ is a unit vector, Q.E.D.

10. $\cos \alpha = \dfrac{6}{7} \Rightarrow \alpha = 31.0027...°$
    $\cos \beta = \dfrac{2}{7} \Rightarrow \beta = 73.3984...°$
    $\cos \gamma = -\dfrac{3}{7} \Rightarrow \gamma = 115.3769...$

11. $[A] = \begin{bmatrix} 0.9 \cos 30° & 0.9 \cos 120° & 6 \\ 0.9 \sin 30° & 0.9 \sin 120° & 2 \\ 0 & 0 & 1 \end{bmatrix}$

12. Snail-like path

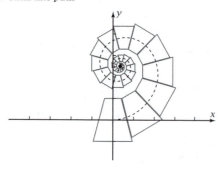

13. Use $[A]^{100}$. The fixed point is in the translation part of the resulting matrix, $(1.6863..., 12.5069...)$, which agrees with the graph.

14.

Iter.	N	L Each	L Total
0	1	12	12
1	5	4	20
2	25	1.3333...	33.3333...
3	125	0.4444...	55.5555...

15. Total length $L = 12 \cdot \left(\dfrac{5}{3}\right)^n$
    For 50th iteration, $L = 12 \cdot \left(\dfrac{5}{3}\right)^{50} = 1.4846... \times 10^{12}$

16. $D = \dfrac{\log N}{\log \left(\frac{1}{r}\right)} = \dfrac{\log 5}{\log 3} = 1.4649...$

17. Major radius $a = 13$ and minor radius $b = 5$

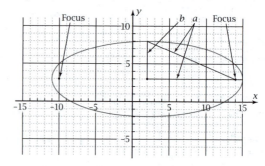

18. • Graph, Problem 17, showing the two foci.
    • Graph, Problem 17, showing the right triangle.
    • $c^2 = a^2 - b^2 = 13^2 - 5^2 = 144 \Rightarrow c = 12$, Q.E.D.

19. $c = ea \Rightarrow e = \dfrac{c}{a} = \dfrac{12}{13} = 0.9230...$

20. Equation is $\left(\dfrac{x-2}{13}\right)^2 + \left(\dfrac{y-3}{5}\right)^2 = 1$.

21. Parametric equations are:
    $x = 2 + 13 \cos t$
    $y = 3 + 5 \sin t$
    The grapher graph agrees with the given figure.

22.

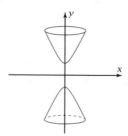

23. $V = \pi x^2 y$
    $V = \pi x^2 (16 - x^2)$

24. $V = \pi x^2 (16 - x^2)$
    Using the Max feature, max V is at $x = 2.8284....$
    (Exact answer is $2\sqrt{2}$.)

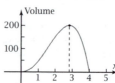

25. A sequence is an ordered set of numbers such as $3, 5, 7, 9, \ldots$.
    A series is the indicated sum of the terms of a sequence, such as $3 + 5 + 7 + 9 + \cdots$.

Precalculus with Trigonometry: Assessment Resources
© 2007 Key Curriculum Press

26. • $d = 32 - 19 = 13$

   • $19 + 32 + \underline{45} + \underline{58} + \underline{71} + \cdots$

   • $t_{300} = 19 + 299(13) = 3{,}906$

   $$S_{300} = \left(\frac{300}{2}\right)(19 + 3{,}906) = 588{,}750$$

27. • $100 + 80 + 64 + 51.2 + \cdots$

   • $S_{20} = 100 \cdot \dfrac{1 - 0.8^{20}}{1 - 0.8} = 494.2353\ldots$

   • Limit $= 100 \cdot \dfrac{1 - 0}{1 - 0.8} = 500$

28. $S_4 = 2 + 5 + 10 + 17 = 34$

29. $S_{20} = \displaystyle\sum_{k=1}^{20} 100(0.8^{k-1})$

30. Equation is $\dfrac{5}{2 + 3\cos\theta}$, as in Problem 31.

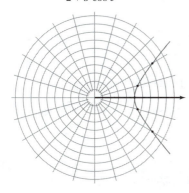

31. No. The point is not a solution to the system of equations because the curve (a hyperbola) has a negative value of r and the circle has a positive value of r there. The graphs are not at this point at the same time as the grapher plots in simultaneous mode.

32. $5\operatorname{cis}330° = 5(\cos 330° + i\sin 330°)$
   $= 4.3301\ldots - 2.5i$

33. $(6\operatorname{cis}100°)(2\operatorname{cis}70°) = 12\operatorname{cis}170°$

34. $(25\operatorname{cis}70°)^{1/2} = [25\operatorname{cis}(70° + 360n°)]^{1/2}$
   $= 5\operatorname{cis}(35° + 180n°) = 5\operatorname{cis}35°$ or $5\operatorname{cis}215°$

35. The negative leading coefficient tells that as x increases, the graph comes down from high values of $f(x)$ and winds up going down again for large values of x.

36.
$$\begin{array}{r|rrrr}
2 & -1 & 13 & -50 & 56 \\
  &   & -2 & 22 & -56 \\ \hline
  & -1 & 11 & -28 & 0
\end{array}$$

   $\therefore 2$ is a zero of $f(x)$, Q.E.D.

37. $v_{av} = \dfrac{f(x)}{x - 2} = \dfrac{-x^3 + 13x^2 - 50x + 56}{x - 2}$
   $v_{av} = \dfrac{(x - 2)(-x^2 + 11x - 28)}{x - 2} = -x^2 + 11x - 28,\ x \neq 2$
   $\displaystyle\lim_{x \to 2} v_{av} = -(2^2) + 11(2) - 28 = -10$

38. Lucy was going down (negative rate) at 10 ft/s.

39. The cubic function has the wrong endpoint behavior because it keeps going down for larger values of x, whereas Lucy actually comes back up again.

40. $f(x) = -(x^3 - 13x^2 + 50x - 56)$
   Sum of the zeros is $-(-13) = 13$.
   Third zero is $13 - (2 + 4) = 7$.

41. Answers will vary.

Test 39 Form B

1. $\vec{b} - \vec{a} = (3\vec{i} + 10\vec{j} - 4\vec{k}) - (8\vec{i} - 2\vec{j} + 13\vec{k})$
   $= -5\vec{i} + 12\vec{j} - 17\vec{k}$

2. $|\vec{a}| = \sqrt{64 + 4 + 169} = \sqrt{237}$
   $|\vec{b}| = \sqrt{9 + 100 + 16} = \sqrt{125}$
   $\vec{a} \cdot \vec{b} = (8)(3) + (-2)(10) + (13)(-4) = -48$
   $\sqrt{237}\sqrt{125}\cos\theta = -48$
   $\cos\theta = -0.2788\ldots$
   $\theta = 106.1931\ldots°$

3. By program, $\vec{a} \times \vec{b} = -122\vec{i} + 71\vec{j} + 86\vec{k}$.
   $(\vec{a} \times \vec{b}) \cdot \vec{a} = (-122)(8) + (71)(-2) + (86)(13) = 0$
   $\therefore (\vec{a} \times \vec{b})$ is perpendicular to $\vec{a}$, Q.E.D.

4. $-122x + 71y + 86z = D$
   $-122(3) + 71(4) + 86(5) = D$
   $D = 348$
   Equation is $-122x + 7y + 74z = 348$.

5. $|\vec{a} \times \vec{b}| = \sqrt{(-122)^2 + (71)^2 + (86)^2} = \sqrt{27{,}321}$
   Area $= 0.5\sqrt{27{,}321} = 82.6453\ldots$

6. $p = |\vec{b}|\cos\theta = \sqrt{125}\cos 106.1931\ldots°$
   $= -3.1179\ldots$

   or: $p = \dfrac{\vec{a} \cdot \vec{b}}{|\vec{a}|} = \dfrac{-48}{\sqrt{237}} = -3.1179\ldots$

7.

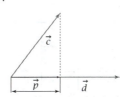

8. Fixed point is $(5, 3, 7)$.
   If $d = 22$, then $\vec{r} = 17\vec{i} + 21 + 11\vec{k}$.
   Point is $(17, 21, 11)$.

9. From the given equation, $\vec{u} = \dfrac{6}{11}\vec{i} + \dfrac{9}{11}\vec{j} + \dfrac{2}{11}\vec{k}$.
   $|\vec{u}| = \sqrt{\left(\dfrac{6}{11}\right)^2 + \left(\dfrac{9}{11}\right)^2 + \left(\dfrac{2}{11}\right)^2} = \sqrt{\dfrac{121}{121}} = 1$
   $\therefore \vec{u}$ is a unit vector, Q.E.D.

10. $\cos\alpha = \dfrac{6}{11} \Rightarrow \alpha = 56.9442\ldots°$
   $\cos\beta = \dfrac{9}{11} \Rightarrow \beta = 35.0968\ldots°$
   $\cos\gamma = \dfrac{2}{11} \Rightarrow \gamma = 79.5243\ldots°$

11. $[A] = \begin{bmatrix} 0.9\cos 30° & 0.9\cos 120° & 6 \\ 0.9\sin 30° & 0.9\sin 120° & 2 \\ 0 & 0 & 1 \end{bmatrix}$

12. Snail-like path

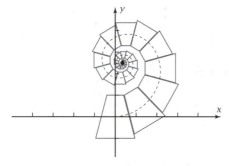

13. Use $[A]^{100}$. The fixed point is in the translation part of the resulting matrix, $(1.6863..., 12.5069...)$, which agrees with the graph.

14.

Iter.	N	L Each	L Total
0	1	12	12
1	5	3	15
2	25	0.75	18.75
3	125	0.1875	23.4375

15. Total length $L = 12 \cdot \left(\dfrac{5}{4}\right)^n$

For 50th iteration, $L = 12 \cdot \left(\dfrac{5}{4}\right)^{50} = 840{,}779.0785...$

16. $D = \dfrac{\log N}{\log\left(\frac{1}{r}\right)} = \dfrac{\log 5}{\log 4} = 1.1609...$

17. Major radius $a = 13$ and minor radius $b = 5$

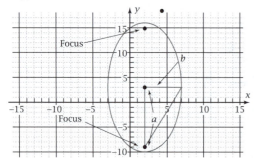

18. • Graph, Problem 17, showing the two foci.
    • Graph, Problem 17, showing the right triangle.
    • $c^2 = a^2 - b^2 = 13^2 - 5^2 = 144 \Rightarrow c = 12$, Q.E.D.

19. $c = ea \Rightarrow e = \dfrac{c}{a} = \dfrac{12}{13} = 0.9230...$

20. Equation is $\left(\dfrac{x-2}{5}\right)^2 + \left(\dfrac{y-3}{13}\right)^2 = 1$.

21. Parametric equations are:
    $x = 2 + 5\cos t$
    $y = 3 + 13\sin t$
    The grapher graph agrees with the given figure.

22.

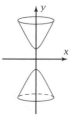

23. $V = \pi x^2 y$
    $V = \pi x^2 (9 - x^2)$

24. $V = \pi x^2 (9 - x^2)$
    Using the Max feature, max V is at $x = 2.1213...$.
    (Exact answer is $\dfrac{3}{\sqrt{2}}$.)

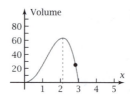

25. A sequence is an ordered set of numbers such as
    $3, 5, 7, 9, \ldots$.
    A series is the indicated sum of the terms of a sequence, such as $3 + 5 + 7 + 9 + \cdots$.

26. • $d = 36 - 17 = 19$
    • $17 + 36 + \underline{55} + \underline{74} + \underline{93} + \cdots$
    • $t_{300} = 17 + 299(19) = 5{,}698$
    $S_{300} = \left(\dfrac{300}{2}\right)(17 + 5{,}698) = 857{,}250$

27. • $100 + 90 + 81 + 72.9 + \cdots$
    • $S_{20} = 100 \cdot \dfrac{1 - 0.9^{20}}{1 - 0.9} = 878.4233...$
    • Limit $= 100 \cdot \dfrac{1 - 0}{1 - 0.9} = 1000$

28. $S_5 = 0 + 7 + 26 + 63 + 124 = 220$

29. $S_{20} = \displaystyle\sum_{k=1}^{20} 100 \cdot (0.9^{k-1})$

30. Equation is $r = \dfrac{5}{2 + 3\cos\theta}$, as in Problem 31.

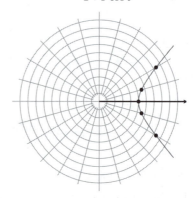

31. No. The point is not a solution to the system of equations because the curve (a hyperbola) has a negative value of r and the circle has a positive value of r there. The graphs are not at this point at the same time as the grapher plots in simultaneous mode.

32. $7 \operatorname{cis} 240° = 7(\cos 240° + i \sin 240°)$
$= -3.5 - 6.0621\ldots i$

33. $(5 \operatorname{cis} 130°)(4 \operatorname{cis} 60°) = 20 \operatorname{cis} 190°$

34. $(64 \operatorname{cis} 80°)^{1/2} = [64 \operatorname{cis}(80° + 360n°)]^{1/2}$
$= 8 \operatorname{cis}(40° + 180n°) = 8 \operatorname{cis} 40°$ or $8 \operatorname{cis} 220°$

35. The negative leading coefficient tells that as x increases, the graph comes down from high values of $f(x)$ and winds up going down again for large values of x.

36.
$$
\begin{array}{r|rrrr}
2 & -2 & 26 & -100 & 112 \\
  &   & -4 & 44 & -112 \\
\hline
  & -2 & 22 & -56 & 0
\end{array}
$$

$\therefore$ 2 is a zero of $f(x)$, Q.E.D.

37. $v_{av} = \dfrac{f(x)}{x-2} = \dfrac{-2x^3 + 26x^2 - 100x + 112}{x-2}$
$v_{av} = \dfrac{f(x)}{x-2} = \dfrac{(x-2)(-2x^2 + 22x - 56)}{x-2} = -2x^2 + 22x - 56, \; x \ne 2$
$\lim\limits_{x \to 2} v_{av} = -2(2^2) + 22(2) - 56 = -20$

38. Lucy was going down (negative rate) at 20 ft/s.

39. The cubic function has the wrong endpoint behavior because it keeps going down for larger values of x, whereas Lucy actually comes back up again.

40. $f(x) = -(x^3 - 13x^2 + 50x - 56)$
Sum of the zeros is $-(-13) = 13$.
Third zero is $13 - (2 + 4) = 7$.

41. Answers will vary.